The Book on Antimony

The Book on Antimony
Dancing with the Black Dragon

My Alchemical Journey with Antimony

*The Book of Nature and the Hidden Secrets
and Mysteries of Antimony Unveiled: Being the
Forbidden Knowledge of Ancient Philosophers
by that celebrated Student, Philosopher, Chemist, Naturalist,
Astrologer, Alchemist, Metallurgist, Sorcerer, Explanator of
the Mysteries of Wizards and Witchcraft; Together with
Recondite Views of Numerous Arts and Sciences—
Obscure, Plain, Practical,
Etc., Etc.,
Etc.*

by

Robert Allen Bartlett

Revelore Press
Olympia, WA
MMXXI

Revelore Press
620 73rd Ave NE
Olympia WA 98506
USA

www.revelore.press

Book Design by Jenn Zahrt
Cover Design by Joseph Uccello.

ISBN 978-1-947544-42-0

First print edition published by Revelore Press in 2021.

Contents

Preface

What this book is about;
THE BOOK ON ANTIMONY

Twentieth century alchemist, Frater Albertus, planned on writing a work titled, *The Book on Antimony*, which, to my knowledge never manifested. The book was to spark interest in preparations of antimony for medicinal use based on spagyric and alchemical principles. In the transition of alchemy to modern chemistry, many valuable ideas, techniques, and products were pushed aside to make room for updated approaches. In England, discussion of alchemical topics was discouraged and later banned in meetings of the Royal Society in favor of the new model of chemical principles. Soon, alchemy disappeared as a bad dream of our ancestors and those who could understand its methods were spread far and few between. There have always been alchemists working in the shadows through time. Frater Albertus pulled alchemy out and into the light on a global scale, as a legitimate avenue of research into new medicines and materials. Part of his research involved preparations of antimony, based especially on the writings of the alchemist Basil Valentine in his *Triumphal Chariot of Antimony* which first appeared around 1604. Frater Albertus hoped to gather enough information together on how to prepare antimony in a variety of ways to produce powerful agents unknown to modern medicine, and also to accumulate as much analytical information on the products as possible so that medical evaluation could more easily be suggested. He taught much of this technology worldwide for many years. I studied and worked with Frater Albertus for about ten years and the book before you presents a documentary of the teachings on antimony I have been able to collect since 1973 based on his initial guidance. So this is my version of *The Book on Antimony*; I think Frater would have been pleased.

I was never sure how best to present all of this information but in the end decided it was best to start at the beginning and unfold the information as it was presented to me. The alchemists called antimony a Black Dragon; this is the story of my involvement with antimony, my dance with the Black Dragon.

Antimony is not subject you hear about very much these days and yet antimony has been with us for centuries as a medicine, a pigment, as a flame retardant, it is used in matches and fireworks even as a semiconductor in modern electronics. In times past antimony was a subject of wonder and miracles as well as scandal.

How to use this book

This is a book of practical laboratory alchemy, but also a historical documentation. Along with some narrative and commentary, the bulk of this volume consists of scans of pages right from my personal notebooks gathered over the last 50 years. Reference notations are generally provided in the upper right corner of note pages where applicable.

The first part chronicles how antimony was introduced to me from the alchemical perspective and the results of practical works stemming from that introduction. The last part is a compendium of works using antimony, with instruction, photographs and some analysis of materials and products.

You can of course read cover to cover and see how antimony was revealed to me or skip through to a subject or process of interest at any time as a reference. I think most of the scans are clearly legible and I wanted to get them scanned before many of the pages start to fade with age. Without circumlocution or holding back vital details, I present this information in hopes that future workers on antimony preparations will have a strong foothold to make rapid advances; it does no good just sitting on my bookshelves.

This is the first of several books on alchemical laboratory works distilled from my collected notes (which I call the *Corpus Spagyricus*) planned for later release.

Part One: Introduction to Antimony

History

Archeological evidence points to man's knowledge of antimony as early as 4000 BCE, not only as a mineral but as a metal used to cast vessels and small ornamental items.

Ancient Egyptians used finely powdered stibnite, which they called Mestem, as eyeliner for both cosmetic and medicinal purposes as mentioned in the Ebers medical papyrus of about 1650 BCE. This fine powder was later called Khol, and you will still see eyeliner sold under this name though it no longer contains antimony. Khol was a term used for centuries to describe anything in a very finely powdered state. Later, Arabic influence changed this to Al-Khol, and still later it became known as Alcohol, meaning the finest powder. It was not until the middle ages that the term alcohol was used to designate the spirit of wine. The Arabic term Al-iksir, from which we get our word Elixir, was also used to designate a finely powdered substance. The word is derived from the early Greek word *xirion*, meaning a dry powder or ash.

Words of the Masters

Roger Bacon 1214–1294 CE

The alchemist Roger Bacon presents a clear description of the antimony work leading to medicines for man and metals. From *Tract on the Tincture and Oil of Antimony*:

Stibium, as the Philosophers say, is composed from the noble mineral Sulphur, and they have praised it as the Black Lead of the Wise. The Arabs in their language, have called it Asinat vel Azinat, the alchemists retain the name Antimonium. It will however lead to the consideration of high Secrets, if we seek and recognize the nature in which the Sun is exalted, as the Magi found that this mineral was attributed by God to the Constellation Aries, which is the first heavenly sign in which the Sun takes its exaltation or elevation to itself.

Bacon points to the fact that antimony was used to bring gold, the Sun, into a very pure state and was thus known as the "Aries of the Philosophers" because astrologically, the Sun is in his exaltation in the zodiacal sign of Aries.

Nicholas Flamel 1330–1417 CE

One of the most popular stories of a successful alchemist is that of Nicholas Flamel. He was a bookseller of modest means with an interest in the Hermetic Arts. He came into possession of a book filled with hieroglyphic figures, which he recognized as a valuable work on alchemy. After nearly thirty years of study he was able to understand the writings and figures in the book and undertake the practical work. Flamel was able to complete the Great Work of confecting the Philosopher's Stone and transmutation of metals. Though he continued to live modestly, he used his newfound wealth in charitable ways such as establishing several free hospitals for the poor, sizeable endowments to the church, and construction of housing for the homeless. His handwritten texts and full documentation of these acts are kept in the Bibliotheque Nationale in Paris.

His method for preparing the Philosopher's Stone is a Dry Way of working with antimony, which some have named "The Flamel Path" in his honor.

PORTRAIT OF NICOLAS FLAMEL.

Basil Valentine 1450? CE

The most authoritative texts concerning the alchemical works with antimony come from Basil Valentine. His true identity is uncertain, although he claimed to be a Benedictine monk writing in the early 15th century.

In 1604, there appeared his work titled *The Triumphal Chariot of Antimony*, which described the preparation of many compounds from the ores of antimony, useful in medicine and alchemy. This text became almost the centerpiece of all future work with antimony and is referred to by many artists with the utmost esteem.

Basil Valentine was well aware of the poisonous nature of antimony in its raw state; in fact he called it "a very great and excellent poison". His methods detail the means of removing the toxic qualities from antimony in order to produce powerful medicinal agents for man and metals.

Following the correct and true preparation of stibnite, there is no more poison to be found in it at all, for the antimonium must be completely transmuted by means of the spagyric art, and a medicine thus be produced from the poison.

Through the years, *The Triumphal Chariot of Antimony* was republished in many editions in several countries. The 1671 edition contains an extensive commentary by medical doctor Theodor Kerkring. Kerkring provides valuable insight on the various preparations of antimony given by Basil Valentine, and provides additional working knowledge to avoid pitfalls and dangers. Kerkring also provides his observations on the use of antimonial products in his own medical practice which serve to corroborate the amazing healing potential of antimony as claimed by Basil Valentine.

The work of Paracelsus was instrumental to the introduction of metallic derivatives in internal medicine. His writings are filled with references to the preparation and use of antimony, and he is in full accord with Basil Valentine regarding the healing virtues of this material.

In the same way that antimony refines gold; it also refines the body in the same form and manner; for within it is the essence, which lets nothing impure remain with what is pure. And no one who is experienced with all archidoxic writings, nor any spagyrist, may fathom the strength and virtue of antimony.

Antimony lends itself to a surprising range of preparation methods and products. Spurred on by the works of Basil Valentine and Paracelsus, there was a great surge of interest in the medicinal use of antimony during the sixteenth century.

There were, of course, antimony preparations made without regard to alchemical principles which caused poisonings. Soon antimony had a bad reputation which prompted the Counsel of Paris to ban its use in medicine. This stand was also adopted by several other countries, and the use of antimony for medicine was banned from 1566 to about 1650.

Eirenaeus Philalethes 1628–1665 CE

Another great adept in the alchemical arts, who appeared in the 1600s, was the American alchemist George Starkey, writing under the name Eirenaeus Philalethes. His works include *The Metamorphosis of Metals*, *The Marrow of Alchemy*, and *An Open Entrance to the Closed Palace of the King*. A close study of these works is highly recommended to the practical artist. Philalethes followed a dry path very similar to that of Flamel. In

The Marrow of Alchemy, Philalethes gives a description of the matter to be used:

> The substance which we first take in hand, is a mineral similar to Mercury, which a crude sulphur does bake in the Earth; and is called Saturn's Child, which indeed appears vile to sight, but is glorious within; it is sable coloured, with argent veins appearing intermixed in the body, whose sparkling line stains the connate sulphur; it is wholly volatile and unfixed, yet taken in this native crudity, it purged all the superfluity of Sol; it is of a venomous nature, and abused by many in a medicinal way; if its elements by Art are loosened, the inside appears very resplendent, which then flow in the fire like a metal, although there is nothing of a metallic kind more brittle.

Philalethes calls this "Our Dragon" and it is a description of stibnite, the sulfide ore of antimony. Philalethes method is known as a Dry Way or via sicca with antimony.

Isaac Newton 1642–1727 CE

The great genius of Isaac Newton was focused on the practice of alchemy for over thirty years. His notes indicate that he believed he was very close to perfecting the Stone of the Wise. Laboratory accidents involving metallic mercury vapors may have led to an early demise, a clear warning that "Dragons" are only approached with due precautions.

Newton was fascinated by the work on antimony and heavily influenced by the works of his contemporary, Eirenaeus Philalethes.

> In Antimony are Mercury (in the regulus), Sulfur (in the redness) and Salt (in the black earth which sinks to the bottom), which three, corrected, separated, and finally united together in the proper manner of Art so that fixation be obtained without poison, give an opportunity to the artificer to approach the Stone of Fire. (Keynes Ms 64)

> For antimony like unto mercury may fitly be compared to a round circle, of which

there is no end; in which the more diligently any man seeks the more he finds, if process be made by him in a right way and due order. Yet the life of no one man is sufficient for him to learn all the mysteries thereof. [...]

But to return to my Philosophy of Antimony, I would have the Reader, before all other things, to understand, that all things contain in themselves operative and vivificative Spirits; which inhabiting in the Body feed and nourish themselves, and are sustained by the Body. Elements themselves want not these Spirits, which (the living GOD permitting that) whether they be good or evil, have their Habitation in them. Men and Animals have in them a living operating Spirit, which receding from them, nothing but a Carkass remains. In Herbs, and all things bearing Fruit, a Spirit of Sanity exists; otherwise they could not, by any Preparation, be reduced to Medicinal use. Metals and all Minerals, are endued and possessed with their own incomprehensible Spirit, in which, the power and virtue of all their possible effects, consists. For whatsoever is without Spirit, wants Life, and contains in itself no vivifying Virtue. Therefore,

you are to know, that in Antimony also there is a Spirit, which effects whatsoever in it, or can proceed from it, in an invisible way and manner, no otherwise, than as in the Magnet is absconded a certain invisible power. [...]

There are other Spirits, wanting speech, which cannot shew themselves visibly in the very act; and they are those which live in Animals, as in Men and the like, in Plants also and in Minerals; nevertheless they have in themselves an occult and operative Life, and manifest and discover themselves by their efficacious power of operating, which they contain in and bear about themselves, and most apparently give testimony of their virtue of healing, whensoever that (by help of the Art) is extracted from them, being accurately separated from their body. After the same manner, the efficacious Spirit, and operative power of Antimony, manifests its gifts, and distributes them among Men, being first loosed from its own body, and freed from all its bonds, so, that it is able to penetrate, and render fit to be applyed to those Uses, which the Artificer proposed to himself in Preparation. (Valentine, 16)

---

from *Essentia Magazine* 2 (Winter 1981)

The Wonders of Antimony
by Frater Albertus

Antimony in its natural form displays an exceptional external appearance. Its ray-like extension in every direction impresses us as a manifestation of energy from a core of enormous potency. There is no metal known that appears in nature like antimony. Several minerals have similar characteristics (uranium ore, for example, which is known to contain enormous amounts of energy, sometimes has an antimonial appearance) but no mineral displays the outstanding spear-like luster of antimony.

However, to the average person antimony is of little significance. One may have heard

of it as an elemental metal, being of a poisonous nature, like arsenic, but beyond this usually little is known. As to any medicinal value of this poison, even less emerges. What, then, is so wonderful about antimony?

The ancients knew about antimony, praising it very highly for its hidden medicinal virtues. During medieval times, a rediscovery of these virtues by Basil Valentine and the "father" of modern medicine, Paracelsus, caused considerable renewed interest. Both found antimony to be of extraordinary curative potency and wrote extensively about it. Valentine called antimony one of the Seven Wonders of the World, praising it as the best blood-purifying agent available. He claimed to have used it for the cure of many diseases, including cancer. These claims were substantiated by Dr. Kerkring of Holland about two hundred and fifty years later when he prepared and used antimonial tinctures in his medical practice. Since that time, the Latin translation of Basil Valentine's *Triumphal Chariot of Antimony* by Dr. Kerkring and subsequent publication in other languages including English have caused considerable interest in antimony and its therapeutic virtues. Unfortunately, attempts to reestablish and confirm these early claims have proven fruitless for a hitherto unexplained reason.

Failure has stalked modern attempts to verify the medicinal potency of antimonial tinctures because of insufficient knowledge of the original alchemistical terminology and symbolism used by Valentine and Paracelsus. When modern chemistry replaced some of the archaic sounding names and symbols with terms that conformed to modern chemical theory, the modern researcher was not able to fathom the true meaning of the original concepts and hence was unable to duplicate the procedures so clearly outlined by Valentine. It is here where the controversy begins, (This does not mean that in former times there were no misconceptions about antimony. On the contrary, ignorance as to how to purify antimony of its powerful poisonous nature so that it could be safely used as a medicine was even in medieval times a stumbling block for those who failed to carefully follow the instructions of the alchemists.)

Contemporary research has established the fact that to unravel some of the alchemistical jargon requires a deep insight into the thought-world of the former alchemists. Only when the meaning of their wording and terminology has been uncovered, a difficult task as there are often great differences from presently established nomenclatures, is it then possible to begin making interpretations and verifications of those results

claimed by the alchemists. Those who have made sincere and diligent efforts to establish the validity of the ancient claims about antimony are literally amazed by the diversity of the procedures involved and their results. Then one appreciates why Valentine calls antimony one of the Seven Wonders of the World and states that one person's life is not long enough to explore all the wonders of the substance.

Nevertheless, the claims made by those who say they have accomplished the freeing of the potencies inherent in antimony give rise to many questions. First of all, why is so little known about antimony if it was once so famous? If it has great curative powers, where are the results of these investigations? If antimony preparations do exist, why is more not known about them? Why is this medicine not used to prove its efficaciousness?

There is sufficient literature available about antimony to fill many bookshelves but, unfortunately, modern interest has concentrated on the commercially profitable metallurgical exploitation of this substance. Very few people have made attempts to probe beyond the poisonous characteristics of antimony and master the proper formulation necessary to reveal its medicinal qualities. Evaluations can only be made after the substance to be tested is sufficiently available and there is hardly enough to be had for this serious clinical evaluation. So it is not surprising that so little is known about the wonders of antimony.

For several decades Paracelsus College and its predecessor, The Paracelsus Research Society, have placed considerable emphasis on the preparation of antimony for therapeutic evaluation. Experiments and tests have shown that careful contemplation is required before any laboratory attempts are undertaken. As statements by former alchemists do not find substantiation in modern textbooks and appear from the outset as impossible because of linguistic misunderstandings, modern researchers understandably face difficulties and even shy away from such an undertaking. Nevertheless, considerable

progress has been made. Efforts being made continue to produce gratifying evidence and further substantiation of the methods advocated by former alchemists for the production of antimonial tinctures and essences.

To produce medications that have their formerly inherent toxins removed so as to become harmless places a tremendous strain on the novice who wishes to enter into this field of research, particularly when no previous alchemistical studies under competent guidance have been completed. If it was not for the evidence at hand that this can be done, at least to a certain extent, the frustration of present-day researchers would be even greater.

However, if the potencies in antimony are so profound, why has modern medical science not made greater efforts to find out more about it, particularly when small quantities of antimonial tinctures have become available for clinical evaluation? The fact is that attempts to place these tinctures into the hands of those legally qualified to test them have failed because authorities such as the Federal Food and Drug Administration

(FDA) have no testing reports to pass judgment upon. Such required testing involves enormous amounts of money and time extending over years. Unless other ways and means become available, it looks like the wonders that are hidden in antimony will remain concealed even though Dr. Kerkring proved in his medical practice that much of the suffering of mankind can be alleviated by antimony.

However, modern medical science considers that the cures claimed by Dr. Kerkring are impossible. This prejudice, and the alchemistical connotations of the work of Valentine and Paracelsus, have prevented serious contemporary scientists from researching the area of antimony as a medicinal substance. Whatever the case may be, there is sufficient evidence on hand to prove that non-toxic and beneficial essences and tinctures can be prepared from antimony. What is lacking is only appropriation and approval by those qualified to legalize medicines. Only in such a way can the Wonders of Antimony be made available to suffering mankind.

Current works in medicine

Although Basil Valentine stressed that antimony could be made non poisonous, many medical applications even to the present, depend on the purgative and emetic qualities inherent in antimony; Tartar Emetic being the longest lasting antimonial preparation in the pharmacopoeias. Modern medicine has developed a few preparations for parasites, but these too rely upon antimony's toxic nature. Dr. David Schein wrote his doctoral thesis, *Basilius Valentinus and his Tinctures from Antimony*, at the University of Munich, Germany based on works performed in 1975 and 1976. In the preface to the English translation of 1980, he laments that, with the time that had passed since its first writing:

> One would therefore expect it to be somewhat out of date by now, but unfortunately no further research has been done in the meantime, concerning Basilius Valentinus and his tinctures from antimony. It seems that the historical sciences or anybody else have no inclination towards experimental research of old chemistry, and I am puzzled, why this is so. I had hoped, that this text, which is really very preliminary, would stimulate further investigation; more chemical research and certainly an examination of the biological properties of such alchemical substances as described here. In vain, nothing has happened, and I myself, having been able to do only little more in this area, am waiting for further opportunities to pursue these studies.

I hope the present volume fills in some of that gap and also stimulates further investigations into the medical virtues hidden in antimony.

Laboratory in 1967

Part Two: The Journey Begins

Early Works

This is where my story of antimony begins. In my younger days, I had a fascination with rocks and minerals. I had collected a nice selection of interesting specimens and was constantly searching for more. It didn't take long to find out that there were things you could do to rocks in order for them to reveal their names. Scratch them on a tile plate, treat them with acid, mix them with common salts and heat them with a candle flame directed by a blowpipe; this was all great fun to me.

I scoured the local library for information on other experiments with minerals and quickly discovered the world of the alchemists. The artwork and mystic symbols struck a deep chord inside of me, and little did I know it would blossom into a guiding force that would follow me the rest of my days.

Very soon, I had commandeered my older brother's chemistry set and established a small laboratory in the corner of my bedroom. My "Grimoire of Art" was a copy of the *The United States Dispensatory*, 1950 edition I inherited. This was a 5-inch thick tome describing the history, preparations, uses and doses of raw materials and drugs; even plant and animal substances were still listed. I learned how to prepare new chemicals from raw materials on hand. I studied the few texts about alchemy that I could find, but they were cryptic, confusing, and very secretive about practical works. *The Story of Alchemy and Early Chemistry*, by John Maxon Stillman provided my first practical introduction to laboratory alchemy and its terminology. I learned how to color metals by external application of various chemicals and tried my hand at making an artificial emerald; the recipe (from the Leyden-Stockholm Papyrus) called for the urine of an ass. I used my own urine, figuring it was the closest I was going to ever

get, and which turned out convenient, since I could blame its later failure on not being enough of an ass.

I filled the house with dense white smoke a time or two, and blew a hole in the ceiling, which prompted my parents to have me relocate my growing laboratory into a wooden shed we had in the backyard. That was perfect; now I had four times as much room! My lab quickly expanded to fill the whole shed.

By the age of fourteen, I had constructed a gas fired furnace and tried my hand at distilling the mineral acids from copper sulfate and potassium nitrate; the vitriol and niter of the ancient sages. Imagine my joy when I successfully smelted lead from a lump of galena and later copper from a piece of malachite. Still, this was just chemistry, and the secrets of the alchemist continued to elude me.

I began to study the writings of witches, wizards, and astrologers to gain an understanding of the secretive language of the alchemists and became quite good at casting and interpreting horoscopes, brewing potions, and casting a spell or two. My studies lead me into herbology and the mystical Qabalah as well as the Ceremonial Magic of the Middle Ages.

By the end of high school, I was fully enmeshed in the teachings of The Golden Dawn as presented by Israel Regardie; in fact I devoured all of Regardie's writings. In one of his works, *The Philosopher's Stone*, I gained new insights into the world of alchemy, but most importantly a name, Frater Albertus of the Paracelsus Research Society in Salt Lake City, Utah. I was in college now, ostensibly earning a degree in chemistry but not learning what I was really interested in.

After purchasing *The Alchemist's Handbook* by Frater Albertus, I realized that here was a man teaching the very things I had been searching after. I quickly applied for admission to the classes offered at the Paracelsus Research Society, which later became Paracelsus College, recognized by the State of Utah.

The backdrop for all of this was what my family called "The Shop." My father owned a die casting business and so I grew up surrounded by the metals and implements of forge and furnace, which supplied my lab with many useful items for alchemy, some of which I still have and use.

My first practical work with antimony was in response to an article written in *Scientific American*, the "Amateur Scientist" column in the late 1960's requiring an antimony electrode. It was easy to find a piece of antimony at the Shop so I constructed it. I still have it. My alchemical journey with antimony, however, began in 1973 after receiving a package containing the transcripts of papers presented at the 1973 International Alchemy Conference held in Stuttgart, Germany. The paper by Joseph Weber on antimony served as my introduction and guide for first experiments with antimony. I have appended it here as it is short but also because it is filled with good information and rare to find.

1973, Seeking the Origins of Alchemy in Egypt

THE SULPHUR OF ANTIMONY AND THE ART OF ITS PREPARATION *

by

Joseph Weber

THEORIES OF PRODUCTION METHODS

In outlining my experiences in extracting the sulphur from antimony preference has been given to the fact that with the exception of the Stone of the Wise no better blood cleansing remedy exists than the extracted sulphur or soul of antimony.

Since blood represents the carrier of life in any warm blooded individual, no emphasis is needed to point out that it should be kept clean in accordance with the alchemistic precept: clean body, pure soul, and pure spirit.

The essential factor contained in antimony and pertaining to its healing potential is its sulphur content or soul.

Besides its excellent action as a blood cleanser the sulphur is also a base ingredient for various additional highly effective alchemistical medications and remedies.

First I wish to draw attention to the fact that there exists a dualism in antimony as in all other manifestations. There is an unfixed and a fixed sulphur of antimony, and both types are applicable remedies for diseases where the blood is either too thick or too thin. The principle is: For thick blood - unfixed, for thin blood - fixed sulphur of antimony

---

* Translated by Siegfried O. Hansch

Alchemical Symposium of 1973 / paper by Joseph Weber,
"The Sulphur of Antimony and the Art of its Preparation"

respectively. Both types are often used in the form of antimony tinctures.

To separate or extract the sulphur out of antimony we require a menstrum analogous to that used in the herbal kingdom. Before we deal with the various methods of extracting the sulphur of antimony, we will proceed with the preparation of this menstrum.

Separation of the three essentials - body, soul, and spirit - from minerals present more difficulties than in the herbal kingdom. Since the three essehtials are more accessible in the herbal kingdom, the production of this menstrum should be based on the spirit from the herbal kingdom, i.e., alcohol. In order to work with this herbal spirit in the mineral kingdom, the two kingdoms must be bridged, i.e., the alcohol has to be magnetized with vibrations from the mineral kingdom. For this reason we use four parts thrice sublimated ammonium chloride grinding to a fine powder between sublimations, adding ten parts of absolute alcohol then macerating same. After the alcohol has been distilled from the extract its vibrations are no longer the same. It has become saturated with mineral influences and can, therefore, be used as a menstrum in the mineral kingdom.

This procedure was described by Basilius Valentinus in his book "The Triumphal Chariot of Antimony", and 250 years later Dr. Kerkring, a Dutchman annotated a reprint of the book. It is for this reason that our honorable teacher Frater Albertus, named this menstruum: Kerkring-Menstruum, abbreviated KM.

Now after we have become familiar with a menstruum with which we can work in the mineral kingdom, we would like to point out some of the possible methods whereby the sulphur of antimony may be separated.

One of the best known methods is that utilizing the glass of antimony. Here too several variations are possible, one of which we shall describe.

Take one part ground antimony ore (Sb_2S_3) and mix in a mortar with eight parts of antimony trioxide (Sb_2O_3). The very finely ground mixture should be heated to about 1000 - 1050° C. in an unglazed crucible. If after about half an hour this mixture is poured out on a copper plate, it turns into a red glass. A longer heating period will change the glass first into yellow and finally into white. In order to obtain glasses of other shades, the mixtures of Sb_2O_3 and Sb_2S_3 should be varied, e.g., one part of Sb_2S_3 and three parts Sb_2O_3, which results in a green glass. After cooling the glass must be ground in a mortar or ball mill to a fine flour-like powder which is then placed in an extractor with six normal acetic acid for the extraction of a golden-yellow tincture. After pouring off this extract, additional six normal acetic acid should be used and the glass again extracted. This procedure should be repeated until the vinegar no longer becomes tincted.

All the extractions are then combined, filtered and distilled in a water bath. A red powder will remain behind over which pour thrice distilled rainwater and distill again. Pour absolute alcohol over the remaining powder and allow to digest for a time. Thereby we obtain a deep red tincture of antimony.

A second, more rational possibility of separation can be carried out by chemical means. For this purpose a saturate solution of sodium-hydroxide (Na OH) and water should be prepared. At normal room temperature you can dissolve 1/3 Na OH in 2/3 water resulting in a 33% solution. We can utilize the interior warmth that developes to more quickly dissolve the antimony and so immediately add ground antimony ore (Sb_2S_3) as much as will dissolve. (About 1/7 part by weight of the solution) Then a 60% acetic acid solution is added to the sodium-antimony mixture, approximately 9/10. This forms a mildly acid reacting solution which should be left for some time. Thereafter this is washed with water

and filtered until litmus paper no longer shows a reaction.
After filtering and drying a red-brown powder remains which
can immediately be extracted with KM, or first with six
normal acetic acid, thus securing either an unfixed or fixed
antimonial tincture. This tincture still contains sulphur of
the sulphur. If, however, a pure antimony tincture is desired, the red powder should be calcined to a white before
extraction; thus burning off the common sulphur.

Another technique of chemical separation is the antimony
chloride method. In this procedure one part Sb_2S_3 is poured
into five parts hydrochloric acid, and boiled for thirty
minutes, during which time it has to be stirred continuously
until no more sulphureous fumes escape. The remaining greyish-
black fluid is a antimony chloride, which if filtered twice
through glasswool, results in an amber-colored fluid from
which the hydrochloric acid has to be distilled. Should a
yellowish mass develop on the sides of the flask, change
receivers and raise the temperature; a reddish, butter-like
mass will come over. The distillation has to be continued
until the remainder forms a crust in the flask. The distilled
antimony chloride is then dissolved in water, neutralized,
and dried under heat. Thereafter grind in a mortar and extract the sulphur of antimony with KM.

It would exceed the limitations of our paper were we to
go into all the possibilities and variations of separating
antimony.

In conclusion, remember that practical alchemy can only
be understood and mastered in its entire depths from one
spiritual psychical background and that events analogously
show the spiritual psychical development or evolution.

After making a few upgrades to the lab, purchasing five pounds each of the oxide and sulfide of antimony as well as five pounds of ammonium chloride, I began a series of experiments on making glass of antimony and sublimating Sal Ammoniac to prepare the Kerkring Menstruum. My initial glasses were dark and opaque, but I was so proud of them, I kept a piece for years as a memento but lost it somewhere in time.

The day finally arrived when I received a letter of acceptance to attend the Prima class of Spring 1974 at the Paracelsus Research Society (PRS) in Salt Lake City, Utah.

Part Three: PRS

PRS Prima 1974

In April of 1974, I attended the first of seven 2-week intensive training courses in the Hermetic Arts taught by Frater Albertus, one of the most well-known practical alchemists of the 20th century. My life changed entirely; I dropped out of college, moved to the primitive heart of Idaho, and devoted my time to the study and practice of alchemical works.

The classes ran from 9:00 a.m. to 5:00 p.m. Monday through Saturday with works in the laboratory running continuously. Dormitory space was provided for everyone to stay onsite. TV, radios, even newspapers were discouraged so that everyone stayed focused on the works and teachings. The library and lecture hall were open 24/7 and students would congregate there in the evenings to share or amend notes of the day and carry on conversations on a variety of occult topics until the early morning hours. This was the scene for the next seven years. Many of the students returned each year and soon became like family and, though we all came from diverse backgrounds, Alchemy united us like brothers and sisters with a common goal.

Atlanta, Idaho 1974

PRS Prima Class 1974

MR. ALBERT RIEDEL

It may come as a distinct surprise to some people today to learn that the historical tradition is still active in the modern world. One of its foremost exponents is a man following in the footsteps of Paracelsus, and who has even founded an institute of higher learning, the Paracelsus Research Society. Like Paracelsus, however, Mr. Riedel is no blind follower of his predecessors in alchemical art and practice. An original thinker, he developed fascinating methods of scientific investigation which neither Paracelsus nor the earlier alchemists have conceived of and would certainly have envied. In his work, the ancient and modern sciences have joined hands to walk together for the benefit of mankind as Parachemy.

He is a man of tremendous energy and creativity—an independent thinker who has inspired by his example and ingenuity a whole new generation of students and researchers. As a consequence of this, they are carrying on the old noble tradition; it will not die out, thanks to him.

Paralab is one of the several products of his creativity and is watched over and supervised by him. Those who know him honor his scientific and philosophical talents which find their way into the development of unique medicaments and extracts. This makes both Paralab and Mr. Riedel outstanding.

He is not only a philosopher and teacher, but the author of several books which are destined, even now, to exert a tremendous influence on the future development of medicine and science. Like Paracelsus, he will not soon be forgotten. History is shaped and moulded by men of his calibre who have such wisdom and humanity.

Dr. I. F. Regardie

PRS Secunda 1975

Frater Albertus' ultimate dream was to create "Tristar," a unified complex, housing a teaching facility, a laboratory producing spagyric products, and a clinic where the products were put into medical practice.

The 1975 Secunda class alchemy instruction was entirely devoted to antimony, which included readings from Basil Valentine's *Triumphal Chariot* and some hands-on work in the laboratory over the two-week period.

The notes I took during class related to the antimony work have been scanned and appear in the following pages.

Within this building are found the alchemical laboratory, office-library, and lecture room.

(Photo by D. Burton)

Left, photo of the lab building at the PRS and, above, of Frater Albertus.

- Alchemy -

LABORATORY ALCHEMY HELPS US TO SEE THE LAWS EXPLAINED AND UNFOLD.

IN THE MINERAL REALM THERE ARE 3 DIVISIONS: 1 MINERAL
                                                  2 METAL
                                                  3 CRYSTALS OR GEMS

ANTIMONY IS ON THE DIVIDING LINE BETWEEN MINERAL AND METAL
ANTIMONY ☿ IS VERY POISONOUS IN ITS RAW OR CRUDE FORM.
THERE APPEARS IN MODERN MEDICAL TEXTS VERY LITTLE ABOUT IT AND
IS THOUGHT TO HOLD LITTLE OR NO VIRTUE.
THE EGYPTIANS USED IT AS MASCARA.
IT WAS NOT UNTIL THE MONK BASILIUS VALENTINUS WROTE ABOUT IT
IN THE 1500's THAT ITS VIRTUES WERE DISCOVERED & MORE COMPREHENSIVELY
AND RECORDED.
   IN HIS TRIUMPHAL CHARIOT OF ANTIMONY HE WRITES FIVE GUIDE LINES
OR STEPS FOR THE SUCCESSFUL ALCHEMIST:

   1. INVOCATION - A SINCERE PRAYER TO THE MOST HIGH FOR HIS
              HELP AND GUIDANCE.

   2. CONTEMPLATION - MOST IMPORTANT. "KNOW THE THEORY FIRST BEFORE
              ATTEMPTING THE PRAXIS"

   3. PREPARATION - THE MANUAL OPERATIONS.   SUCH AS:
          CALCINATION - TO MAKE IT WHITE AS CALX
          SUBLIMATION - DRY DISTILLATION
          REVERBERATION - TO IMMERSE IN HEAT OR FIRE
          CIRCULATE - TO CIRCULATE MAKING A CIRCLE C NOT REFLUX ℞
          PUTREFACTION - TO DECAY
          DIGESTION - GENTLE HEAT TO OPEN UP
          DISTILLATION - FOR LIQUIDS
          COHOBATION - TO JOIN TO GETHER AGAIN
          FIXATION - BRING TO A FIXED STATE WHEREIN IT IS HARD TO SEPARATE

   4. USES - DETERMINE THE USES. WHERE AND WHERE NOT TO USE IT
        AS ~~the~~ WELL AS WHEN.

5. DOSES — WE MUST JUDGE THE DOSE AT NOT TOO MUCH NOR TOO LITTLE. PROPER DOSAGE IS VERY IMPORTANT.

FOR THE PREPARATION OF ANTIMONY INTO A PURE MEDICINE DIGESTION AND PUTREFACTION ARE MASTER KEYS TO THE PROCESS AS WELL AS THE ALL IMPORTANT REGULATION OF THE FIRE. FOR FIRE IS THE ROOT OF THE WHOLE MATTER. "REGULATE IT PROPERLY"

TO BEGIN THE PROCESS ON ANTIMONY:

1. TAKE THE PURE ANTIMONY SULFIDE AND PULVERIZE IT AS FINELY AS POSSIBLE.

2. SPREAD THINLY ON AN EARTHENWARE DISH AND PLACE THIS IN A CALCINATORY FURNACE OVER A MODERATE HEAT.

3. AS SOON AS SMOKE APPEARS STIR WITH AN IRON ROD UNTIL THERE IS NO MORE SMOKE, AND THE ☿ STICKS TOGETHER IN SMALL GLOBULES.

4. REMOVE FROM FIRE AND PULVERIZE TO A FINE POWDER THEN RETURN IT TO THE FIRE AGAIN.

5. THIS PROCESS IS REPEATED UNTIL THE ANTIMONY DOES NO LONGER SMOKE OR STICK IN GLOBULES AND HAS THE APPEARANCE OF PURE WHITE ASHES.

6. PLACE THIS CALCINED ☿ IN A CRUCIBLE AND SET IT OVER A VIOLENT FIRE. UNTIL THE ANTIMONY BECOMES LIQUID. TO TEST THIS DIP A ROD OF IRON INTO THE MOLTEN MASS THEN PULL IT OUT AND EXAMINE THE GLASS WHICH ADHERES TO IT. IF IT IS CLEAR, PURE AND TRANSPARENT IT IS ALL RIGHT AND HAS ATTAINED ITS DUE MATURITY THIS MATURITY IS PERFORMED SOLELY BY VULCAN OPERATING ON THE SECRET AND CONCEALED NATURE.

7. WHEN THE ANTIMONY HAS BECOME VITREFIED AS DESCRIBED, HEAT A FLAT BROAD COPPER DISH OVER THE FIRE AND POUR THE ☿ IN AS CLEAR AND THIN A STATE AS POSSIBLE — THUS WE WILL OBTAIN THE GLASS OF ANTIMONY.

Alchemy.

CRUDE ANTIMONY ORE IS CALLED ANTIMONY TRISULFIDE (Sb_2S_3)

IT HAS ALSO BEEN CALLED STIBIUM BY THE CHALDEANS AND IN GERMAN, SPEISGLAS MEANING SPEAR LUSTER WHICH DESCRIBES ITS PHYSICAL APPEARANCE OF ITS CRYSTALLINE STRUCTURE, WHICH APPEARS AS MANY SILVERY RAYS WITH DIFFERENT CENTERS OF EMMANATIONS.

THE MAGNETIC POLAR ROTATION CAUSES THE CRYSTAL RAYS TO BE MIXED IN THEIR DIRECTION

ANTIMONY ORE

GANGE OR EXCESS SURROUNDING ROCK

THE MINERAL REALM OFFERS MEDICINES ~~WITH~~ WITH THE HIGHEST VIBRATORY RATES OR GREATEST POTENCIES, BECAUSE THEY HAVE BEEN INFUSED FOR AGES WITH RADIATIONS (CELESTIAL ETC.) WHEREAS PLANTS AND ANIMALS ARE , RELATIVELY SPEAKING, SHORTLY INFUSED.

THE SYMBOL FOR ANTIMONY IS ♁. JUST AS ALL PLANETARY SYMBOLS ARE COMPOSED OF EITHER A CIRCLE, CRESENT, OR CROSS IN SOME COMBINATION. AND JUST AS METALS ARE RULED BY DIFFERENT PLANETS AND CAN BE SIGNIFIED BY THE DIFFERENT PLANETARY SYMBOLS SUCH AS TIN = ♃ GOLD = ☉, MERCURY ☿ ETC. SO IT IS WITH ANTIMONY. WE SEE THE SYMBOL FOR URANUS ♅. THIS PLANET WAS DISCOVERED BY HERSCHEL SO FOR THE SYMBOL THEY USED THE MONOGRAM "H" AND SYMBOLIZED A PLANETARY ORB WITH IT. ♅ WHEREAS THE TRUE SYMBOL FOR URANUS IS ♅ THIS IS THE RULER OF ANTIMONY ♅.

COMMERCIAL ~~——~~ ANTIMONY TRIOXIDE IS PRODUCED FROM THE PURE METAL (WHICH IS DEAD).

FOR ALCHEMICAL PURPOSES WE SHOULD USE THE PURE ORE AS IT COMES FROM THE GROUND. SEPARATE THE GANGE FROM IT, GRIND IT, AND ROAST IT <u>SLOWLY</u> SO THAT IT OXIDIZES SLOWLY TO PURE WHITE.

THIS WHITE TRIOXIDE IS THEN PLACED IN A CRUCIBLE AND PLACED IN AN REVERBERATORY FURNACE SO THAT IT FUSES INTO A CLEAR GLOSS. WHICH CAN BE TESTED BY PLACING A COLD

IRON ROD INTO AND PULLING IT OUT, THEN OBSERVING THE glass WHICH STICKS TO IT. IT SHOULD BE TRANSPARENT. THIS WILL TAKE APPROX. 2-3 Hrs. WITH Regulation OF THE Heat (Higher OR LOWER) VARYING SHADES OF glass CAN BE OBTAINED. Yellow, RED, green, AMBER, Black, white, clear. (THIS VARIATION IN color IS VERY IMPORTANT)

$$Sb_2S_3 \xrightarrow{\overset{S_2}{\uparrow}} \text{CALCINE} \rightarrow Sb_2O_3$$

THE Heat REQUIRED TO CHANGE THIS ANTIMONY TRIOXIDE INTO A clear glass IS (W/O BORAX FLUX) ABOUT 1100°~1200°C. THE glass MUST BE TRANSPARENT OR IT IS NOT MATURE.

ANOTHER WAY TO PREPARE THIS glass OF ANTIMONY IS TO USE BORAX AS A FLUXING AGENT. IN THIS PROCESS WE TAKE:
  1 part BY WEIGHT OF CRUDE ANTIMONY TO,
  2 parts BY WEIGHT OF BORAX
THESE ARE GROUND IN A ~~crucible~~ MORTAR AND PLACED IN A CRUCIBLE WHERE THEY ARE THEN SUBJECTED TO THE FURNACE AND FUSED. (THE BORAX Helps THE ANTIMONY TO MELT UNDER A LOWER Heat) THIS PRODUCES A RED glass called pyropus.

USING THE ANTIMONY TRIOXIDE WE CAN ALSO ADD BORAX AND FUSE THIS AT A LOWER TEMPERATURE IF OUR FURNACES ARE NOT ABLE TO go THIS HIGH. IN THIS PROCESS WE USE THE PROPORTIONS (BY weight)
  8 parts ANTIMONY TRIOXIDE
  1 part BORAX

WHEN OUR glass IS MATURE, THAT IS TRANSPARENT, WE MUST POUR IT ONTO A HEATED COPPER DISH AS THINLY AS possible (TO ASSIST GRINDING). THE COOLED glass IS FINELY GROUND, THE FINER THE BETTER. AND THE RED, yellow OR WHATEVER color MUST BE EXTRACTED FROM IT, BUT FIRST THE BORAX MUST BE

completely (as possible) washed from this ground glass with disti.
hot water. In this it is preferable to circulate the glass
in a soxhlet extractor with several changes of water. Since
borax is an alkaline substance and readily dissolves in water
we can test this rinse water with litmus or PH paper
until there is a neutral reaction showing no or at least
a negligable amount of borax left. (There will always be some
trace amounts of borax when it is used as a flux this is why
it is Best to use no borax flux.)

→ once the glass has been completely washed of borax (or as
much as possible) it is dried so no moisture remains.
Now the color which tincts the glass must be extracted
this is the ♀ of ☿ and it is this sulfur which is the medicine
we seek, the glass that will be left is the body or salt
which contains the emetic virtue and all its poisonous qualities.

To extract this medicine we need a menstruum which is
adapted to the mineral kingdom. Valentine tells us to use
the spirits of wine But by this he does not mean the
pure wine of grapes only, for this is only adapted to the
vegetable kingdom. It must undergo a process which will
associate or magnetize it to the mineral realm.

For this process we use 4oz ammonium chloride which has
been sublimed 3 times. Ammonium chloride formerly called
hart's horn because derived from deer antlers which have
been ground and sublimed. Also known as sal ammoniac.
(can also be derived from urine)

To sublime a substance we can use two enameled or
canningware glass dishes set up thus:

CRYSTALS OF SUBLIMED
SUBSTANCE

POWDER TO BE SUBLIMED

HEAT

Once this ammonium chloride has been sublimed 3 times it must be carefully preserved in a clean <u>dry</u> bottle (glass stoppered preferably) until ready to be used.

Now 10 oz of alcohol are rectified using potassium carbonate (also called sal tartari, salt of tartar, winestone or argol and is prepared from calcined grape wine.) This potassium carbonate is made anhydrous by drying in an oven before use. (The proportions are 25gms potassium carbonate / 1000ml alcohol.) Add the pot. carb. to the already 190 proof alcohol and allow to macerate overnight in a separatory funnel. We will see that the moisture remaining in the alcohol has been absorbed by the pot. carb. and separated itself and sunk to the <u>bottom</u>. This is now separated and the alcohol is distilled carefully one more time at 76°C. To this absolute alcohol is now added the sublimed ammonium chloride and is allowed to macerate circulate or preferably soxhlet extract until a strong golden yellow tincture is obtained.

This tincture (containing the ☿ and ♀ of the sal ammoniac) is then distilled 3 times to remove the golden ♀ which is put aside. The alcohol is now clear but it contains traces of the ☿ (from sal ammoniac) or spirit of the mineral realm (the alkahest) This alcohol has now been, as it were, magnetized to the mineral realm by its association with the sal ammoniac just as a pin retains some of the magnetism when associated with a magnet.

This is now the menstruum we use to extract the color or sulfur from the now powdered, dried, glass of antimony. And is called the Kerkring menstruum (abbreviated KM)

Now to extract this sulfur from our glass we place the powdered glass into a circulator (not reflux ↑ but circulate ↺)

This should be done under vacuum so no moisture is absorbed

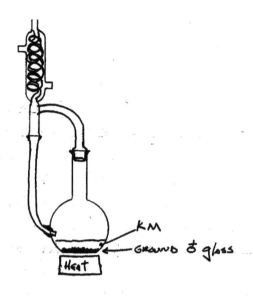

KM

GROUND ♂ glass

Heat

WHEN THE glass is ADDED TO THE CIRCULATOR OR THE THIMBLE OF A SOXHlet EXTRACTOR AND THE KM IS POURED OVER IT, THE WHOLE MUST BE CIRCULATED FOR 3 MONTHS TO OBTAIN ALL THE TINCTURE.

WHEN THIS TINCTURE IS OBTAINED A PORTION OF THE KM IS DISTILLED OFF SO THE MEDICINE OR ♀ IS NOT SO DILUTE.

THIS MEDICINE IS THE BEST BLOOD PURIFIER WE CAN HAVE.

(NOTE: DIFFERENT COLORED glasses WILL GIVE DIFFERENT MEDICINAL PROPERTIES)

THIS IS EXPLAINED FURTHER SO READ ON.

ROBERT ALLEN BARTLETT

Alchemy:

When the cohesive force is present the substance is held together - it is alive. The spirit is present.

When it only ADHERES or sticks to something else it is dead. The soul is there but the spirit is gone.

In the KM we seek the SPIRIT of Sal Ammoniac to infuse it into the alcohol. This mineral spirit is the alcahest.

We know now that: 8 pts Antimony Trioxide plus
                                    1 pt Borax
will fuse in a crucible under a Fischer Burner and produce a yellow glass when poured onto a heated copper plate or other convenient dish.
          And that 1 pts crude antimony ore plus
                             2 pts Borax
will produce a RED glass.
So it is that by regulation of the fire and time in the fire and Borax flux we can produce all the colors of the rainbow clear, white, grey, black, blue, RED, yellow, green, orange, violet, etc. etc.
          These colors will indicate the virtue that is within that particular glass according to the planetary color system:
          green glass - the green ray, ♀ (Netsach)
          RED glass - the RED ray ♂ (Geburah)
          yellow glass - the yellow ray ☉ (Tiphareth)
          clear glass - the pure white light (Kether)

Within this one ☉ you will find the virtue of all 7 planetary influences.

Alchemy:

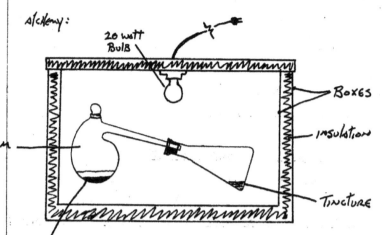

20 watt Bulb

Boxes

insulation

Tincture

Antimony Glass and KM

THIS IS ANOTHER WAY to OBTAIN THE TINCTURE OF ♁ without using a Soxhlet. This method will of course Take Longer. A Sandbath can also Be used. After the Tincture Has come over once, it can Be poured over the glass again and the slow distillation can Be Repeated several times. In this way the Sulfur of ♁ is mixed with the KM in what is known as the Chemical Marriage.

To Remove any EXCESS moisture that may Have Been Absorbed By The KM or Tincture of ♁ we can place The Stoppered Flask in The Freezer and with it a can containing Another empty Flask and Funnel with Filter paper. Now the moisture will Freeze and crystallize out and The Alcohol will not. So when Both Flask and can are Frozen The Tincture or KM can Be Filtered and a Top placed on The can and kept in The Freezer until Done. In This way The Ice Crystals are Filtered out and we obtain The Pure Alcohol.

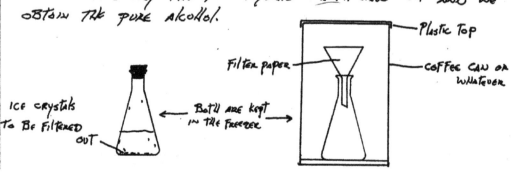

Plastic Top

Filter paper

Coffee can or whatever

Ice crystals to Be Filtered out

Both are kept in The Freezer

ROBERT ALLEN BARTLETT

POTENCIES : DOSES

HOW DO WE KNOW WHAT IS FULL STRENGTH IN OUR ANTIMONY TINCTURE?

IN PHARMACY THE RATIO O 1 PART TO 1 PART (BY WEIGHT) IS USED THAT IS:

1 PART GLASS OF ♁ (BY WEIGHT) IS EXTRACTED BY AN EQUAL WEIGHT OF KM. THIS PRODUCES WHAT IS KNOWN AS THE "MOTHER TINCTURE". THIS MOTHER TINCTURE IS VERY POTENT AND IS DILUTED WITH WATER TO PRODUCE THE PROPER DOSAGE (USUALLY 1 DROP ♁ TINCTURE TO 10-20 DROPS WATER)

THE TINCTURE OF ♁ GLASS USUALLY COMES OUT REDDISH TO YELLOW EVEN FROM OTHER COLORED GLASS SUCH AS GREEN.

THE VIRTUE IS IN THE RED OIL. THIS IS THE ♀ OR QUINTESSENCE OF ♁.

IN THE PLANT KINGDOM THE QUINTESSENCE IS THE ☿. THE QUINTESSENCE OF A SUBSTANCE IN THE MINERAL REALM CAN BE EITHER THE ♀ OR ☿.

TO PURIFY ANTIMONY FUME

START WITH ANTIMONY FUME WHICH IS AN IMPURE OXIDE.
DISSOLVE IN HYDROCHLORIC ACID — BOIL IT.
FILTER IT (GLASS FILTER PAPER)
TAKE WHAT IS FILTERED AND POUR IN DISTILLED WATER
(≈ 20 PTS WATER / PT SOLUTION) THIS WILL FORM THE PRECIPITATE ANTIMONY OXY-CHLORIDE WHICH IS WHITE. KEEP WASHING AND DECANT. GET ALL THE ACID OUT
DRY THIS OXY-CHLORIDE AND PUT IN SOLUTION OF SODIUM BICARBONATE (WEAK SOLN) TO NEUTRALIZE IT. THIS GIVES OFF CO_2. TEST PH (7)
DRY IT WASH IT WELL.

LIME CAN BE USED IN place OF SALT OF TARTAR

USE A SEPARATORY FUNNEL TO SEPARATE THE
WATER / POTASSIUM CARBONATE MIXTURE FROM THE ALCOHOL ———
THEN DISTILLED UNDER A VACUUM TO AVOID MOISTURE ABSORBTION

CONSTANT DISTILLATIONS AND CIRCULATIONS ACTIVATE
AND STRENGTHEN THE SUBSTANCE.

THE ALCOHOL WILL NOT DISSOLVE It BUT ANY MOISTURE IN THE
ALCOHOL WILL DISSOLVE SOME OF THE POISONOUS PARTS. THIS IS
WHY THE ALCOHOL MOST BE PURE AND FREE FROM ALL
MOISTURE. OR ELSE POISONS WILL CONTAMINATE THE TINCTURE
YOU OBTAIN.
TAKE YOUR TIME AND BE SURE ALL IS PURIFIED.

Tertia Notes

Between Secunda and Tertia I worked in my lab in Atlanta and soon came into a source of stibnite through some odd circumstances detailed further ahead. I wanted to lump together the notes taken in Tertia with those of Secunda since this was the majority of teachings received at the PRS concerning antimony. Future classes were devoted to other topics with only some commentary and student questions answered regarding antimony.

In the third year class at PRS, again devoted to the work on antimony, we spent time reading through Basil Valentine's *Triumphal Chariot of Antimony*, with commentary by Dr. Theodor Kerkring in 1685 and published by James Elliot & Co., London 1893. We would take turns reading and Frater Albertus would add commentary. Page numbers in the notes refer to that edition of *Triumphal Chariot*.

P.42 PAGE NUMBERS FROM TRIUMPHAL CHARIOT —

ALCOHOL IS NOT WINE, WINE IS NOT ALCOHOL — BUT CONTAINS ALCOHOL

VINEGAR IS NOT ACETIC ACID AND VICE VERSA BUT VINEGAR

CONTAINS ACETIC ACID. FROM BACTERIAL ACTION

SOUR WINE — VINEGAR — ORGANIC SUBSTANCE

VINEGAR ACTS ON SUBSTANCES DIFFERENTLY THAN SPIRIT OF WINE

— p.35 TRUE SOUL — p.99 1ST SEPARATION OF $\bar{\text{V}}$ FROM $\bar{\text{♁}}$

— TO GRIND FINE MAKE PASTE OF $\bar{\text{♁}}$ w/ VINEGAR

RECTIFICATION OF VINEGAR — 1ST A WATER COMES OVER THEN

acetic acid.
— WINE
— APPLE CIDER ETC.

VINEGAR OF ANTIMONY — USE REGULAR VINEGAR UNTIL YOU

KNOW HOW TO PRODUCE VINEGAR OF $\bar{\text{♁}}$

& GLASS OF $\bar{\text{♁}}$ POUR OVER IT RECTIFIED VINEGAR. EXTRACT YELLOW TINCTURE

(EXTRACTED $\bar{\text{♁}}$ w/ $\frac{\text{S}}{\text{V}}$ GIVES OIL AFTER ☉)

"   "   " /VINEGAR " POWDER " ☉

WHEN WASHING POWDER (P.100) GO ONLY TO PH 7

NO FURTHER. IT WILL TURN SOUR AGAIN SHOWING YOU

HAVE ARRIVED AT THE VINEGAR OF $\bar{\text{♁}}$. IT TASTES LIKE

VINEGAR. THIS IS THE ANTIMONIAL ACID.

— VINEGAR FIXES — MAKES SOLID.

HOW CAN INORGANIC $\bar{\text{♁}}$ CONTAIN VINEGAR? Biological TRANSMUTATION

— YOU CAN HAVE TINCTURES THAT ARE DEAD —

(LIKE BLOOD WITHOUT ITS LIFE FORCE)

THE SWEET POWDER — NOT LIKE HONEY BUT ACID-LESS

P.102 — EXTERNAL MEDICINE ALSO INTERNAL

LEPROSY = HANSEN'S DISEASE

MELANCHOLY - IMPURE BLOOD CANNOT CIRCULATE AS IT SHOULD
 AND CARRY THE SPIRIT FREELY TO ALL PARTS.

PURE BLOOD CAN RESIST POISON.

☿ ☆THE BEST BLOOD PURIFIER.

STICH IN THE SIDE - KIDNEY IMPURITIES - STONES. ETC.

 KIDNEYS - WASHING MACHINES OF THE BLOOD.

— IF IT IS BUILT UP BY FORCE IT GETS TORN DOWN BY
FORCE - ☿ WORKS GRADUALLY.

HEALTHY BLOOD — HEALTHY SPIRIT

THE VINEGAR FIXES WHAT IS TO BE FOUND IN THE ☿

THIS TINCTURE WILL WORK DIFFERENTLY THAN THE KM EXTRACT

 ~~SPIRIT OF~~ KM EXTRACT - EXPANDS AND HEATS

 VINEGAR EXTRACT - COOLS AND CONTRACTS

INFLAMATIONS EXPAND THE VESSELS

IMPURITIES CAN CONTRACT THE VESSELS

 7-BASICS LOOSENS THE IMPURITIES THEN THE
☿ PURGES THEM OUT.

THIS IS WHERE DOSAGE IS SO IMPORTANT.

TOO MUCH CAN PURGE US TOO FAST - CAUSING CLOTS ETC.

VINEGAR FIXES - LIKE PHOTOGRAPHY. NOT EVERY AND
 DOES THIS.

P. 103

MARBLE ASH TRAY ETC. WILL WORK JUST AS WELL AS THE EGG

THIS IS THE POISON OR SALT USED EXTERNALLY

LUPUS - RAW FLESH THAT WONT HEAL. EATS AT THE FLESH. NOT CANCER

" POISON ATTRACTS TO IT, ITS OWN "

P 105.   BOCCHUS - GOD OF WINE -

JUNO - WIFE OF ZEUS - THE SUBSTANCE OR EARTH

VULCAN - FIRE GOD - THE FIRE

LET IT RISE BUT NOT ESCAPE - DISTILL IT.

HOLD IT W/ A STRING - CONTROL ITS RISING.

WHEN ETHANOL IS OXIDISED ACETIC ACID IS

PRODUCED

$$H-\overset{\overset{\displaystyle H}{|}}{\underset{\underset{\displaystyle H}{|}}{C}}\overset{\overset{\displaystyle H}{|}}{\underset{\underset{\displaystyle H}{|}}{C}}-OH$$

$$H-\overset{\overset{\displaystyle H}{|}}{\underset{\underset{\displaystyle H}{|}}{C}}-\overset{\overset{\displaystyle O}{||}}{C}-O-H$$

ACETIC ACID BOILS AT 117° - 118° C

WINE VINEGAR - THE FIXED SPIRIT.

WINE - 17% ALCOHOL, SO THE SPIRIT WITHIN WHEN FIXED

   IS SIMILARLY LOW. THE WINE MUST BE RECTIFIED.

GLACIAL ACETIC ACID - DILUTE BY 2/3 = 6N ACETIC ACID

                       WATER

                         33% ACETIC ACID

p. 100

  FOR SOXHLET - FILL THIMBLE 2/3 w/WATER

AND ADD AS MUCH ACETIC ACID TO THE FLASK

AS IS NECESSARY - THIS WAY WE ALWAYS HAVE 6N

ACETIC ACID IN THE THIMBLE. THIS IS DONE BECAUSE OF

THE DIFFERENCE IN BOILING TEMPERATURES.

"WE ALWAYS PREFER MACERATION"

AFTER OBTAINING THE RED POWDER (p 100) IT IS EXTRACTED

w/ KM GIVING US THE FIXED TINCTURE.

(WE CAN ALSO MORE FIXED VEGETABLE EXTRACTS)

THE FIXED POWDER IS STILL POISON BUT CONTAINS

THE PURE ESSENCE WHICH IS EXTRACTED W/ KM

THIS - INFLAMATION

EMOLLIENT SOOTHS INFLAMATIONS

  EX: KIDNEY STONES. ANTIMONY TO CLEANSE THE BLOOD

SINCE IT INFLAMES WE USE FIXED TINCTURE TO EASE THE

INFLAMATION. OIL TO COAT TISSUES AS EMOLLIENT - THIS CAN

BE SOMETHING WITH AN AFFINITY FOR THE KIDNEYS ♀

I.E. OIL OF SAGE OR COPPER. MIXED WITH THE KM IN THE

☿ EXTRACT. (FIXED OR UNFIXED ACCORDING TO THE NEED)

IN THIS WAY THE ☿ ACTS LIKE THE VEHICLE OR CHARIOT FOR THE SPECIFIC MEDICINE

☿ PURIFIES THE BLOOD (CARRIER OF LIFE) EVEN TO THE FINEST

CLOGGED CAPILLARIES — LETTING THE FULNESS OF LIFE FLOW

THRU AND RAISE US UP.

DIFFERENT COLORED GLASS AND THEIR COLORS DO NOT NECESSARILY

PRODUCE MEDICINES OF DIFFERENT PROPERTIES.

SULFUR OF SULFUR — RED OIL

    IT IS AMOST EXCELLENT PRESERVATIVE — KEEPS THINGS PLIABLE

— MUST HAVE GOOD HEALTH 1ST IN ORDER TO PRESERVE IT OTHERWISE

WE PRESERVE OUR IMPERFECTIONS ALSO.

IT IS THE PREPARATION OF ☿ THAT PRODUCES DIFFERENT

MEDICINES.

- THE EXCESS OF THE COLOR RAY SHOWS US THE VIRTUE WITHIN

NEPTUNE — ZINC — OLIVE — ENDURING INTELLIGENCE — ☿

                COLOR

- NOT HIGHER OCTAVES — BUT OTHER POLARITY OF THE ANCIENT PLANETS

THAT IS A HALF TONE.

ZINC IS LIKE COPPER BUT CONTAINS LESS SULFUR.

- TUES = ♂ RAY IN OLD SYSTEM IN NEW SYSTEM DAY IS ÷ INTO

    NIGHT ƒ DAY RULER BY DAY — REST BY NIGHT

P.103 - THIS POWDER, LIQUIFIED IS STILL POISON - EXTERNAL USE ONLY   MOIST ATMOSPHERE IS NECESSARY TO LIQUIFY

P.105 - 1ST OPERATION   CALCINATION & ULTRIFICATION

2ND OPERA   DIGESTION TO EXTRACT OIL

COAGULATION - CIRCULATION

DISTILLATION INTO OIL

FIXATION - FORMATION OF FIRE STONE

- THE FIRESTONE CAN ONLY WORK ON METALS WHEN IT IS FERMENTED THAT IS THE ADDITION OF GOLD IN SOLUTION TO ACT AS AN ENZYME

PROPER USE IS IMPORTANT

P.106 - FOOTNOTE - THE BODY MUST BE PURGED W/ GENERAL REMEDIES — (7 BASICS)

THESE PREPARATIONS CANNOT CURE THOSE DISEASES WHICH HAVE PROGRESSED BEYOND REDEMPTION — AFTER THAT POINT ONLY THE HOLY SPIRIT W/ IN AS A GIFT CAN CURE.

LIVE A LIFE THAT WILL MAKE YOU WORTHY TO RECEIVE SUCH A GIFT OF THE HOLY GHOST (SPIRIT)

QUARTAN FEVER — FEVER W/ VIOLENT ERUPTIONS EVERY 4 DAYS
FIRE STONE = STONE OF MERCURY

ROBERT ALLEN BARTLETT

THE OIL OF ☉ WILL WORK ON THE TISSUES & SERUM

TO PURGE

- BORON - (BORAX) - IS VERY POWERFUL (USED IN GASOLINE & ROCKET FUEL

VINEGAR OF ☉ = VINEGAR OF THE SAGES

OMPHACIUM - JUICE OF THE UNRIPE GRAPE

P109-10 - MOISTURE DISTILLED OFF LEAVING TARTAR

SPIRIT OF VINEGAR - ACETIC ACID

SPIRIT OF SALT - (NOT AS TODAY HCl) BUT FROM TABLE SALT EXTRACT ITS

SPIRIT OUT

CALX OF GOLD - IT'S SALT

P113 - SUBLIMATE THE 2 SUBSTANCES

SPIRIT OF VITRIOL - FROM COPPER SULFATE ← THE ORE OF COPPER

BECAUSE IT CONTAINS ALOT OF ♀

* - WE CAN ALSO USE IRON SULFATE - OR PYRITE

* - OR PURE SULFUR VIVE

Edulcoration - SWEETEN - REMOVE THE SALT OF AMONIA

TINCTURE OF CORRALS - RED CORRAL EXTRACTED W/ KM

QUINTESSENCE OF RHUBARB - ITS ☿

AQUA☿ FONTIS - NITRIC ACID

P 121 - THIS FIXED RED POWDER IS NOT POISONOUS

COLCOTAR OF VITRIOL - IRON SULFATE

p.129 - MINERAL VINEGAR - ANTIMONIAL ACID - MERCURY OF ☉ FIXED

THIS IS THE ALCAHEST OF ☉ (FIXED)

Tartar - Potassium Tartrate or Bitartrate
↑ WINE STONE

Salt of Tartar - Potas. Carbonate

Two Keys P 128
1 - SPIRIT OF WINE ~~only~~   UNFIXED   PURGATIVE PROPERTIES
2 - VINEGAR   FIXED cleanses w/ sweats etc

P 131 - USE SUBLIMED TARTAR

P 166 - LATERA - RED clay FIREBRICK - USED AS A
Filtering media similar to diatomaceous earth.

P 170 - STRAIN w/ GLASS wool
↑
WE ARRIVE AT A COMBINATION OF ♀ OF ♀ AND ♀ OF ♁
BECAUSE THE COMMON SULFUR HAS NOT BEEN CALCINED OUT
FROM THIS RED POWDER WHICH IS NOT YET FIXED (THE VINEGAR

KERMES - ANTIMONY OXYSULFIDE

ONLY NEUTRALIZED THE LYE) AND PRODUCE EXTRACTS OF
RM AND VINEGAR (GN) CONTAINING ♀ OF ♀ AND ♀ OF ♁
THIS RED POWDER CAN BE CALCINED THEN VITRIFIED
WITH LESS HEAT.

Rx THE RED POWDER - EXTRACT w/ VINEGAR DISTILL OFF THE
VINEGAR FROM TINCTURE - Rx POWDER THAT REMAINS
AND EXTRACT w/ KM TO PRODUCE THE FIXED TINCTURE

ROBERT ALLEN BARTLETT

♁ EXPERIMENT #2

① POUND ♁ ORE TO FINE POWDER

② DISSOLVE 1 PORTION IN A PRE-MIXED SATURATED **6N**
SOL'N OF NaOH - PLACE ON HEAT TO DIGEST.
COLOR 1ˢᵗ GREY THEN BRICK RED - ORANGE. SIMMER 2 HRS & SET ONE NITE

③ DISSOLVE NaOH IN WATER - HEAT IS GIVEN OFF.
UTILIZE THIS INNER HEAT TO DISSOLVE A SECOND PORTION
OF ♁ - AGAIN 1ˢᵗ GREY THEN BRILLIANT ORANGE. GREEN ON SETTLING

SKIM OFF A PORTION OF THIS LIQUID AND FILTER W/
GLASS WOOL - THE ORANGE SEDIMENT FILTERS OUT AND
THE FILTRATE IS A CLEAR ᴳᴿᴱᴱᴺᴵˢᴴ WISKEY COLORED LIQUID. 〔TEST SAMPLE〕
THIS IS THE ANTIMONY OXYSULFIDE IN SOLUTION
THIS WAS NOW LEFT IN THE SUN TO DIGEST. OVER NIGHT

④ TO THIS FILTRATE WE ADD NOW SOME 6N ACETIC ACID
A REDDISH PRECIPITATE IS FORMED - CONGEAL°ᴰ OR SEPARATED
THE ANTIMONY AND SULFUR. THIS RESEMBLES COFFEE GROUNDS.
☞ ADD ACID UNTIL NEUTRAL OR EVEN A LITTLE ACIDIOUS.
NOW WASH WITH WATER AND LET THE PRECIP. SETTLE
OUT - ~~SETTLE~~ SIPHON OUT THE WATER AND WASH AGAIN.

⑤ - ADD MORE WATER TO LIQUID DERIVED FROM ③ TO
DISSOLVE MORE ♁. NOW FILTER W/ GLASS WOOL - A PURE CLEAR
FILTRATE IS NOT ESSENTIAL THOUGH DESIRED. COLOR IS GREENISH

| 1 | SOL'N TO VINEGAR → ³⁰⁰ᵐᴸ - REDDISH ᶠᴵᴺᴱ ORANGE POWDERY PRECIP. SETTLES ON BOTTOM |
| 2 | VINEGAR TO SOL'N - REDDISH ORANGE POWDER PRECIP. FLOATS ON TOP |

³⁰⁰ᵐᴸ   ²⁵⁰ᵐᴸ   COARSER   LUMPY FOAMY

ADD SOL'N UNTIL NEUTRAL   (DO NOT LEAVE THE ALKALINE SUBSTANCE IN GLASS AS IT WILL BE ETCHED)   6N ACETIC IS USED TO PRECIPITATE W/.   PRECIP. UNTIL SLIGHTLY ACIDIC

POUR ALL IN A LARGE CONTAINER AND WASH ⊗ WITH WATER TIL NEUTRAL (FILTER ALL THE GRIT OUT AND USE ALL THE ORANGE POWDER AND LIQUID. GRAVE IS THROWN OUT.)

⑥ ♂ DISSOLVED IN LYE AND FILTERED WAS DRIED. THE FILTRATE WAS THE LYE. THE ♂ ♂ SULFUR REMAIN IN THE FILTER, IT MUST BE WASHED W/ HOT WATER TO REMOVE ALL THE LYE. THE RESIDUE IS THE KERMES WE WON'T. NOW CAN WE GET THE ♀ OF ♂ OUT? YELLOW-ORANGE THE FILTRATE — DRIED CONTAINS THE LYE AND A PORTION OF THE ♂ WHICH CAN BE PRECIPITATED. IT IS A GREEN LIQUID AFTER RE-DISSOLVING IN WATER BEFORE PRECIPITATION. THE LYE CHANGED IT AGAIN — AND NOW THE ♂ CAN BE PRECIPITATED PARTIALLY BY THE ADDITION OF H_2O

TAKE THE BROWN POWDER:
    EXTRACT — W/ VINEGAR
        W/ KM
          CALCINE EXTRACT

♂ - PURIFIES THE BLOOD (THE CARRIER OF THE LIFE FORCE)
♀ - PRESERVATIVE. (EMOLLIENT) FROM CORRUPTION
  - IRON ♀ - EXTRACT SAME AS ♂ PROCESS
   P — ♏ - ENERGIZER

ROBERT ALLEN BARTLETT

T-HEAD

IRON - BRAIN DAMAGE - FIND CAUSE 1st AND RECTIFY 1st

I.E. LIVER DAMAGE TYING UP LINES TO BRAIN.

USE ♃ OR TIN TO RECTIFY THEN IRON. TIN + ♀

TO SOOTHE.

— COMPLEX MEDICATIONS EX. TIN + ♀ FOR LIVER + IRON + ♀

FOR GALL AND HEAD.

— WORK ON NERVES - SOMETHING TO SOOTHE FRAYED ENDS

— EVERYTHING IS INTER CONNECTED SO <u>CONTEMPLATE</u> BEFORE

GIVING A MEDICINE THE TRUE CAUSE.

THE INTERMIXING OF THE 3 ESSENTIALS PRODUCE
THE MULTITUDE OF EXPRESSIONS. ALL IS COMPOSED
OF THE 3 IN DIFFERENT PROPORTIONS.

EXP. #2 cont.

~~BEFORE~~ TAKE A SMALL GROUND SAMPLE OF THE RED BROWN
PRECIPITATE AND CALCINE OVER A BURNER IN AN
EARTHEN WARE DISH. SULFUR IS DRIVEN OFF AND
IT BECOMES GREY AS IT LOOKED IN THE ORE STATE
IT GLOBULES UP IN ONLY MINUTES
— IF HEAT IS TOO HIGH THE REGULUS IS MADE —
THE GREY STATE IS ATTAINED MUCH SOONER
GRIND AND REPLACE ON FIRE TO CALCINE

— FILL ONE FLASK PARTIALLY W/ THE BROWN POWDER
AND COVER W/ 75% VINEGAR & 25% H_2O
PLACE IN SAND BATH.

— FILL ANOTHER FLASK PARTIALLY W/ THE BROWN PRECIPITATE AND
COVER W/ ~~ETOH~~ — ~~ETOH~~ ABSOLUTE ALCOHOL (WE CAN
USE KM IT WE HAVE IT) TSOSIL SAYS TO USE RECTIFIED
SPIRITS OF WINE ♆ PLACE IN SAND BATH.

— FILL A 3RD WITH THE BROWN PRECIPITATE AND COVER W/
6N ACETIC ACID. STOPPER AND PLACE IN SAND BATH

ROBERT ALLEN BARTLETT

Rx THE CALCINED PRECIPITATE - FILL A THIMBLE AND EXTRACT

EDULCORATE THE ~~TINCTURES~~ TINCTURES FROM THE CALCINED ORE AND THE RAW ORE.

Rx PRECIP, CALCINE AND FUSE INTO GLASS OF ☿ W/OUT FLUX

VINEGAR OF ☿ — P 43 P 98 FOOTNOTE   NAME ONLY BECAUSE IT TASTES LIKE VINEGAR. 3 ESSENTIALS

P. 171

P 170 - MERCURY NOT FOUND IN ☿ (WEAKEST)   THE STONE IS MADE
        AS 1ST SUBSTANCE   W/ UNFIXED ☿

ITS MERCURY IS FIXED W/IN

— FIRE STONE MADE W/ UNFIXED ☿ IT FIXES THE OIL AND SALT

RAIN WATER PURIFIED BY THE O_2 & N_2 IN AIR
  * DISTILLED WATER IS HARMFUL TO DRINK BECAUSE WE NEED
SOME OF THE INORGANIC MINERALS FOR OUR SYSTEM
RIVER WATER - HARD WATER - IT CONTAINS MINERALS LEACHED FROM
      THE GROUNDS OF COURSE TOO MUCH MINERAL CONTENT
      CAN ALSO BE BAD.
RAIN WATER - SOFT WATER - MINERAL FREE - MUCH PURER
      FOR OUR PURPOSES. (SMOG FREE COLLECTION AREA)

P 171

HORSEDUNG - CONSTANT - UNIFORM HEAT CAUSED TO PUTREFACTION
        MOIST HEAT

BALNEUM VAPOROSO - STEAM BATH
    BODY OPENS

P. 172 - THE RED POWDER NEED NOT BE WASHED.
    CAREFULLY RECTIFY THE VINEGAR -
    ITS OWN SALT IS THE FIXED RED POWDER

173 - FOOTNOTE - USE CONDENSER RATHER THAN IMMERSING INTO
            WATER AS SHOWN ON PAGE 174

SOUL OF SATURN - OIL OF LEAD

SAL PRUNELLAE - FUSED POTASSIUM NITRATE   (FUSED STICKS)

INFLAMED BLOOD - HAVE A TEMPERATURE OR FEVER

PREVENTIVE MEDICINE IS THE BEST - DON'T WAIT AROUND.

    OUR MAIN OBJECTIVE IS TO TAKE MEDICINES WHEN WE ARE

    HEALTHY, TO KEEP US HEALTHY

    - LET ∅ SPEAK FOR ITS SELF   BECAUSE THAT WHICH IS IT

    IS IMBODIED IN IT.

    FROG'S SPOWN - ~~TADPOLE~~ JELLY LIKE SUBSTANCE

        TOADS - CONTAIN POISON   (THIS ALSO CONTAINS A POISON TO
                                    PRESERVE IT FROM BEING EATEN

        PARACELSUS - INCINERATE TOAD IN CLOSED VESSEL INTO SALT

        SPRINKLE ON POISIONOUS WOUND AND IT WILL EXTRACT THE

        POISION

EXP. #3 VINEGAR OF ANTIMONY

PULVERIZE ORE

WEIGH 9 LBS WATER

" 3.8 LBS ANTIMONY

$\frac{6}{14}$ $\overline{9}$

PUT THESE TOGETHER IN A LARGE STOPPERED
VESSEL AND LET DIGEST

AMOUNT

HEAT

(SIDERAL INFLUENCES)
INFLUENCE OF MOON ✓   NEW — FULL

TIME REQUIRED
WILL DEPEND ON THESE

— THE ENZYMATIC ACTION ASSISTS THE PUTREFACTION PROCESS
SOME OF THESE ENZYMES MAY BE LOST DURING THE
PRODUCTION OF THE KERMES — SO DIFFERENCES IN FERMENTATION
TIMES MAY BE NOTICED BETWEEN THE KERMES AND THE
RAW ORE.

ROBERT ALLEN BARTLETT

THE longer THE DIGESTION THE MORE will BE DISSOLVED

BROWN ♂ SOXHLET EXTRACT w/ 75% AA
w/ ABSOLUTE ALCOHOL

ONCE WE SEE THAT BASIL & KERKRING HAVE LEAD US ARIGHT IN THE <u>PREPARATIONS</u> WE GAIN CONFIDENCE IN THEIR ADVICE ON THE <u>USES</u>

VINEGAR GIVES US A FIXED POWDER FROM WHICH WE PRODUCE THE FIXED ESSENCE OF ♁ — NO MATTER WEATHER WE USE RAW ORE, GLASS, CALCINED ORE, KERMES, ETC P.100 ♁ ← THE YELLOW POWDER

ACETIC ACID → ACETATE — TAKE TIME & WE CAN DISSOLVE ALL THE ♁ OR AT LEAST ⅔ — STILL POISONOUS AT THIS POINT BUT IT CONTAINS THE PURE ESSENCE FIXED W/IN P 101 — THE EARTHY SEDIMENT IS STILL POISONOUS BUT THE EXTRACT w/ ♑ IS GOOD MEDICINE

OUR PIONEERING WORK & RESEARCH CAN HELP IN THE PROGRESS OF THESE THINGS

ROBERT ALLEN BARTLETT

P 172. DISSOLVE in its own salt

    1oz   in 4oz.
    ↑   ↑
    salt   VINEGAR

P 171 - FERMENTED & USED IN MAKING THE VINEGAR CAN
BE USED IN PRODUCING MORE LIKE SOURDOUGH
STARTER.

P 169 CIRCULATION will gradually SEPARATE THE oil
TO THE BOTTOM - THE SPIRIT will FLOAT ON TOP.
DEXTEROUS DISTILLATION - USE THE LEAST HEAT POSSIBLE
GENTLY WHIRL THE RETORT WHILE DISTILLING TO FURTHER
AID THE SEPARATION. FILTER TO REMOVE OIL SEDIMENT

BOSOM BK OF GEO. RIPLEY

THE GREEN LION ~ COLECTANEA CHEMICA

℞ ☿ — SEE T.C. P 109 FOOTNOTE GREEN GLASS

50% ACETIC ACID AND 50% WATER HAS BEEN FOUND THE BEST PROPORTION AS AN EXTRACTION MEDIA (VINEGAR EXTRACTION)

P H1 WORKS OF PARACELSUS    PURE SWEET ANTIMONY OIL
      1 MEASURE = 1 qt

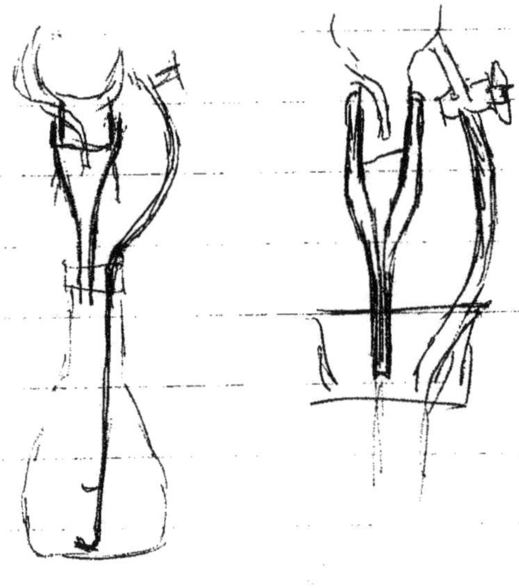

YOU DO INFLUENCE YOUR WORK

ROBERT ALLEN BARTLETT

ANTIMONY EXPERIMENT #2 TERTIA CLASS

I. GRIND ☿:

   A. FINELY POWDER

II. DISSOLVE 1 PORTION ☿ IN PRE-MIXED LYE SOLUTION:

   1. 6N NaOH WAS USED IN ENAMEL POT

   2. GREY COLOR AT FIRST MERGING INTO BRICK-RED OR

      DARK ORANGE

   3. PLACE ON HEAT TO DIGEST 2 HRS LET SIT OVER

      NIGHT. REHEAT IN MORNING 1 HR.　(CONTINUED STEP VI)

III. DISSOLVE NaOH FLAKES INTO WATER UNTIL SATURATED

   1. HEAT IS PRODUCED.　THIS GIVES THE

   2. DISSOLVE PONDERED ☿ INTO THIS SOLUTION. — OXY SULFIDE

      A. SLUDGE DEVELOPS ON BOTTOM

      B. COLOR FIRST GREY THEN BRIGHT ORANGE

      — ON SETTLING THERE IS A GREENISH COLOR

   3. THIS WAS LEFT TO DIGEST w/OUT HEAT OVERNIGHT

IV. FROM THE SOLUTION PRODUCED IN STEP III A SMALL

SAMPLE WAS FILTERED INTO A CYLINDER - USING GLASS WOOL

   1. ORANGE SEDIMENT FILTERS OUT LEAVING A GREENISH

      TINGED WISKEY COLORED LIQUID (CLEAR)

   2. TO THIS CLEAR SOLUTION (IV 1) WAS ADDED 6N

      ACETIC ACID.

   3. A BROWNISH RED PRECIPITATE WAS FORMED. ACID WAS

      ADDED UNTIL SLIGHTLY ACIDIOUS ON PH PAPER

      SHOWING ALL THE LYE WAS NEUTRALIZED.

   4. AFTER ALLOWING THIS PRECIPITATE TO SETTLE TO THE

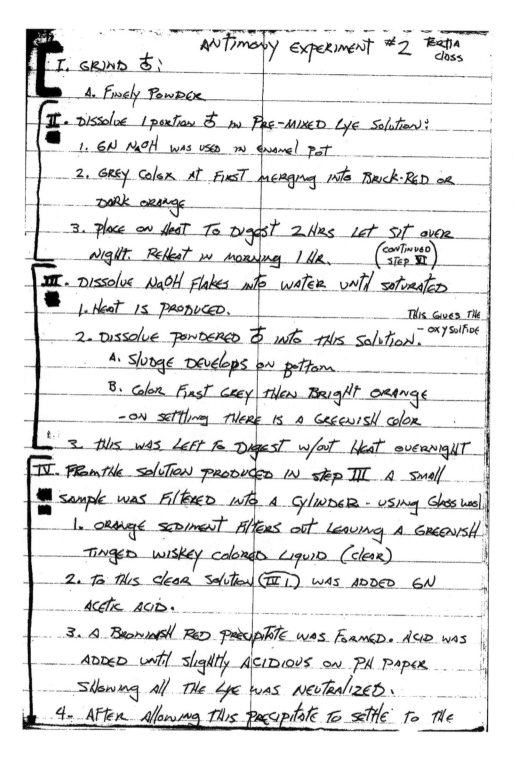

BOTTOM OF THE BEAKER THE LIQUID WAS ~~SIPHONED~~
SIPHONED OFF AND DISCARDED.

5. MORE WATER WAS ADDED TO WASH THE PRECIP.
AGAIN, PH PAPER SHOWED NEUTRAL.

6. AFTER ALLOWING PRECIP. TO SETTLE — THE LIQUID WAS
AGAIN SIPHONED OFF AND DISCARDED.

7. THE REMAINING PRECIP. & LIQUID WERE PLACED
ON A HOT PLATE TO EVAPORATE BEFORE FINAL
DRYING. THIS POWDER CONTAINS ⚷OF⚷ AND ⚷OF ☿

V. PREPARATION OF THE BROWNISH RED PRECIPITATE
(AS IN IV) OR ANTIMONY OXYSULFIDE FROM THE REMAINING
SOLUTION PREPARED IN STEP III :

1. ADD MORE WATER TO SOLUTION DERIVED AT IN III
THIS WILL PUT MORE OF THE ☿ AND LYE INTO SOLUTION.

2. NOW FILTER LIQUID WITH GLASS WOOL TO REMOVE
ALL THE GANGE SETTLED ON BOTTOM

A. THIS CONSISTS OF THE CLEAR LIQUID AND THE ORANGE POWDERY
ANTIMONY—SULFUR IN SOLUTION AND SUSPENSION.

B. THE GANGE APPEARS AT THE BOTTOM AS A GRITTY
SAND. THIS WE DISCARD.

3. ADD MORE WATER UNTIL ALL THE ORANGE OXYSULFIDE
IS WASHED OUT AND ONLY GRIT REMAINS.

4. NOW, TO THIS SOLUTION WE ADD 6N ACETIC ACID
AND IMMEDIATLY THE ORANGE TURNS TO A DARK

ROBERT ALLEN BARTLETT

RED-BROWN SIMILAR TO COFFEE GROUNDS.

* PRELIMINARY TEST: 2 BEAKERS — one (A) CONTAINS THE FILTERED SOLUTION. one (B) CONTAINS 6N ACETIC ACID. TO BEAKER (A) WE ADDED ACETIC ACID — A RED BROWN PRECIP. FORMED AND FLOATED ON TOP. TEXTURE SIMILAR TO COTTAGE CHEESE. TO BEAKER (B) WE ADDED THE SOLUTION — A RED BROWN PRECIP. WAS FORMED BUT THIS TIME SANK TO THE BOTTOM AND HAD A MUCH FINER TEXTURE.

THIS WAS DONE FIRST on step V

5. SOLUTION AND ACETIC ACID WERE ADDED UNTIL ALL SOLUTION WAS USED UP AND PRECIPITATED OUT. THE pH SHOWED SLIGHTLY ACID INDICATING ALL THE LYE HAD BEEN NEUTRALIZED.

6. WATER WAS NOW ADDED TO THIS PRECIP. (WHICH WAS ALL PLACED IN A LARGE CONTAINER) IN ORDER TO WASH OUT ANY REMAINING LYE AND ACID.
   1. AFTER SETTLING THE LIQUID WAS SIPHONED OFF AND DISCARDED. NEW WATER WAS POURED IN AND STIRRED. ALLOW TO SETTLE — REPEAT SEVERAL TIMES UNTIL PH SHOWS NEUTRAL.

7. AT NEUTRAL PH — NOW FILTER SOLUTION AND COLLECT BROWN POWDER FOR DRYING —

VI. FILTER SOLUTION PREPARED IN STEP II:

1. A clear yellowish-orange liquid is drawn off.

2. A yellow orange residue is left in the funnel on the glass wool. Discard sand-like gange

3. The liquid was placed on the heat in an enamel dish to evaporate the water off.

4. When dry there remained a dirty white salt (part green part yellow part brown). This is the lye which still contains part of the ☿ and sulfur.

   A. The yellow residue is the ☿ and sulfur derived from the ore — the gange was discarded during filtration. This is (the yellow residue) called the Kermes mineral.

5. To the dried white salts (lye water, see ③+④) hot water was added to remove the ☿ and sulfur still within them. On adding the water we obtained a green liquid and a blueish-grey sediment. This is to be collected and washed —collect wash water and evaporate

6. Use hot water and wash the yellow residue or Kermes mineral — (VI 2 & 4A)

   A. Wash til neutral

   B. Collect wash water and evaporate, with water obtained in VI-5.

VII. PRECIPITATE FORMED IN STEP IV, ON NEARING DRYNESS
WAS TESTED FOR PH:

1. PH SHOWED ALKALINE (≈ 9)

2. THIS SHOWS MORE OF THE NaOH WAS LEACHED OUT
AND NEEDS TO BE WASHED OUT AGAIN.

3. WATER WAS ADDED TO THE PRECIP. AND STIRRED
ALLOW TO SETTLE AND REPEAT WASHINGS TILL NEUTRAL
THEN EVAPORATE EXCESS WATER AND DRY PRECIP.
UNDER GENTLE HEAT.

VIII. TO COLLECT BROWN POWDER ARRIVED AT IN
STEP II-7:

1. SIPHON OF ALL CLEAR WASH WATER AFTER ALLOWING
PRECIP. TO SETTLE.

2. SPREAD OUT LARGE SHEETS OF BROWN WRAPPING
PAPER OR SUCH-LIKE AND LADLE THIS SOUPY
BROWN POWDER ON TO IT.

3. SPREAD AND LET DRY.

4. COLLECT.

IX. TEST TO SEE IF A STRONGER VINEGAR SOLUTION
WILL EXTRACT (BY MACERATION) A DARKER TINCTURE FROM
GLASS OF ☿

1. PLACE GROUND GLASS OF ☿ IN FLASK

2. COVER W/ 75% ACETIC ACID + 25% WATER MENSTRUM

3. STOPPER AND LET DIGEST IN SAND BATH.

X. TAKE POWDERED BROWN PRECIPITATE FROM **VIII** : 5/4/76

1. PLACE 1 PORTION ON CALCINING DISH:

    A. SULFUR IS GIVEN OF AND CAN BE IGNITED

    B. GLOBULES ARE FORMED.

    C. COLOR IS DARK GREY TURNING LIGHT IN A SHORT TIME.

       1. TOO MUCH HEAT CAUSES THE REGULUS TO BE FORMED.

    D. GRIND AND REPLACE ON FIRE AGAIN.

2. PLACE 1 PORTION OF THE PRECIP. INTO A FLASK.

    A. COVER W/ 75% ACETIC ACID $ 25% H_2O

    B. COVER AND LET DIGEST IN SANDBATH.

3. PLACE A 3RD PORTION IN ANOTHE FLASK AND COVER
W/ ABSOLUTE ALCOHOL - LET DIGEST IN SANDBATH.

    A. WE CAN USE KM IF AVAILABLE.

4. PLACE A 4TH PORTION IN ANOTHER FLASK AND COVER
W/ GN ACETIC ACID - STOPPER AND LET DIGEST IN SANDBATH

XI. PREPORATION OF THE VINEGAR OF ☿ : 5/4/76

    ↖ AN ALCOHEST

1. POWDER ORE.

2. RATIOE OF H_2O TO ☿ GIVEN BY BASIL VALENTINE = 6-14

    ☿ H_2O

3. WEIGH WATER - WE HAVE 9 Lbs $\frac{6}{14} \times \frac{3.8}{9}$

4. DIVIDE INTO TWO GALLON JUGS 4.5 Lbs H_2O
ADD 1.9 Lbs POWDERED ☿ STOPPER AND
LET DIGEST IN SAND BATH.

XII. PREPARATION OF ☿ GLASS FROM THE CALCINED BROWN
PRECIPITATE DERIVED FROM **X**-1 : 2:00 PM S/S

1 HEAT CRUCIBLE $ ADD 1ST SOME OF THE BROWN
PRECIP. HEAT W/ FISCHER BURNER.

ROBERT ALLEN BARTLETT

2. DIFFICULTY IN GETTING it TO FLUX.

    A. WE TRIED RAW ORE

    B. CALCINED BROWN PRECIP.

    C. UNCALCINED PRECIP₃

3. SUGGESTED PROBLEMS

    A. NOT ENOUGH HEAT?

    B. $\mathrm{D\,\sigma\,\hbar_?\,\sigma}$ IN $\mathrm{\Theta}$

4. THEY HAVE ATTAINED THE MOLTEN STATE 2:30 BUT HAVE NOT MATURED

XIII. 6N VINEGAR EXTRACTIONS   4/27/76   3:30 pm

    1. GLASS OF ☿ - S/2 LITTLE COLOR - CLOUDY

    2. CALCINED ☿ ORE | S/2 GOLDED TINCTURE OF ☿

    3. RAW POWDERED ☿ ORE S/2 DARK WINE TINC. ☿ OF ☿ / ☿ OF ☿

    4. S/4 REMOVE EACH TINCTURE AND FILTER SEPARATELY

    5. S/5 REPLACE TINCTURES INTO EXTRACTORS AND DISTILL LIQUIDS OFF. SAVE LAST RESIDUES AND PLACE ON SEPARATE DISHES FOR FINAL DRYING

    6. COLLECT DRY POWDERS & GRIND

    7. ADD WATER TO WASH OUT EXCESS ACID - LET EVAPORATE.

    8. POWDER FROM:

        A. CLASS OF ☿ - MOSS GREEN - GRAY - MOST POWDER

        B. RAW ORE - DARK BRICK RED - 2ND AMOUNT MOST

        C. CALCINED ORE - LIGHT TAN - 3RD

5/6/76 11:00 AM

XIV. TAKE MORE OF THE BROWN PRECIPITATE FROM VIII

1. Fill one THimble AND place in extractor. extract w/ absolute alcohol.

2. Fill one THimble ~~extractor~~ AND place in another extractor. extract w/ 75% acetic acid 25% H_2O

3. Fill a third THimble w/ THE calcined Brown precipitate FROM X-1 AND extract w/ 50/50 acetic acid - water.

5/7/76 4. THe extraction w/ alcohol Has a clear golden yellow Tincture this is the unfixed Tincture of ♁ AND sulfur.

5. THe THimble #2 (above) Has a slight pinkish or light red extract also ♁ ? ♀

6. THe THimble #3 (above) Has slight traces of a Tincture this is of ♁ only.

7. extracts #5 & 6 are to be evaporated AND washed carefully - dried then extracted w/ alcohol to produce THe fixed Tincture of ♁ ? ♀ (#5) AND of ♁ only in (#6)

Sources of Antimony

ROBERT ALLEN BARTLETT

The antimony source material for most of the practical works illustrated herein came about in a very strange way. I had returned to Atlanta after the Secunda class at PRS anxious to begin working with antimony again with my newly acquired guidance. The previous year had been devoted to the Prima work with herbal alchemy; now we were edging the powerful mineral kingdom, with antimony as the gateway. I pulled out and dusted off the antimony compounds purchased earlier and began attempts towards making the tincture of antimony as described by Basil Valentine, but my resources were running low.

Is it synchronicity? The universe really does give us what we need when we need it. I was sitting in a pub in Atlanta one Friday afternoon, not more than a month after returning from Secunda, when Glen, a local friend walked in and sat down. He said he was quitting his mining job to pursue his own small gold mine up the Yuba River and asked me if I would like to take over the job for him. I asked him what he was mining, and he said Stibnite! My eyes lit up as my jaw hit the table. What were the odds of that, and only sixteen miles downriver. I got the contact info and immediately set off to meet Bill Weatherby, the mine owner. Bill was used to his previous worker Glen, a brawny six-foot-plus mountain man, and so he questioned whether I could handle the work involved. With my interest in geology and previous experience at the Shop I was able to speak the language of metals and machines enough to convince him I could. He said we start Monday at six in the morning, and thus began my adventure in stibnite mining.

There aren't many areas in the US where stibnite can be found in large deposits. It so happened that an area close by was one of them.

Here are the details on the deposit:

Geology, Geochemistry, and Mineral Resources of the Lower Part of the Middle Fork Boise River Drainage Basin, Boise and Elmore Counties, Idaho

By Thor H. Kiilsgaard *and* Cole L. Smith

U.S. Geological Survey Bulletin 2064-AA

Hermada Antimony Mine

The Hermada antimony mine (fig. 9, loc. 5) is in the western half of sec. 13, T. 6 N., R. 9 E. Mine workings consist chiefly of the Hermada pit and the North pit, which is about 2,500 ft north of the Hermada pit. Both workings are along the west side of the East Fork of Swanholm Creek, about 3 mi northeast of the junction of Swanholm Creek and the Middle Fork Boise River. In addition to the Hermada and North pits (fig. 9, loc. 4), several thousand feet of bulldozer trenches, many of them more like roads than trenches, extend along hillsides west of the Hermada pit. In 1992, the Hermada property consisted of 13 unpatented mining claims and 5 patented claims (Hermada and Hermada Nos. 1, 2, 4, and 6).

The Hermada claims were staked in 1947. The most active period of mining operations at the property was from 1947 to 1950. Original exploration was by adits, but these were obliterated by subsequent development of the Hermada open pit, which is about 250 ft long and as wide as 125 ft. Mining in the Hermada pit was by bulldozer and handsorting of selected pieces of ore. According to Popoff (1953), in 1947–48 the Hermada Mining Company mined and shipped 207.65 tons of crude ore that averaged 32.05 percent Sb. A high-grade ore sample collected in 1948 contained 35.3 percent Sb, 12.4 percent S, 0.05 percent As, 0.11 percent Pb, 46.0 percent SiO_2, 0.30 percent CaO, 1.30 percent FeO, 4.7 percent Al_2O_3, and nil gold and silver (Popoff, 1953). From 1947 to 1950, 4,600 tons of ore averaging 11.7 percent Sb was produced from the mine and trucked to the Talache mill at Atlanta, Idaho. From these shipments, the mill produced 776 tons of concentrate that averaged 59.92 percent Sb. Antimony ore also was produced from the Hermada mine in 1951 and 1952 and concentrated at the Atlanta mill. As of 1992, total output from the mine was about 1,502,000 pounds of antimony according to unpublished U.S. Bureau of Mines records. Almost all of this antimony was mined from the Hermada pit.

The Hermada deposit is in biotite granodiorite (fig. 10, unit Kgd), and consists of a broad zone of north-northwest-striking faults and narrow andesitic dikes along which are quartz-stibnite veins that are irregular in strike length and thickness. The longest vein explored to 1950 was 115 ft (Popoff, 1953); it commonly was only a few inches thick, but some shoots were as thick as about 5 ft. The overall width of the mineralized zone was about 100 ft. Stibnite was the principal ore mineral, although other antimony minerals, including kermesite, stibiconite, cervantite, and valentinite, were also present. At the Hermada pit, the northerly trending Hermada zone is intersected and crosscut in at least three locations by younger northeast-striking dacitic dikes.

Biotite granodiorite along dikes in the Hermada zone is hydrothermally altered to sericite and clay minerals. Locally, the alteration is so intense that identification of the original rock is difficult. The andesitic dikes also are altered and decomposed locally to a brownish, earthy material. The quartz-stibnite veins are in the granodiorite, contiguous with or near the northerly trending dikes (fig. 10). Mineralized lenses in the veins are in granodiorite that has undergone sericitic and silicic alteration. Near mineralized shoots, the granodiorite has been mostly replaced by quartz, much of which has been broken and granulated by postmineral faulting.

The Hermada deposit was explored under a Defense Minerals Administration (DMA) contract in 1951 and 1952. The exploration work consisted of extensive bulldozer trenching in the North pit, several thousand feet of bulldozer trenching west of the Hermada pit and driven west to intersect north-striking veins projected south from the Hermada pit (Kiilsgaard and Zoldak, 1955, unpublished DMA report available in Spokane field office). Exploration in the North pit exposed a north-striking quartz-stibnite vein a few inches thick that was cut by a large, northeast-striking shear zone that postdates quartz-stibnite mineralization. Pulverized stibnite was found in the shear zone. A quartz-stibnite vein about 10 in. thick was exposed in a bulldozed cut about 2,400 ft S. 60° W. from the Hermada pit. Native antimony was found in a northeast-trending dacite dike, about 1,100 ft south of the Hermada pit. Sparse pyrite and flecks of stibnite also were found in altered biotite granodiorite intruded by a northeast-striking dacite dike that was intersected in the adit about 260 ft from the portal. The final 60 ft of adit intersected highly altered biotite granodiorite in which there was numerous north-striking quartz stringers as thick as 5 in. and much pyrite but no stibnite.

Svensson Antimony Prospect

The Svensson antimony prospect (fig. 9, loc. 1) is along the eastern side of sec. 10, T. 6 N., R. 9 E., about 0.5 mi east of Swanholm Creek and about 4 mi north of the intersection of Swanholm Creek and the Middle Fork Boise River. Mine workings at this prospect explore several small, discontinuous stibnite-bearing quartz veins that cut Cretaceous biotite granodiorite.

Mineral exploration at the prospect has been concentrated at two locations (1) a caved adit, the portal of which is at an altitude of 5,800 ft, and that, according to Bill Weatherby (oral commun., 1992) extended about 120 ft southeast into the hillside, and (2) a large bulldozed pit about 140 ft long, 70 ft wide, and 20 ft deep, the bottom of which is at an altitude of 5,930 ft and 400 ft southeast of the portal of the adit. Several other bulldozed cuts are northeast and east of the principal workings. All of the workings are on the Hope Nos. 1 and 2 unpatented claims.

The large bulldozed pit was excavated in 1952 as part of a Defense Minerals Exploration Administration (DMEA) contract let to Oscar V. Svensson, Boise, Idaho, for the purpose of exploring three parallel stibnite-bearing quartz veins that strike N. 15° W. and dip 50°–60° NE. The veins range from 2 to 12 in. in thickness, are about 5 ft apart, and consist chiefly of a hanging-wall gouge zone along which are quartz veins that contain disseminated, fine-grained pyrite and minor amounts of stibnite. Biotite granodiorite within the vein zone is strongly altered to sericite and clay minerals and, locally, stained by limonite derived from oxidized pyrite. Samples of the veins collected in 1952 ranged from nil to 7.5 percent Sb. Atomic absorption analysis of two samples of the vein material collected in 1986 showed 0.08 and 0.09 ounces of gold per ton. Semiquantitative spectrographic analysis of the two samples showed 200 and more than 1,000 ppm As and 100 and more than 1,000 ppm Sb. Svensson reported that prior to 1951, several tons of quartz, some of it containing 6–8 percent Sb, was mined from the pit, production that was a justifying reason for the subsequent DMEA contract. No significant amount of stibnite, however, was discovered by the DMEA exploration program.

The lower, caved adit was driven by the Weatherby family during the 1960's to test the veins explored by the large open pit. A few tons of quartz and stibnite are reported to have been mined from the adit, but the work did not find a significant amount of antimony (Bill Weatherby, oral commun., 1992).

About 570 ft N. 20° E. of the large open pit is a veinlet of quartz containing disseminated stibnite. The vein strikes N. 25° W., dips 50° NE., is about 4 in. thick, and was explored in 1952 over a strike length of 70 ft by bulldozer trenching. Two samples collected from the vein in 1952 contained 0.30 and 0.06 percent Sb. One of the samples contained 0.44 percent As and 0.10 percent Pb (Popoff, 1953).

About 850 ft east of the large open pit, on top of the hill, two parallel quartz veins about 5 ft apart strike N. 19° W., dip 60° NE., and range from 2 to 12 in. in thickness. The veins were explored by bulldozer trenching over a strike length of 140 ft in 1952. Stibnite was found in the veins but not in an amount sufficient to warrant additional exploration.

Another quartz vein tested in 1952 is 950 ft N. 50° E. of the large open pit. The vein strikes N. 12° W., is as thick as 12 in., contains trace quantities of stibnite, and was explored by a crosscutting bulldozer trench.

Stibnite-bearing quartz veins at the Svensson prospect are in a northwest-striking zone about 850 ft wide. The veins are small and discontinuous. Locally, they contain concentrations of stibnite, but the overall antimony grade is low.

Weatherby Prospect

The Weatherby antimony prospect (fig. 9, loc. 2) is in the north-central part of sec. 14, T. 6 N., R. 9 E., along a southwest-flowing tributary of Swanholm Creek, about 3.25 mi north of the junction of Swanholm Creek and the Middle Fork Boise River.

The prospect consists of a sloughed bulldozed cut and a caved adit a few feet below, which is reported to be about 150 ft long and to have been driven in the 1960's (Bill Weatherby, oral commun., 1992). Both the bulldozed cut and the adit trend S. 20° E. Several tens of tons of hand sorted quartz, stibnite, and altered biotite granodiorite were observed on the adit dump in 1986. The handsorted material probably was stockpiled in anticipation of acquiring a volume large enough to warrant shipping, but apparently that volume was not collected. Some of the pieces of ore are too large to have come from the adit and probably are from the bulldozed cut. Quartz of the hand sorted material contains fine-grained pyrite and stibnite. Many pieces of ore have slickensides and are coated with gouge; they may have been mined from a fault zone. Atomic absorption analysis of a selected sample of the dump ore yielded 0.35 ounces of gold per ton. Semiquantitative spectrographic analysis of the same sample yielded more than 10,000 ppm (1 percent) Sb, 1,000 ppm As, and 5 ppm Ag. No vein or fault was seen in the sloughed workings, but the trend of the workings suggests that the workings were driven on a vein that strikes about N. 20° W.

The Weatherby Mine

Looking into the dragon's lair

Now, hunting dragons is not easy work and very dangerous. After reading about the adventures of Paracelsus in the mines of the Fugger's and the subterranean intelligences one might run into, I decided to construct a little talisman to appease them or at least prevent some mischief. Sometimes at the end of a workday when we were packing up to leave, I would stand at the face and turn off my lamp. Black, blacker than black; no light whatsoever. Slowly I would walk towards the portal and as soon as I rounded the bend, I could see a single star in an otherwise black infinity. As I moved closer, the star became a shaft of light and a new world came into view in living color. I thought of Plato's cave dwellers.

Robert Allen Bartlett

Talisman For The Earth Element

Atlanta, ID.
1976

Gathering Dragon Scales

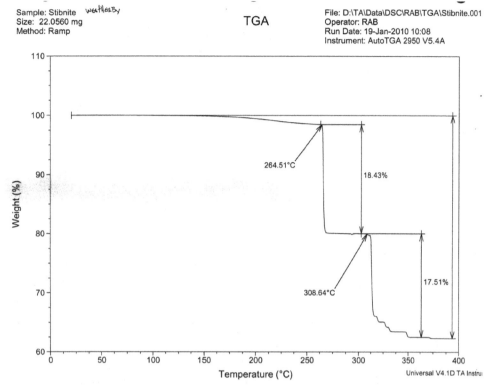

Sample: Stibnite weatherby
Size: 22.0560 mg
Method: Ramp

TGA

File: D:\TA\Data\DSC\RAB\TGA\Stibnite.001
Operator: RAB
Run Date: 19-Jan-2010 10:08
Instrument: AutoTGA 2950 V5.4A

264.51°C

18.43%

308.64°C

17.51%

Weight (%)

Temperature (°C)

Universal V4.1D TA Instru

Above, TGA of Stibnite from the Weatherby mine. Below is a photo of the Arc Emission spectrum of the Stibnite bounded by Iron spectra for wavelength alignment in an optical comparator. The results of the same analysis on Hermada Stibnite are appended on the next page.

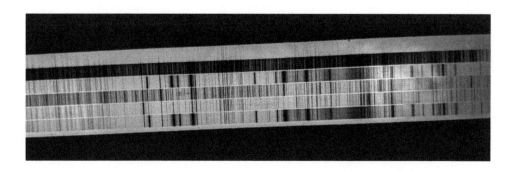

SPECTROGRAPHIC ANALYSIS

BOISE ASSAYING

& METALLURGY

1519 Main Street

(208) 345-6336

Boise, Idaho 83706

Client _____

Date _7/78_____

Sample ID: HERMADA ANTIMONY ORE

Lab No:

ELEMENT	%	ELEMENT	%	
Aluminum	.03	Manganese	.0003	
Antimony	> 10	Molybdenum	< .003	
Arsenic	—	Nickel		
Barium	—	Phosphorus	—	
Beryllium	—	Platinum	—	
Boron	—	Silicon	MC	
Cadmium	—	Silver	.0005	
Calcium	.2	Sodium	< .1	
Chromium	—	Tin	—	
Cobalt	—	Titanium	.001	
Columbium	—	Tungsten	—	
Copper	.1	Vanadium	—	
Gold	—	Zinc	.001	
Iron	.3	Zirconium	—	
Lead	.006	Hg	—	
Magnesium	.003			

MC - Major Constituent
Tr - Trace
Remarks:

Bartlett
Spectroscopist

Unless Otherwise noted, results are semiquantitative
only and may be 1/3/ to 3 times the actual amount present.

Sb By IODOMETRIC TITRATION: 62% (8/78)

Sb ≈ 60%

ROBERT ALLEN BARTLETT

HERMADA StiBNiTE

I performed this analysis of Weatherby and Hermada stibnite while in college and working for Boise Assaying and Metallurgy, part time; but that part of the story comes later. By far, the largest amount of source stibnite came from the nearby Hermada Mine.

Sample ID: Hermada Stibnite   **Percent solids:** 100

	Digestion information
	3050
Amount:	2.87
Dry amt.:	2.87
Prep. date:	4/1/03

	Analysis date	Inst. used	Dilution factor	Instrument result (mg/L)	Instrument rep. lim. (mg/L)	Sample rep. lim. (mg/kg)	Sample result (mg/kg)
Al	4/1/03	59 ICP	8	0.262	0.07	9.76	36.46
Sb	4/1/03	59 ICP	8	224.900	0.07	9.76	31344.95 *
As	4/1/03	59 ICP	8	1.678	0.03	4.18	233.87
Ba	4/1/03	59 ICP	8	0.000	0.003	0.42	0.42 U
Be	4/1/03	59 ICP	8	0.006	0.003	0.42	0.81
Cd	4/1/03	59 ICP	8	0.000	0.005	0.70	0.70 U
Ca	4/1/03	59 ICP	8	2.378	0.08	11.15	331.43
Cr	4/1/03	59 ICP	8	0.062	0.01	1.39	8.61
Co	4/1/03	59 ICP	8	0.000	0.007	0.98	0.98 U
Cu	4/1/03	59 ICP	8	0.614	0.006	0.84	85.56
Fe	4/1/03	59 ICP	8	23.450	0.01	1.39	3268.29
Pb	4/1/03	59 ICP	8	0.000	0.06	8.36	8.36 U
Mg	4/1/03	59 ICP	8	0.000	0.2	27.87	27.87 U
Mn	4/1/03	59 ICP	8	0.136	0.003	0.42	18.89
Ni	4/1/03	59 ICP	8	0.128	0.02	2.79	17.90
K	4/1/03	59 ICP	8	0.000	1	139.37	139.37 U
Se	4/1/03	59 ICP	8	0.076	0.05	6.97	10.56
Ag	4/1/03	59 ICP	8	0.035	0.007	0.98	4.89
Na	4/1/03	59 ICP	8	0.000	0.08	11.15	11.15 U
Tl	4/1/03	59 ICP	8	0.000	0.2	27.87	27.87 U
V	4/1/03	59 ICP	8	0.000	0.007	0.98	0.98 U
Zn	4/1/03	59 ICP	8	0.419	0.007	0.98	58.43

Digestion: 5mL HNO₃ @ 70°C 15 min

+3 mL HNO₃ @ 70°C 15 min

+5 mL H₂O₂

+3 mL HCl

Dilute to 50 mL

* Most of the Sb dropped out of solution as the oxychloride

ICP metals analysis of Hermada Stibnite

The third major source material was known as "Antimony Fume," and this came from Paralab. The exact source of this is unclear, though Paralab had many 55 gal. drums filled with it. The letter below refers to another possible source Paralab was looking at and so not the material that was on hand and already in production, but the method of manufacture indicated is what I understand was the Paralab Fume.

Sb Fume Source

January 14, 1980

Paracelsus Research Society
P.O. Box 6006
Salt Lake City, Utah 84106

ATTN: Dr. David Schein

Dear David,

In accordance with our conversation in November, I have enclosed some information on Sb_2O_3 as produced and/or sold by Harshaw Chemical Co. I checked with their technical people and was given the following information as regards the production method.

1. Concentrate of Sb_2S_3 (mostly flotation cons) from sources in So. Africa, Canada, and Bolivia are placed in a kiln fired with fuel oil with a rapid air stream passing over concentrate. It is a two stage process – crude roast and kiln finish roast.

2. Temperature of approx. 1000°F rapidly sublimes Sb off primarily as Sb_2O_3. $\frac{1}{2}\%$ – 2% will be Sb_2O_5. No true Sb_2O_4 exists. (Temperature seems low to me.

3. Process takes less than 12 hours. About 90% – 95% extraction of Sb. Sublimate collected in bag house.

4. Very low percentages of impurities. Primary one is AS which seems to get trapped as part of Sb_2O_3 crystal structure – taking place of Sb atom. Bulk of crystalline structure is cubic (senarmonite) and only 10% or so is needle like crystal of valentinite. Price of H material in 50 lb. sacks is $1.75 lb.

There are several grades and I have enclosed samples of type H (KR) and the high purity Blue Star which is low arsenic. This material is produced in Europe by a proprietary procedure not known by Harshaw Scientists. Supposedly a deviation of the sublimation process.

If you have specific questions on the process, you can talk to the Technical Director at Harshaw, Dr. Hal Halbedel at (216) 721-8300.

From my point of view, the low percentage of impurities in this material would make attempts at determining the mechanisms involved in experiments much easier. In a comparison of the KR sample to the Sb fume, I used in class, I found much larger quantities of AS Pb B Na &nSn in the fume. In my effort in class to produce an oil of Sb and to observe any signs of transmutations of elements as you described to me, I found that the Na and much Pb was dissolved in acetic acid while SN Sb & As were not, except in trace amounts. The alcohol soluble fraction of the Sb gum was primarily Na, Pb, Ca & Mg with Al, Si and Fe in ml minor percentages. Only a trace of Sb As & B observed in this fraction. Thus, at first glance, it seems that an ether extraction of the alcohol soluble fraction would be more a Na & Pb extraction than a Sb extraction. I am hoping to get a copy of your thesis soon, so I can try some further work on analysis of different fractions, etc.

I would think that it would be beneficial if you could do parallel runs on the Sb fume vs. ore to the Harshaw sublimates and send me samples of each step so I can see what goes where. I could then let Bob know which elements to shoot for on the AA to get exact percentages in the various samples.

I didn't see any great shifts in element percentages in my initial study, but am not equipped really to do more than follow the various elements from sample to sample and give indications to Bob to quantitatively determine with the AA. I would say, though, that on what I did in class, it seems that I was more likely to produce an oil of Na, Pb, Ca, Mg, Fe, Si or Al than Sb.

Let me know when your thesis will be available and what you think of this Harshaw materials, etc.

I will be at this address until January 24. If you like, call me some evening.

My best wishes to you all,

BV/mu

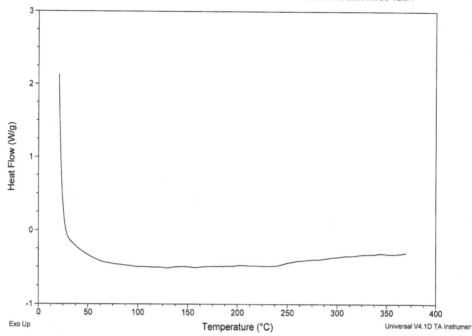

DSC scan of the Paralab Antimony Fume

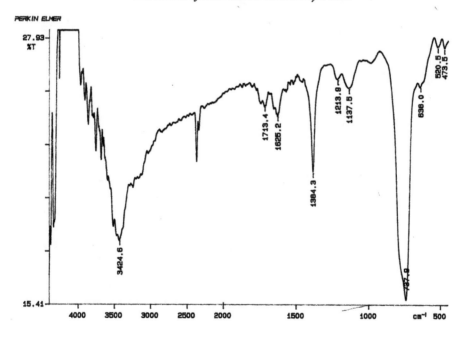

FTIR scan of the Paralab Antimony Fume

Sample ID: Sb FUME   **Percent solids:** 100

Sb-27-005A   **Digestion information**

Amount:	3050	
Amount:	1.52	
Dry amt.:	1.52	
Prep. date:	9/30/02	

	Analysis date	Inst. used	Dilution factor	Instrument result (mg/L)	Instrument rep. lim. (mg/L)	Sample rep. lim. (mg/kg)	Sample result (mg/kg)
Al	9/30/02	59 ICP	24	0.593	0.07	55.26	468.24
Sb	9/30/02	59 ICP	24	90.200	0.07	55.26	71210.53
As	9/30/02	59 ICP	24	25.710	0.03	23.68	20297.37
Ba	9/30/02	59 ICP	24	0.012	0.003	2.37	9.55
Be	9/30/02	59 ICP	24	0.000	0.003	2.37	2.37 U
Cd	9/30/02	59 ICP	24	0.941	0.005	3.95	742.50
Ca	9/30/02	59 ICP	24	2.059	0.08	63.16	1625.53
Cr	9/30/02	59 ICP	24	0.000	0.01	7.89	7.89 U
Co	9/30/02	59 ICP	24	0.000	0.007	5.53	5.53 U
Cu	9/30/02	59 ICP	24	0.044	0.006	4.74	34.74
Fe	9/30/02	59 ICP	24	1.888	0.01	7.89	1490.53
Pb	9/30/02	59 ICP	24	1.171	0.06	47.37	924.47
Mg	9/30/02	59 ICP	24	0.398	0.2	157.89	313.89
Mn	9/30/02	59 ICP	24	0.056	0.003	2.37	44.29
Ni	9/30/02	59 ICP	24	0.000	0.02	15.79	15.79 U
K	9/30/02	59 ICP	24	0.000	1	789.47	789.47 U
Se	9/30/02	59 ICP	24	0.123	0.05	39.47	97.42
Ag	9/30/02	59 ICP	24	0.007	0.007	5.53	5.84
Na	9/30/02	59 ICP	24	40.200	0.08	63.16	31736.84
Tl	9/30/02	59 ICP	24	0.000	0.2	157.89	157.89 U
V	9/30/02	59 ICP	24	0.000	0.007	5.53	5.53 U
Zn	9/30/02	59 ICP	24	8.520	0.007	5.53	6726.32

Paralab Sb Fume
↓
Aqua Regia Extraction
↓
Analysis By ICP
TJA 61E ICAP

9/30/02
RaB

Above: Metals analysis of the Fume by ICP.
Facing page: Analysis for Mercury in the Antimony Fume by Cold Vapor AA

Sb-27-005A
Sb FOMG

MέTHOD / Hg Soil

Linear Regression					
Date	04/30/03				
Type	SOIL				
Calibration					
Concentration	Absorbense				
0.000	0.000				
0.500	0.012				
1.000	0.024				
2.000	0.048				
4.000	0.102				
Linear Correlation	0.9995				
In y=mx+c m =	0.0255				

Sample ID	Absorbense	Dilution	Concentration mg/l	Sample weight g	Concentration mg/kg
ICB	0.000		0.000		NA
ICV	0.024		0.941		NA
MB	0.000		0.000		NA
BS	0.024		0.941		NA
BSD	0.022		0.863		NA
Sb-27-005A	0.103	63	254.457	1.08	23.561

Table 2. Physical and chemical properties of some antimony compounds.

Compound	Formula	Crystalline form and properties	Melting point °C	Boiling point °C	Solubility in cold water
Antimony	Sb	Silver white metal hexagonal	630.5	1750	insoluble
bromide, tri-	$SbBr_3$	col., rhomb.	96.6	280	decomposes
chloride, penta-	$SbCl_5$	white liquid or monoclinic	2.8	79	decomposes
chloride, tri-	Butter of antimony $SbCl_3$	col., rhomb., deliq.	73.4	283	very soluble
fluoride, penta-	SbF_5	col. oily liquid	7	149.5	soluble
fluoride, tri-	SbF_3	col., rhomb.	292	subl. 319	very soluble
hydride (=stibine)	SbH_3	inflammable gas	-88	-17.1	slightly soluble
iodide, tri-	SbI_3	ruby-red, hexagonal	170	401	decomposes
oxide, penta-	Sb_2O_5/Sb_4O_{10}	yellow powder	380/930	-	very slightly soluble
oxide, tetra-	Natural cervantite Sb_2O_4	white powder	930	-	very slightly soluble
oxide, tri-	Natural senarmonite Sb_2O_3	white, cub.	656	subl. 1550	very slightly soluble
oxide, tri-	Natural valentinite Sb_2O_3	col., rhomb.	656	1550	very slightly soluble
potassium tartrate	Tartar emetic $K(SbO)C_4H_4O_6$ $1/2H_2O$	col. cry.	100	-	soluble
selenide	Sb_2Se_3	grey cry.	611	-	very slightly soluble
sulfide, penta-	Sb_2S_5	yellow powder, prism	dec. 75	-	insoluble
sulfide, tri-	Natural stibnite Sb_2S_3	black, rhomb.	550	ca 1150	insoluble
sulfide, tri-	Antimony orange Sb_2S_3	yellow-red, amorph.	550	ca 1150	insoluble

amorph. = amorphous, col. = colourless, cry. = crystal, cub. = cubic, dec. = decomposes; deliq. = deliquescent, rhomb. = rhombic/ortho-rhombic, subl. = sublimes. Based on information in ref. (57).

Experiments with Stibnite, Kermes, Glass, Regulus, etc.

I sorted through the pile of mine tailings and chipped out a box of high grade ore to take home. With 10 or 20 pounds of freshly mined stibnite on hand, I was ready to begin experimenting and putting into practice the information gathered in class at PRS. These experiments were performed in the laboratory in Atlanta during the periods between classes.

The furnace (facing page) was a pile of insulating fire brick (E-23) fired by a Fischer burner my dad gave me at age 12. The photo next to it is of a later furnace but same basic design and same burner used.

Sal Ammoniac sublimated three times for preparing Kerkring Menstruum

I have included here a selection of pages from an early notebook during that time (1976 to 1979). They are crude and sometimes a bit confusing, I know; but they do contain some interesting observations and tid-bits. Most of these experiments were qualitative exploratory adventures to get the feel for what antimony can do. Note: The scanner blacked out some highlighted dates; they weren't purposely redacted.

ADDED ♁ FROM Sal AMMONIAC OF LAST
SUBLIMATE TO THE NEW KM TINCTURE TO
ACT AS AN ENZYME IN PREPARING KM.

PREPARATION OF GLASS OF ♁ FROM
♁ FUME. 8 Tsp POWDERED ♁ FUME
1½ Tsp BORAX FLUX
PLACE 1 Tsp IN CRUCIBLE PLACE IN FURNACE
UNDER HIGH HEAT. ♁ FUSES INTO BLACK
BUBBLING MASS. SULFUR IS PURGED OFF
DURING THE BUBBLING. MORE ♁ MIXTURE IS
ADDED AS THE SUBSTANCE IN THE CRUCIBLE IS
MOLTEN.
ALL OF ♁/BORAX MIXTURE ADDED, THE SULFUREOUS
DISCHARGES BECOME LESS AND LESS — THE
WHOLE BECOMES A BRIGHT RED MOLTEN MASS.
AN IRON ROD IS INSERTED FROM TIME TO
TIME TO CHECK ON THE MATURITY OF THE
GLASS — IN THE FIRST STAGES IT IS BLACK
THE GLASS BECOMES MORE CLEAR AND OF A
DARK YELLOW COLOR. IT APPEARS FINALLY AFTER
≈ 1 HR TO BE CLEAR AND MATURE. WE POURED
IT OUT ONTO A HEATED BRASS DISH. THE
THINNER PORTIONS WERE CLEAR BUT THE
CENTER PORTION WAS FOGGY
AND THERE WERE SEVERAL WHITE SPOTS
OF IMPURITIES. THIS CAN BE REGROUND
AND MELTED AGAIN UNTIL MATURITY IS
ATTAINED.

███████ THE GLASS WAS GROUND AND REPLACED INTO CRUCIBLE THEN INTO THE FURNACE. AFTER FUSING AND HEATING FOR 45 MIN (MUCH SMOKE GIVEN OFF) THE GLASS LOOKED MATURE WHEN THE IRON ROD WAS INSERTED AND EXAMINED. THE GLASS WAS AGAIN POURED ON A COPPER DISH BUT ~~SHOWED~~ CLOUDINESS IN IT SO IT WAS REPLACED INTO THE HOT CRUCIBLE IN THE FURNACE AND MELTED AGAIN FOR ≈ 1/2 HR. THEN IT WAS POURED AGAIN THIS TIME GIVING A CLEAR DARK AMBER COLORED GLASS. (WT. 21 GRAMS)

███████ - THE ANTIMONY FUME (PART OF IT ≈ 1/4 LB) WAS SPREAD ON A COPPER DISH AND ROASTED OVER A MEDIUM HEAT TO DRIVE OFF SOME OF THE EXCESS SULFUR. ROAST 2 HRS. THE Ŏ IS NOW EVEN DARKER THAN AT THE BEGINNING. PLACE 12 TSP. OF THIS Ŏ W/ 2 TSP BORAX. GRIND TOGETHER. PLACE 1TSP IN CRUCIBLE AND HEAT VIOLENTLY OVER FURNACE (BEGIN 7:00 PM) BUBBLING OCCURS AS THE EXCESS SULFUR IS DRIVEN OFF BUT THERE IS NOTICABLY LESS SMOKING. TESTING W/ IRON ROD SHOWS FIRST A DARK BLACK OPAQUE GLASS THEN A CARAMEL BROWN. THEN A GLOSSY YELLOW WITH TRANSPARENT YELLOW PORTIONS THIS STAGE WAS REACHED AFTER 1 1/2 HRS. AFTER 1 HR 45 MIN. THE IRON ROD TEST SHOWED TWICE THAT THE GLASS WAS MATURE; BUT WHEN POURED OUT THERE WERE STILL GLOSSY STREAKS ALL THRU IT. - IT WAS BROKEN IN PIECES AND RETURNED

TO THE FIRE.

2 HRS 10 MINS. IN THE FIRE TOTAL TIME AND ▮▮▮
THE IRON ▮▮▮ SHOWS CLEAR GLASS. IT WAS
POURED ONTO A COPPER DISH AND A BEAUTIFUL
▮▮▮▮ AMBER GLASS WAS FORMED. TOTAL YIELD 56 GRAMS.

▮▮▮▮▮ TINCTURE DERIVED FROM ALCOHOL OVER
3X SUBLIMED SAL AMMONIAC (FOR KERKRING MENSTRUUM)
WAS FILTERED OFF AND SET ASIDE FOR DISTILLATION.

▮▮▮▮▮ 6 OZ. OF 3X SUBLIMED SAL AMMONIAC,
WHICH WAS USED PREVIOUSLY TO PREPARE KM ▮
▮▮▮▮▮ AND STILL CONTAINED SOME OF THE ♁,
WAS ADDED TO 15 OZ GLACIAL ACETIC ▮▮▮▮.
THIS WAS SEALED IN A JAR AND ALLOWED
TO MACERATE. YELLOW TINCTURE ALREADY
APPEARED.
THIS WILL BE USED TO EXTRACT A POWDER
FROM ♁ WHICH WILL IN TURN BE USED TO
PREPARE THE FIXED ANTIMONIAL TINCTURE.

5/19/76 - MIX 16 TSP ♁ FUME WITH 2½ TSP BORAX
MELT IN CRUCIBLE 1 TSP AT A TIME UNTIL MOST
OF THE SULFUR IS PURGED OFF (START 11:35)
2:40 PM - NO CHANGE IS TAKING PLACE - THE GLASS
IS NOT MATURING BUT STAYING BLACK. IT
WAS POURED OUT TO BE GROUND AND DIVIDED
INTO SMALLER PORTIONS (TOTAL WT. 80 GRAMS) ← IMMATURE GLASS WT.
CLOSE EXAMINATION SHOWED CLEAR AMBER SPOTS
MARKING THE BEGINNING OF MATURITY.

5/20/76 - 7:30 pm Place 12 Tsp. Antimony Fume in a
Brass dish and calcine slowly on electric Hot
plate. 8:30 large glass slag-like globules Have
formed. The ☉ is taken off and ground then returned
it is darker grey now. Measure is 8 Tsp.

9:30 pm - Test sample of calcined ore from the mine
with Borax to see if Glass can be produced. Ratio- 8:2
9:50 - No change at all. Antimony not fluxing   ☉:Borax
Heat turned off. This ore will have to be precipitated
out into Kermes mineral because of the silica mixed
with it.   5/21/76

10:10 Remove Fume from Hot plate and Grind.
Measure 8 Tsp. Add 1 Tsp Borax and grind together
Add 1 Tsp. of this to crucible and place in furnace
over High heat. (Time 10:20) The ☉ mixture seems
much more willing to liquify with only 1/3 the
smoke of the previous pourings. (Note - The Moon
is in a perfect trine aspect to Uranus at
11:30 MDT) (12:10 LMT) Add ☉ mixture as needed.
12:00 Iron rod still shows glass is dark ☽ immature
Poured out at 12:10 still immature, dark glass.
Total wt - 67 grams immature Glass

5/22/76 - Add 1/2 of the broken up glass produced
on 5/19/76 to a crucible and place in
Furnace of moderate Heat. Add more glass
as the First gets red Hot and molten
(9:10 pm)

██████ ▁ - place tincture DERIVED FROM alcohol
AND 3X ♎ Sal ammoniac into 500ml Retort
place in SANDBAth To warm AND PRODUCE
A vacuum prior To Distillation.

10:25 No change in maturity of Glass. ≏ ½ was
poured onto a copper dish. The other Half was
RETURNED To the fire - Still DARk with greenish Gloss
11:00 poured The Remaining Glass out. Still unchanged
AND immature.

██████ - TURN on SANDBAth containing Retort with
TINCTURE FOR KM (under vacuum) To Low Heat
Let Distill very slowly. Start 9:30 am
Distillate is colored slightly yellow.
(OFF at 11:00 pm ≏ ½ is Distilled over (2½ oz))

5/28/76. GATHERED several pounds of ☿ ore FROM the
Hills AROUND us. (HERMADA mine)
TURN on Retort containing KM To Low at
5:00 pm

6:10 pm place ≏ ½ of the Glass produced on 5/20
(This was immature Gloss) into a crucible in the
FURNACE at a MODERATE Heat. When molten ADD
¼ Tsp BORAX AND mix in. Alot of smoke is given
off AND The Rod shows The Glass is clearing.
6:25 - pour out The Glass - is shows quite a
GREATER DEGREE of maturity. Though not Fully
MATURE.

REPLACE IN FURNACE AND ADD THE REST ~~OF THE~~
THE GLASS PRODUCED ON 5/20. WHEN MOLTEN ADD
¼ TSP BORAX. MUCH SMOKE GIVEN OFF AGAIN.
6:50 - CRUCIBLE CRACKED AND GLASS LEAKED ALL OVER.
- 8:45 - 47 GRAMS of GLASS WAS SALVAGED, GROUND
AND PLACED IN FURNACE WITH A NEW CRUCIBLE ~~AND~~
9:20 - ADD ½ TSP BORAX
10:00 - SMALL CHANGE IN MATURITY IS HAPPENING
POUR GLASS OUT.

████ - CLEAN OUT RESIDUE IN RETORT AND SAVE ~~████~~
FOR THE FUTURE PREPARATION OF KM.
SAVE DISTILLATE TO BE DISTILLED AGAIN TWO TIMES.

████ PLACE KM IN CLEAN DRY RETORT AND HEAT
IN SAND BATH. HEAT RECEIVING FLASK ON HIGHER
HEAT. PUT THEM TOGETHER WHILE HOT AND LET
COOL THUS PRODUCING A VACUUM. RETURN TO
SAND BATH AT LOW HEAT. OFF AT 11:00 PM

████ GRIND ẞ GLASS (CLEAR AMBER) TO FINE POWDER AND
PLACE IN PAPER THIMBLE SET UP IN EXTRACTOR WITH
WATER TO WASH OUT BORAX FLUX. TOTAL WT. ~~████~~

████ - TURN ON SANDBATH WITH KM ~~████~~
AT 10:00 AM.
TURN ON EXTRACTOR TO WASH OUT BORAX FROM
ẞ GLASS. ~~████~~

[redacted] - change wash water in extractor washing
♁ glass.

clean and dry retort & receiver - heat
both with KM in retort then put together
and let cool.

[redacted] - change wash water in extractor washing
♁ glass. again.

Turn on sandbath to distill KM a third
time at low, under vacuum off at 12:30pm

[redacted] - Turn on sandbath to distill the ~~last~~
portion of KM. It is now a crystal clear
liquid.

[redacted] change wash water in extractor and
continue to wash out the Borax ~~flux~~.
The wash waters are saved and show
a yellowish-white precipitate (the Borax) which
has a pH of about 10.

WT of KM: 56 grms

[redacted] At the end of the day we removed the
thimble containing the ♁ and placed in in
a warm spot to dry.

[redacted] Empty now dry ♁ from thimble and
grind finer. Replace in thimble for rewashing

[redacted] place ♁ in thimble in extractor
and wash with water again to remove
more of the Borax. (9:30 AM)

[redacted] - Turn off extractor at 10:00 pm
water in flask cloudy and alkaline. water
in extractor body - pH. 8

ROBERT ALLEN BARTLETT

6/9/76 - collect stinging nettles and place in blender with water. Blend to a thick mush-like consistency. Add 9 cups of this to the steam distillation apparatus.

Fill a large thimble w/ 2 oz finely ground chamomile and place in extractor. Use a menstruum of clear grape wine fortified with once distilled grain alcohol (≈ 30 cc.)

■ set up extractor with ☿ again to be washed once again.

6/10/76 - Turn on extractor with chamomile ■ and extractor with ☿. Also turned on steam distillation apparatus (8:45 am)
    11:30 - liquid in steam receiver is coming over but no signs of oil.

The chamomile extraction was taking so long and at such a high degree of heat that a vacuum of 14 inches-mercury was applied and the heat turned down a little.

■ xtractor with ☿ being washed and pH checked showed it was slightly acid, that is all borax is washed out and it is ready to be dried.

Steam distillation apparatus was turned

OFF A 10:30 PM - DISTILLATE WAS CLEAR AND HAD A VERY STRONG NETTLE SMELL. NO SIGNS OF VISIBLE OIL ON TOP.

6/11/76 - ADD 1000 ml OF WARM WATER CONTAINING ½ TSP YEAST AND ½ CUP SUGAR TO THE FECES OF THE STEAM DISTILLED NETTLES, AFTER DRAWING OFF MOST OF THE DARK TINCTURE WITH IT CONTAINING THE CRUDE SULFUR

CONTINUE DRYING THE THIMBLE CONTAINING THE WASHED & GLASS POWDER.

6/14/76 - DISTILL THE DISTILLATE FROM THE NETTLES STEAM EXTRACTION. - STRONG SMELL BUT LITTLE IF ANY VISIBLE OIL.

6/15/76 - DISTILL ALCOHOL FROM NETTLES

6/16/76 - TURN OFF CHAMOMILE EXTRACTION

5:00 PM - ADD 56 GRAMS OF THE DRIED POWDERED GLASS OF ANTIMONY TO 56 GRAMS OF THE PREPARED KERCKRING MENSTRUUM STOPPER WITH GROUND GLASS AND LUTE SET ASIDE FOR DIGESTION.
THE POWDERED GLASS APPEARS LIGHT YELLOW
(VERY SLIGHT TINCTURE 3/19/77)
1/13/78 NO TINCTURE

THIS DAY. PLACE UNDER 20 m/Hg VACCIUM.

- LEACHED OUT SALTS OF SAFFRON, ALOES & MYRRH
SET ASIDE TO EVAPORATE AND CRYSTALLIZE.

7/25/76 - BEGAN DISTILLATION OF CHAMOMILE MACERATED
WITH ALCOHOL AND ACETIC ACID (BEGUN ON 6/25/76)
IN A RETORT UNDER VACUUM

- CONTINUED SOXHLET EXTRACTION OF CHAMOMILE WITH
CHAMOMILE WINE.

- BEGIN MACERATION OF 15 GRAMS POWDERED CAYENNE
AND 50 GRAMS POWDERED MYRRH IN 70%
ISOPROPYL ALCOHOL (15 OZ) FOR A LINIMENT

FROM WEATHERBY'S]

7/26/76 - BEGAN MACERATION OF CALCINED ☿ ORE (PRE-
PARED DURING THE WINTER OF 75-76) 1 OZ. WITH
6N ACETIC ACID (90 ML.) IN DIGESTIVE HEAT

BEGAN MACERATION OF RED KERMES (ANTIMONY OXYSULFIDE)
(PREPARED FROM TECH. GRADE ANTIMONY TRISULFIDE FROM
MATHESON, COLEMAN & BELL, DISSOLVED IN LYE SOLUTION
AND PRECIPITATING W/ ACETIC ACID AND WASHING
AND DRYING DURING SUMMER-FALL 75)
1 OZ KERMES AND 90 ML 6N ACETIC ACID.
PLACED IN DIGESTIVE HEAT. - (DRIED OUT)
1/13/77

BEGAN DISTILLATION OF ACETIC ACID PREPARED
WITH 3X SUBLIMED SAL AMMONIAC (STARTED

ON 5/18/76) BY DECANTING TINCTURE INTO A
RETORT, HEATING TO BOILING ON SANDBATH,
REMOVING FROM HEAT AND ATTACHING HOT
RECEIVER AND ALLOWING TO COOL — THUS OBTAINING
A VACUUM FOR FURTHER DISTILLATION

7/28/76 — GROUND 1 OZ OF HIGH GRADE ♁ ORE FROM
HERMADA MINE (ATLANTA) AND COVERED W/ 2 OZ.
OF 50% ACETIC ACID — SET TO DIGEST.

— TRIED TO PREPARE A SMALL QUANTITY OF ♁ GLASS
USING THE RED KERMES AND BORAX FLUX
IN A RATIO OF 2:3 RESPECTIVELY. AFTER
MELTING THEY TURNED TO A CARAMEL OPAQUE
GLASS MIXED WITH THE REGULUS OR METALLIC
ANTIMONY WHICH SMELTED OUT. SMALL STREAKS
OF CLEAR AMBER GLASS WERE PRESENT. TOTAL
TIME IN FURNACE WAS ½ HR. EASY TO MELT,
TRY CALCINING THE RED POWDER TO GREY FIRST
THEN MAKING GLASS.

— WHILE WASHING A CALCINING DISH WITH HCl
(WHICH WAS USED IN CALCINING RAW ♁ ORE) AND RINSING
WITH WATER, I NOTED THE PRECIPITATION OF THE
WHITE ANTIMONY OXYCHLORIDE. THIS PROMPTED
REMEMBERING THE IMPURE ANTIMONY FUME WHICH
CAN BE CLEANED IN THIS WAY TO FORM A PURE
OXIDE FOR THE PREPARATION OF ♁ GLASS.
150 ML OF CONC. HCl (20°Bé) WAS PLACED IN A
FLASK AND HEATED WHILE DISSOLVING AS

ROBERT ALLEN BARTLETT

MUCH OF THE GREY ☿ FUME AS WOULD GO INTO
SOLUTION (1-2 oz). THIS FORMED A DARK BLACK
LIQUID WHICH WAS BROUGHT TO A BOIL THEN FILTERED
THROUGH GLASS WOOL GIVING A GOLDEN CLEAR LIQUID.
A SMALL AMOUNT OF UNDISOLVED PARTICLES SETTLED TO THE
BOTTOM BUT WERE REMOVED BY DECANTING INTO ANOTHER
VESSEL. THIS 150 ml OF CLEAR GOLDEN SOLUTION
WAS POURD INTO A 2000 ml FLASK ¾ FULL OF
WATER. THIS INSTANTLY FORMED A BEAUTIFUL
SNOW WHITE PRECIPITATE WHICH IS THE OXYCHLORIDE
OF ☿. THIS IS TO BE DECANTED AND WASHED
SEVERAL TIMES TO REMOVE THE ACIDITY. LET STAND
AND SETTLE OVER NIGHT.

— BEGAN CALCINATION OF RED KERMES PRECIP.
IT SEEMS TO PROCEDE MUCH FASTER THAN THE
RAW ORE.

7/29/75 — PREPARED MORE OF THE ☿ FUME ACCORDING
TO THE FORMULA USED YESTERDAY.
COMBINE YESTERDAY'S YEILD WITH TODAYS AND
BEGIN WASHING WITH WATER AND DECANTING

— DISOLVED 2 oz RAW ☿ (COMMERCIAL)
WITH 200 ml CONC. HCl. STRONG H₂S GAS
IS GIVEN OFF. HEAT TO HELP SOLUTION OF ALL
☿. AFTER DIGESTING ½ Hr, 50 ml MORE HCl WAS
ADDED AND DIGESTED UNTIL BUBBLING STOPPED.
SAND AND UNDISSOLVED GRIT ARE COLLECTING ON THE
BOTTOM, ON SETTING A DARKER MATERIAL

SANK TO THE BOTTOM AND A CLEAR GREENISH
LIQUID ON TOP. DECANT AND FILTER
ADD 100 ml MORE HCl TO THE SLUDGE WHICH
REMAINS. MORE $\bar{\partial}$ IS DISSOLVING
ALLOW THIS TO DIGEST OVERNIGHT AND THE
PREVIOUSLY OBTAINED FILTRATE TO SETTLE.

- GROUND 1 OZ COMMERCIAL REAGENT GRADE, $\bar{\partial}$ TRICHLORIDE
AND COVERED WITH 150 ml OF 50% ACETIC ACID.
SEAL IN JAR AND PLACE IN DIGESTIVE HEAT
  2. YELLOW TINCTURE (3/14/77)

- CONTINUED CALCINATION OF THE RED KERMES
WHICH IS NOW A LIGHT RED-GREY AND
GETTING LIGHTER.

- FILLED A NEW THIMBLE WITH CHAMOMILE
AND PLACED IT IN THE SOXHLET (REPLACING THE
ONE IN THERE) WHICH WAS STARTED ON 7/29/76,
AND ADDED 100 ml MORE CHAMOMILE WINE.
SAVED AND DRIED THE PREVIOUSLY EXTRACTED
HERB FOR CALCINATION.

8/2/76 - BEGAN DISTILLATION OF FILTERED SOLUTION OF
HCl AND Sb_2S_3

- ADDED 2000 ml OF WEAK SOLN OF SODIUM BICARB.
(pH 8) TO THE WHITE $\bar{\partial}$ OXYCHLORIDE PREPARED
ON 7/29/76. LIGHT ~~effervescence~~ BUBBLING
OCCURS AS THE $\bar{\partial}$ OXIDE IS FORMED AND
THE CHLORINE COMBINES WITH THE SODIUM.

CO_2 gas is given off, leaving Sb_2O_3 and
salt water (pH 7) This is decanted and washed
several times to remove all the salt.

- Ground 2oz of ♁ ore and placed in a
16oz glass vessel. Slowly added ☆ 5–10 cc
of concentrated Nitric Acid (white fuming). Instantly
A thick red vapor of nitric oxide evolved.
More acid was added slowly as the fuming
continued and the vessel became very hot.
Test with lead acetate paper showed no hydrogen
sulfide being given off as I suspected it
would.
Note: when testing the HCl & ♁ mixture w/
lead acetate paper – the paper was coated
with a bright metallic coating as though
it were spray painted silver. This was
evidently caused by the chlorine precipitating
out the lead.

- While this was taking place, 3 more macerations
were begun – 1. 1oz. calcined ♁ ore with
90 ml absolute ether (anesthetic). 2. 20grams
commercial ♁ trichloride with 60 ml of
absolute ether. 3. 1oz. raw ♁ ore with
60 ml absolute ether. Place in incubator

To the above ♁/nitric solution, acid was
added to dilute to 5 oz liquid in all
shaken well and placed in the →

INCUBATOR TO DIGEST. THE FORMERLY BLACK POWDER IS NOW A GREENISH WHITE WITH DARKER PARTICLES OF GANGE SINKING TO THE BOTTOM.

8/3/76 - CONTINUED DISTILLATION OF THE HCl & ☿ SOLUTION. AS IT CONCENTRATES IN THE RETORT IT BECOMES DARKER AND DARKER YELLOW TO ABOUT THE APPEARANCE OF URINE

- DISTILLATION OF CHAMOMILE WITH ALCOHOL/ACETIC MENSTRUM (6/26) IS GETTING CLOSE TO THE END (OF 1ST DISTILLATION) ← THE DISTILLATE COMES OVER NOW AS CLEAR GOLDEN COLORED DROPS. THE HERB RESIDUE IS BEGINNING TO TURN DARK BROWN TO BLACK. A BEAUTIFUL CLEAR GOLDEN TINCTURE.

- PURIFIED FUME WAS PLACED IN A TRAY TO DRY AFTER DECANTING AND SIPHONING OFF THE WASH WATER. (FROM 7/28/76)

- BEGAN REDISTILLING THE DISTILLATE FROM THE SAL-AMMONIAC/ACETIC MACERATION (7/26). SAVED THE DARK RESIDUE (≈30cc DARK GOLD COLORED) FOR FURTHER USE IN THE FUTURE. DISTILLATE MEASURED 250 ml. SLIGHTLY YELLOW COLORED.

- RAN A SMALL EXPERIMENT TO PRODUCE THE REGULUS OF ☿ ACCORDING TO VALENTINE: 8 GRAMS CRUDE TARTAR FROM GRAPE JUICE, + 12 GRAMS RAW ☿ ORE (EQUAL PARTS BY VOLUMEN) + 4-5 GRAMS POTASSIUM

ROBERT ALLEN BARTLETT

NITRATE. GROUND THESE TOGETHER AND PLACED IT SCOOP BY SCOOP INTO A HOT CRUCIBLE IN THE FURNACE. IT DETONATED AND SHOT OFF SPARKS AND SMOKE, THEN QUICKLY FUSED INTO A MOLTEN MASS THIS WAS POURED ONTO A COPPER PLATE AND COOLED. ON COOLING THERE REMAINED A BRITTLE, DARK BROWN, OPAQUE, GLASS-LIKE SUBSTANCE WITH A WAXY LUSTER. ON BREAKING IT UP INTO SEVERAL PIECES, SMALL GLOBULES OF SILVER ☿ METAL WERE FOUND THESE WEIGHED 12 GRAINS IN ALL. THIS WAS SET ASIDE. THE BROWN GLOSSY SUBSTANCE WAS GROUND (WT 18 GRAMS) AND PLACED IN A TEST TUBE THEN COVERED WITH ≈ 40 ML ABSOLUTE ETHER. SEALED AND PLACED TO DIGEST. SEE P 142 TCA

8/4/76 - CONTINUED DISTILLATION OF HCl/☿ SOLUTION.
    - TURNED OF SOXHLET CONTAINING CHAMOMILE
    SAVED HERB AND EXTRACT WAS BOTTLED TO
    DECANT.
    - MIXED EQUAL PARTS ☿ ORE AND POTASSIUM CARB.
    AS PER KERCKRING'S ADVICE ON P. 142 TCA. TO
    PRODUCE THE REGULUS OF ☿. ON POURING THE
    EASILY FUSED SMOKELESS MIXTURE THE SAME
    GLASSY SUBSTANCE WAS FORMED AS YESTERDAY
    ONLY THIS TIME THERE WERE NO GLOBULES OF
    ☿ REGULUS. ONLY THE GLASS. MICROSCOPIC OBSERVATION
LEADS ME TO BELIEVE THE REGULUS IS FINELY SUSPENDED
IN THIS GLASS AND THAT FURTHER PURIFICATION IN THE
FURNACE WILL COAGULATE IT.

(FROM 7/28/76)

- A SMALL PORTION OF THE PURIFIED, DRY, WHITE FUME WAS PLACE IN A CRUCIBLE AND HEATED A SHORT TIME. THIS PRODUCED A YELLOWISH OPAQUE GLASSY SUBSTANCE (NOT ENOUGH TO POUR) PERHAPS THE ADDITION OF FLUX WILL HELP.

- BEGAN MACERATION OF 20 GRAMS RAW ☿ ORE WITH 100 ML ACETONE. PLACE IN INCUBATOR TO DIGEST.

- CONTINUED WASHING KERMES PREPARED SEVERAL WEEKS AGO AS A DEMONSTRATION OF THE PROCESS OF PRECIPITATION. PH NOW SHOWS SLIGHTLY ACID. DECANT AND DRY.

8/5/76 - DISTILLED ACETIC ACID PREPARED WITH SAL AMMONIAC - SET UP TO DISTILL A THIRD TIME.
   - BEGAN MACERATION OF 1 HANDFUL OF GINKO LEAVES (GROUND) AND 4 OZ. GRAPE WINE.

8/9/76 - FUSED TOGETHER TWO TSP. BORAX AND 2½ TSP. PURIFIED WHITE FUME (PREPARED 7/28) IN THE FURNACE. POURED THE MOLTEN SUBSTANCE ONTO A FLAT COPPER DISH. THIS WAS THEN A CLEAR GOLDEN YELLOW GLASS OF ☿
   TOTAL WT. 23 GRAMS

- SET UP TO DISTILL THE ACETIC ACID PREPARED WITH SAL AMMONIAC A THIRD AND FINAL TIME.

ROBERT ALLEN BARTLETT

- STRAIN GINKO MACERATION AND BEGIN DRYING HERB. SAVE EXTRACT TO FILTER.

8/9/76 - MIXED 48 GRAMS PURIFIED ☿ FUME (7/28) WITH 10 GRAMS BORAX. PLACED 1 TSP. INTO HOT CRUCIBLE IN FURNACE. IT TAKES SEVERAL MINUTES TO FUSE AND WHEN POURED GIVES A CLOUDY YELLOW GLASS. LEFT IN A HIGH HEAT FOR A LONGER TIME GIVES A CLEAR YELLOW GLASS MELTED THE REMAINDER OF THE ☿/BORAX MIXTURE IN DEGREES AND LET DIGEST AT A HIGH HEAT FOR A SHORT TIME (≈10 MIN.) WHEN POURED THIS ALSO GAVE A CLOUDY GLASS WHICH WAS GROUND AND REPLACED INTO THE CRUCIBLE WITH THE ADDITION OF 1 GRAM BORAX — HIGH HEAT. TEST WITH IRON ROD SHOWS CLEAR YELLOW GLASS. WHEN POURED IT WAS CLEAR IN PLACES AND LIGHTLY CLOUDY IN OTHERS. REQUIRES MORE HEATING. ON GRINDING AND RE-MELTING THE SUBSTANCE GOT A LITTLE DARKER YELLOW BUT MUCH LESS CLOUDY. (WT 30 GRAMS)

- BEGIN DISTILLATION OF ACETIC ACID — SET UP YESTERDAY

8/10/76 - REMELTED THE CLOUDY GLASS IN HOT FURNACE. THE GLASS WAS DIVIDED INTO TWO PORTIONS. TO THIS 1ST PORTION WAS ADDED A QUARTER TSP BORAX. THIS DIDN'T APPEAR TO SPEED UP THE MELTING TO MUCH. AFTER THE WHOLE ☿ SUBSTANCE WAS A UNIFORM LIGHT

RED IT WAS POURED. THE SECOND HALF WAS MELTED AND THE SAME PROCEDURE WAS FOLLOWED. BOTH POURINGS GAVE A CRYSTAL CLEAR YELLOW GLASS. (TOTAL WT 49 GRAMS)

— SET UP SOXHLET WITH ≈ 1 OZ DRY WILD LETTUCE USED ROSEMARY WINE (7/74) FOR A MENSTRUM.

— CONTINUED DISTILLATION OF ACETIC ACID.

+ 8/11/76 · PLACED 1 OZ. ANTIMONY TRISULFIDE INTO INTO FLASK ADD 4½ OZ HCl. DIGEST IN SUN FOR SEVERAL HOURS UNTIL IT STOPPED BUBBLING

— TURN ON SOXHLET WITH ROSEMARY WINE AND WILD LETTUCE. VACUUM OF 20 IN.

— CONTINUED DISTILLATION OF ACETIC ACID.

→ ADDED ½ OZ CONC. NITRIC ACID — VIOLENT BUBBLING OCCURS OF RED NITRIC OXIDE LET THIS COOL AND STOP FUMING OVER NIGHT

— SAVED THE 3X DISTILLED ACETIC ACID WHICH CAME OVER AND SEPARATELY SAVED THE RESIDUE FOR MAKING MORE KM/ACETIC (YEILD 250 ML)

ON SETTLING ≈1½ HRS THERE WAS A THIN LAYER OF SAND AT THE BOTTOM, A CLOUDY YELLOW ORANGE LIQ., AND A SPONGE-LIKE GREEN SUBSTANCE FLOATING ON TOP

ROBERT ALLEN BARTLETT

2/2/77
green lion/alcohol

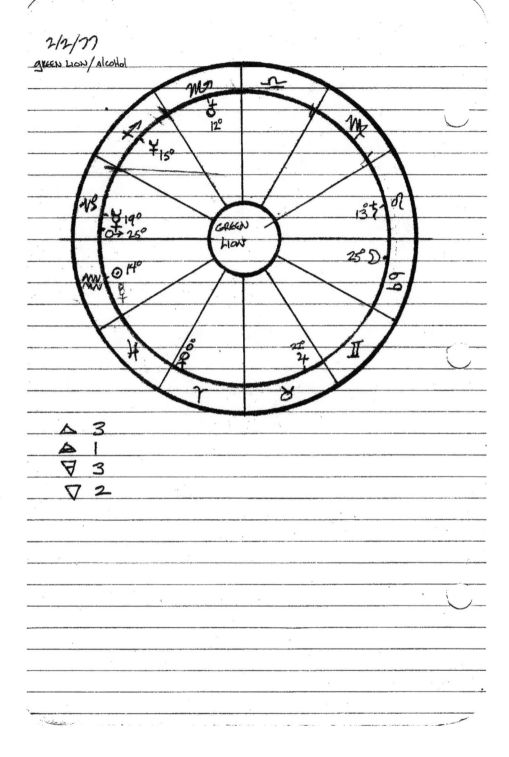

△ 3
◭ 1
▽ 3
▽ 2

— SEPARATED THE SELF HEAL BEGUN 11/30/76 INTO
TWO VESSELS. CONTINUE DIGESTION.

1/22/77 — REDISTILLED THE CHERRY WINE AGAIN
MAKING IT 5 TIMES (THIS LAST TIME THE
POTASSIUM CARBONATE WAS ADDED) WATER WAS SEPARATED.
ALCOHOL DISTILLED AT 76°C THEN STOPPERED
WITH SEVERAL GRAMS ANHYDROUS POTASSIUM CARB.

1/23/77 — DRAW OFF GREENISH BLUE TINCTURE
PRODUCED WITH 6N ACETIC ACID ON THE
CALCINED ORE (WEATHERBY'S) BEGUN WINTER OF 75-76
AND PLACED IN RETORT. DISTILL OFF THE (7-26-76)
ACID SLOWLY. (ADD ACID BACK TO CALCINED Ō TO EXTRACT MORE)
WHEN DRY A GREEN SALT REMAINS. WASHED W/ RAIN
WATER AND DISTILLED TO DRYNESS.

BEGAN SLOW DISTILLATION OF THE CHAMOMILE - ACETIC/
ALCOHOL MIXTURE (VRM) IN SANDBATH.

2/2/77 — PLACED ≈ 1 OZ RECTIFIED CHERRY WINE
(5× Ō TWICE W/ KCO₃) ONTO GREEN POWDER
LEFT FROM 1/23/77 STOPPER WELL.

2/12/77 — PLACED GREEN POWDER AND ALCOHOL
FROM 2/2/77 IN LARGE TEST TUBE AND PLACED
IN WARM SANDBATH (≈ 120°F) TO EXTRACT.
ALREADY THERE IS A LIGHT BLUISH GREEN TINT.
(MARCH 12, DEFINITE BLUE GREEN TINCTURE)

ROBERT ALLEN BARTLETT

HEATED 3 parts ōre, 1.5 parts SUBLIMED SULFUR, 1.5 CRUDE SULFUR VIVE, 3 ports IRON FILINGS. TO REDNESS FOR 5 HRs. THEN COOLED SLOWLY. (DOES NOT POUR) ("Hortman's" GOLD)

3/14/76 - THE SOLID GREY BLACK MASS FROM YESTERDAY WAS REMOVED FOR THE CRUCIBLE AND GROUND. THEN PLACED IN DISH TO ROAST OFF EXCESS SULFUR. GROUND AGAIN AND ADDED TO IT, TWO PARTS FUSED AND GROUND BORAX. GRIND TOGETHER.

- PLACED THE 30 CC COLLECTED $-A INTO RETORT TO DISTILL IN SANDBATH. (VACUUM)

- CHamomile IN ACETIC/Alcohol IS COMING OVER w/ ☿ AND ♀ CONJOINED IN A CLEAR GOLDEN TINCTURE RESIDUE OF HERB IS DARK BROWN AND BLACK.

3/31/77 - DISSOLVED 3 Tsp. NaCl (SEA) IN ≈100 ml OF 4 MONTH OLD URINE (CLEAR) THEN ADDED 1 Tsp CuSO$_4$. FOAMING OCCURED RAPIDLY. ADDED ½ Tsp SAL AMMONIAC (ONCE ☾). LET SIT SEVERAL HRs. FILTER TWICE. SAVE DARK BLUE SOLUTION.
- ADD SOLUTION TO IRON FILINGS FOR THE PARACELSIAN METHOD OF PRODUCING CROCUS OF MARS

5/18/77 - DISSOLVED SEVERAL POUNDS Sb$_2$S$_3$ FROM HERMADA MINE IN 1.5 gal. CONCENTRATED NaOH SOL'N. HEAT FOR 3 HRs. ☿ LET SETTLE OVER-NIGHT. STRAIN TO REMOVE GANGE AT BOTTOM. ADD CONCENTRATED HC$_2$H$_3$O$_2$

To precip. Kermes mineral Sb_2S_3 (Red Brown Powder)
Decant and wash 5 times
Till neutral. Decant. Ladle ppt.
onto paper spread on ground
to dry.

5/24/77 Collected rain - let settle several
days open to air. Seal with
cloth and place in warm place to Ferment.

6/5/77 - Placed 5.5 oz Kermes into Soxhlet
w/ acetic acid (conc). Place in sand
on hot plate. Circulate.

6/11-12/77 collected 5 gallons Filtered Rainwater
(electric storm)

6/19/77 - Distilled acetic acid from amber tincture
of ☉ and ♀ obtained from Kermes 6-5-77
collect Residue.

6/20/77 Added 2ml. of fermented dew water
- collected on last year's wesak moon - to
a half gallon of rain water, hopefully
to act as a catalyst to hasten the
fermentation of the rain water.

Robert Allen Bartlett

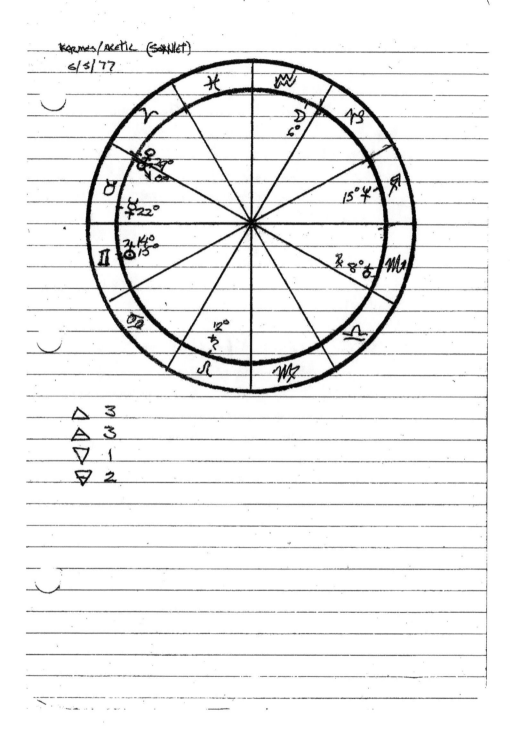

Kormes / Acetic (Solvet)
6/5/77

△ 3
△ 3
▽ 1
▽ 2

2/18/78 – Stopped extraction of willow Bark/Poppy seeds of 2-15-78 and filtered the extract through very thin course paper into a separatory funnel. The red extract is full of drops of thick clear oil that float on the surface and also form an emulsion in the liquid.

2/19/78 – Calcined the willow/Poppy residue of 2-18-78 to grey salts leached out with H_2O and let evaporate.

4:30 pm – Began distillation (on low) of the vinegar of antimony experiment of 8-29-76. ≈ 800 ml of liquid and ≈ 9 oz of the ore which has taken on a syrupy consistency and seems almost greasy. pH = 5 ≈ comes over at 98°C Heat setting 3

2/20/78 – Began soxhlet extraction of a large thimble (≈ 5-6 oz) of finely (4:30 pm) powdered sulfur vive using glacial acetic acid as a menstrum.

2/22/78 – 1:am the temperature of the vinegar of antimony experiment (distilling) has dropped from 98 to 93°C and the distillate coming over last

2/22/78 (cont.) is milky white with a pH of ≈ 2-3

2/22/28 - Heat on Vinegar of Antimony exp.
is slowly increased thru the day
until it reaches high setting where it
is left to sublimate the residue.
- Yellow crystals have formed on the inside
of the side arm of the distilling flask.
(High setting at 4:00 pm)

- The acetic acid of the sulfur Soxhlet (2-21)
extraction is a deep golden red now.

2/23/28 - 8:AM Begin lowering the
heat on the Vinegar of Antimony exp.

8:30pm - Removed the residue from
the flask and placed it in a
stainless steel sublimator. This consisted
of ground ore and what appeared to
be chunks of crude ☿ Regulus.
This was heated over a gas stove burner
slowly at first then high.

12pm - Decrease heat then cool all
the way over-night.

2/24/78 - Ground the ☿ ore residue in
the sublimator and mixed ≈ 2 tablespoons
of ☿ fume with it. This was put
back in the sublimator (3pm) and heat applied

Photo of Regulus formed during the Vinegar of Antimony distillation. One of only a few samples that remain from this time period.

1/9/79 - Began Soxhlet extraction of 25g ♂ Fume
w/ glacial acetic acid
very dark amber clear extract after 24 hrs.

1/10/79 - Began maceration of 150 grams Kermes
with glacial acetic acid 350 ml (10:10 pm)

— placed a new thimble of 25g Fume into the Soxhlet
extractor of 1-9-79 and continued extraction.

1/11/79 - Filtered ~~together~~ the two HCl solutions
of antimony ore and kermes of 8-6-78
top layers of both sediments is white then grey
going to the color of undissolved substance
(black for ore and red brown for kermes)
Filtered solution from ore is golden and clear
solution from kermes is of a ~~blue~~ pale golden yellow
— placed equal portions (~ 10 ml) of the two filtered
solutions in a beaker and began adding
a solution of ammonium polysulfide (made by passing
H_2S into a dilute NH_4OH solution). A bright
orange precipitate of Sb_2S_3 forms immediately.

1/12/79 - Filtered the orange Sb_2S_3 precipitate
of 1/11/79 to collect and dry the powder

1/14/79 - Placed 75g powdered magnetite into a flask
and covered with 200 ml glacial acetic acid
stoppered and allow to macerate in a warm
place

Anecdotes on uses

All of the materials produced up until this time were still suspect in my eyes. Did they work medicinally as advertised or was it just "snake oil." I had some occasion to try them out on willing subjects. One day while sitting in the sun relaxing in Atlanta, a truck and horse trailer came speeding up our driveway and came to a sudden halt. The driver, quite distraught, asked if we had a gun. He needed it to put down an injured horse in the trailer. I didn't have a gun but said let's have a look. The horse had apparently sliced its leg open on a piece of loose sheet metal within the trailer. The owner had wrapped the wound with cloth, rope, wire, anything he could find to stop the bleeding; there was blood everywhere in the trailer and the horse was beginning to get weak. We opened the bandage and there was a slab of flesh like a large steak hanging there and blood was squirting out still. Just days before, I had read an Ayurvedic text where it was suggested to pacify the blood flow from a wound by applying oil. I ran inside and grabbed a bottle of the oil of egg derived from the yolks and smeared it all over the wound. Like a charm, the bleeding stopped and we were able to clean the area with water. I asked the owner if he would mind trying something that should speed the healing process. After seeing what the oil of egg did, he was all in. I applied a Fixed Tincture of Antimony directly on the wound. The horse initially flinched from the alcohol but then became very tranquil; maybe it was just from loss of so much blood. I made a strong decoction of Stinging Nettles, a Martial plant with amazing tonic and blood building capabilities and fortified it with a healthy dose of Fixed Antimony. I put some of this into a bowl of water and approached the horse. He was very thirsty and drank the whole thing. We repeated this in the morning as the owner was getting ready to take the horse to a veterinarian. The horse seemed no worse from the wear and was able to enter the trailer without effort or need for coaxing. About three weeks later the horse owner returned to Atlanta with other horses, but he told me that the horse we treated was alive and well. He said that when he got to the vet, he was quite amazed at the state of the wound; there was no swelling or infection at all. In fact, all the vet had to do was change the dressing. It must have impressed him because he asked the owner what he had put on the wound to heal it so rapidly and without infection or swelling. All the owner could say was "pure magic."

Another incident I recall from this time involved a human. Sandy, another Atlanta resident, was prone to gall bladder inflammations that would occasionally flare up quite painfully. She had medication for it but had run out and the nearest pharmacy was 90 miles down a bumpy dirt road. I found her one day sitting outside the local pub doubled over in pain and sobbing. She told me the problem and said that even with her medicine the attacks last for several days, and she is pretty much bedridden for that time. We were getting a reputation as medicine makers in town, so I asked her if she would try a potion I would make for her. She agreed, and I went home to prepare it. The gall bladder is under the rulership of Mars, so I mixed my trusted friend, Stinging Nettle again, as a spagyric tincture blended with Fixed Tincture of Antimony. Within half an hour I returned, and Sandy drank a dose of the tincture. I left her the bottle and wished her well as I went off to take care of some business. When I returned in an hour, there was Sandy, standing, no, dancing around in no pain whatsoever. When she saw me, she ran up and gave me a hug that nearly busted a rib or two; she was so happy and thoroughly amazed at how fast the medicine worked and so much better than her current medication from the doctor.

Part Four: College Years

In the second year of classes, Frater Albertus announced that Paracelsus Laboratories (Paralab) was being reorganized and would soon be in production. Paralab was to begin preparing herbal and mineral materials in the alchemical tradition and offer them for research and use in the alternative healthcare fields that were beginning to emerge at that time. At the end of class, we were allowed some private one-on-one talks with Frater Albertus. I expressed a burning desire to work at Paralab, and Frater Albertus encouraged me to return to school and finish my degree in chemistry; my work at Paralab would be waiting.

Thanksgiving day of that same year we struck a 2- or 3-inch vein of high-grade stibnite in the Weatherby mine. We dug out the rock that had been blasted and piled it outside, even though it was blizzarding. I saved aside a few personal specimens for later. We began the process of timbering the newly exposed cavity and had already placed the 18-inch-diameter fir tree posts and cap. Ready to start the cross timbers, my partner (an old time, experienced miner) said "stand back I think it's going to do something"; seconds later a huge boulder fell from the ceiling right through the wooden cap like it wasn't even there. Suddenly the walls started collapsing, and we started running down the tunnel not knowing when it would stop; it was very exciting. Obviously we made it out but the cave-in took out four 8-foot-long sets, and the 5th and 6th were not looking very safe. Weatherby decided to close the mine and move on to a silver deposit he had discovered elsewhere. The Kobolds were telling us to move along as well; I left them an offering, and we departed in peace.

I was out of a job but quickly found temporary employment with a lumber company working in the area of the Hermada Mine (essentially a hill or two over from Weatherby Mine). One evening after work I walked up the road leading to the mine and was met by a large older gentleman who said his name was Gibb Svensson, the caretaker of the property. I asked him about the mine and told him I had worked for Bill Weatherby. He perked right up, he knew Bill and soon was regaling me stories of the mine when it was open; it had been closed for many years. It was getting dark, and I told Gibb I should be getting back to camp. It was easier to camp out near the job site for the week and return home on weekends. Gibb offered me one of the old miner's bungalows, and I gladly accepted. Gibb was an old timer, living there in the woods for months alone, so he thoroughly enjoyed having company and would greet me each evening with hot coffee and mining tales. One such evening he told me to follow him and we walked along an overgrown road for about a quarter of a mile, when there in the middle of the road was a dump truck–size pile of high grade stibnite. Gibb said, "take what you want, it's been sitting here going to waste." Over the time period of the job, I was able to cart out about 500 pounds of good stibnite as a source material which has lasted up to the present.

After two horrendous fatalities within the logging company, I decided there has to be a better way, and I soon found myself taking Frater's suggestion of returning to school (best advice ever). It didn't take much money to live in the mountains, 90 miles from civilization, so I really didn't have the funding for college. Things have a way of turning out when the time is right. I was able to start school at Boise State University in 1977 under a Basic Educational Opportunity Grant provided by the university. I still needed an income, so I went to the assayer's shop in town where we would occasionally drop off samples from the mine. I knew the owners, George the mining engineer and Larry the geochemist, of "Boise Assay and Metallurgy"; and they remembered me so I asked if they would hire me part time while I was in school. Yes, I was in, and Larry took me under wing, teaching me how to operate a carbon arc spectrograph the size of a Buick (they have hand-held models now) requiring photographic film development and examination under an optical comparator line by line. The film and results obtained on a specimen of Hermada stibnite are reproduced in the Sources section above. I was instructed in a number of physical and wet chemical methods for separating minerals, which have come in handy over the years, and later trained on the relatively new Atomic Absorption Spectroscopy (AA), and the very sensitive Graphite Furnace AA. The grand finale of training was Fire Assaying; almost a lost art but with roots as far back as 2600 BCE and an intimate relationship with alchemy throughout time. This is a fascinating technique we will mention later on.

With working at Paralab in mind, I was on a fast-track at school to get out in three years. I was able to transfer credits from pre-viously attended San Jose State University classes, and that helped cut some time off. If there were any interesting ideas that came up during classes, I would often try them out on samples of my own experiments at home in my lab, for example, looking at things under different lights, especially ultraviolet. Sometimes I would construct a simple instrument like a polarimeter or even replicate an old apparatus and apply it in my works. In the final year, all chemistry students were required to pursue an independent study project of their own choosing. With some reserves, my advisor allowed my project, "Investigation of the Spagyric Technique" and handed me the key to my own small lab room on campus. Part of the project involved preparation of an oil from antimony, which I was able to gather analytical information on. I used some of the antimony fume purchased from Paralab earlier; the notes that were typed up later and the infra-red scan captured are appended.

| PRODUCT: | OIL FROM ANTIMONY (unfixed) | EXP. NUMBER: Sb-85-OA1 |

DATE	TIME	PROCEDURE
4/18/78		Began maceration extraction of 4 oz. of antimony fume (sample #Sb-85-OA1A) (Sb_2O_3) from a smelter (Paralab) with acetone.
6/1/78		Filtered the golden tincture produced and filtered again into a roto-evaporator where the bulk of the acetone was removed. Some Sb_2O_3 concentrated to the bottom. Red oil remains. 5 ml. diethyl ether was added dissolved the red oil which was then filtered from the solid remaining (sample of solid #Sb-05-OA1B). Allowed ether to slowly evaporate from lightly closed vial.
3/20/79		There now remains @ .5 ml. of a viscous, clear amber-red oil which floats in distilled water. (sample #Sb-85-OA1C). Addition of HCl and H_2S shows no ppt of Sb_2S_3. Phosphomolybdic acid reagent shows negative for Sb.

NAME: *Robert Allen Bartlett*

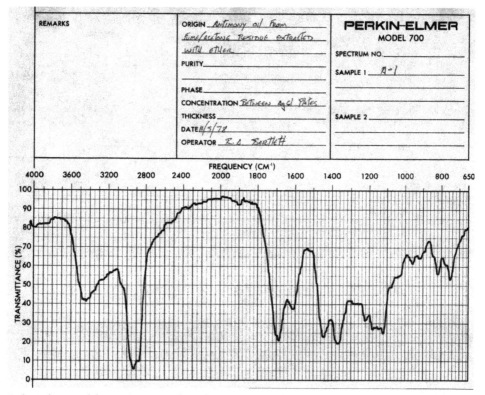

| REMARKS | ORIGIN _Antimony oil From_ _Fume/acetone Residue extracted_ _with ether_ PURITY | **PERKIN-ELMER** MODEL 700 SPECTRUM NO. SAMPLE 1 _A-1_ |
| PHASE CONCENTRATION _Between AgCl Plates_ THICKNESS DATE _11/5/78_ OPERATOR _R. A. Bartlett_ | SAMPLE 2 |

Infrared scan of the Antimony Oil produced as part of my independent research project. The scan is poorly resolved by today's standards but it was the technology available at the time so I thought it was pure treasure.

A test bench and reagents were set up for analyzing my own samples using techniques I was learning at college. These were classical wet methods and not instrumental.

During my final year at college, the Dean of Chemistry was presenting a special graduate course on the history of chemistry. I cornered him in his office one day and asked if I could attend even though I was an undergrad. It took some convincing, but he hesitatingly agreed. At the end of the course we were required to write upon a topic covered. I chose to write about spagyrics. Some days after submitting my paper I stepped into the elevator of the chemistry building and there was the Dean holding my paper! He was quite excited about it and said he just now made a personal copy. He wrote A+ 100% on it. I felt prepared for Paralab. Evidently Frater Albertus liked the paper also, as edited versions appeared in *Parachemy* and *Essentia*, the official journals of the PRS and Paracelsus College and again later in a publication by Phameres.

Upon graduation, everything was set to move to the Salt Lake City area near Paralab, and so off we went to a new chapter of our story.

Photos of the basement laboratory in Boise during the college years, including an image of the same furnace from my first lab

Part Five: Paralab

When we arrived at Paralab we were greeted by old friends and met some new ones, took a tour of the lab, noting areas that needed improvement and wherein it was announced that they couldn't afford to pay me at present. Thanks to the generosity of friends and family, I had a roof overhead and food to eat, so I was good to go without pay; I had no interest in that part anyway.

My first task was to organize the mineral extractions lab. The chemist before me left no notes, and there were about 50 assorted glass jars on tables and shelves, some of which looked very interesting, some entirely corroded, but they had no labels. There was no way of telling what all of this stuff was so eventually it was decided to dispose of it. Except for the jars and a few boxes of empty

jars, the mineral lab looked pretty empty.

Starting from scratch, we set up lab benches and equipment racks along the walls, a central island lab bench with sinks at both ends, a 10 liter Soxhlet extractor in the corner, rotary evaporator, vacuum system, and fume hood; now we were ready for work. It wasn't long until I received a letter of employment.

Frater Albertus outside of Paralab

Paralab

Paracelsus Laboratories, Inc., General Offices, P. O. Box 455, West Jordan, Utah, 84084, U.S.A.

June 16,1979

Robert Bartlett
544 E. 11900 So.
Draper, UT

Dear Robert:

We wish you to know that we have very much appreciated the work you have done at Paralab since your arrival the end of May. Not only have you worked voluntarily with us during the regular business hours but you have worked as well many hours in addition to this.

Your particular kind of help has been very much needed at Paralab. Now that you have completed your schooling, which was undertaken for the purpose of being able to one day work at Paralab, we are happy to be able to place you on the Paralab payroll as of July 1,1979.

Your begining salary we have already discussed, but should you have any further questions regarding this, please do not hesitate to ask us.

Our best wishes to you as Paralab's Chief Chemist and for the success and progress of the work that lies ahead of you.

Sincerely,

Mary Adams
General Supervisor
& Office Manager

Paralab and Paracelsus Laboratories are registered Trademarks for Pharmaceuticals and related Chemicals

Paracelsus Laboratories

NATURAL HERBAL and MINERAL
PREPARATIONS with a DIFFERENCE

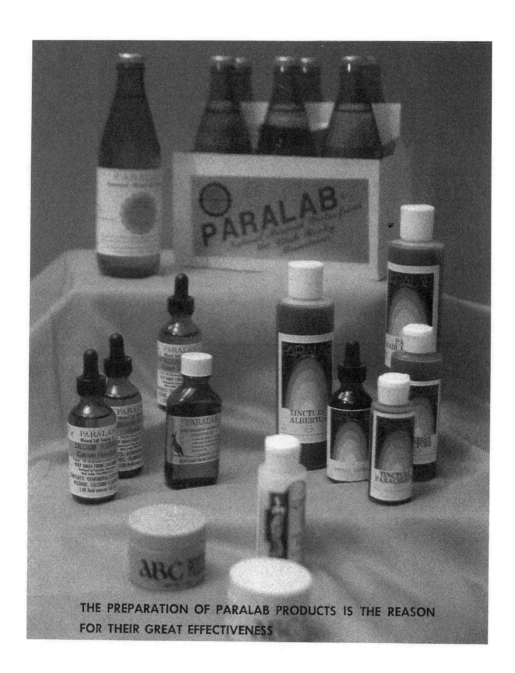

THE PREPARATION OF PARALAB PRODUCTS IS THE REASON
FOR THEIR GREAT EFFECTIVENESS

A word about chemical instrumentation

You can skip through this section and come back to it as a reference to help understand some of the analytical data presented in the following pages. I am inserting it here because I've included scans from different instruments on a variety of finished products and their intermediates during production and placed them within the discussion of the different experiments presented. Through the years, the rise of chemical analysis technology has been a constant amazement for me. Analyses that would have taken hours, even days when working at Paralab can now be accomplished in minutes with much greater accuracy. It also meant gaining a certain degree of mastery in operating some very hi-tech and finicky instruments over the years.

There are a number of analytical methods represented here and each sheds some light on the nature of the materials tested. Much of this work was accomplished long after Paralab had closed; I kept myself employed as a chemist at the bench level so as to have access to instrumentation in a number of materials testing laboratories over the years. In some cases there is analytical data that has been collected on a material at different points in time to see if significant changes had occurred as it aged. Following the charge given by Frater Albertus to gain analytical data on these products, I respectfully submit herein for all.

In the bulk of the data presented here, thermal properties were collected by Differential Scanning Calorimetry (DSC) and Thermogravimetric Analysis (TGA); Metals analysis by Flame Atomic Absorption spectroscopy (AA) and later by Inductively Coupled Plasma (ICP) . Thin Layer and Paper Chromatography (TLC) methods were used in the early days to investigate the number and nature of components in a sample; later I was able to employ Gas Chromatography (GC), High Performance Liquid Chromatography (HPLC), and Fourier Transform Infrared (FTIR) spectroscopy at various points in time.

I present here a short synopsis of each technique and the type of data it presents for reference and introduction to the information presented ahead.

TGA –Thermogravimetric Analysis

Thermogravimetry studies the change of a sample mass as a function of temperature. The measurements of these changes are made using a thermobalance in which tests are accomplished according to a programmed heating rate in a suitable enclosed system with a controlled atmosphere.

For this study, a TA Instruments 2950 Thermogravimetric Analyzer was used with Ultrapure Nitrogen as a cover gas to prevent oxidation and so more closely resemble the conditions inside a distillation flask or retort. Samples were heated at a rate of 20° C per minute from room temperature (20° C) to 600 °C. Given the small sample size of 20 to 50 mg this rate was selected to mimic "distillation by degree" within a convenient time span allowing for multiple sample runs.

TGA data can be used for guidance on high temperature distillation of materials. On the next page is a thermogram showing

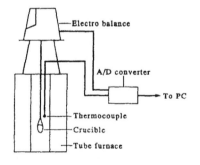

weight loss of powdered cedar leaf as the temperature rises. This is an overlay of two separate runs showing the methods' reproducibility.

The *"Golden Chain of Homer"* describes the *"Anatomy"* of minerals by distillation. We can see many of these transitions occurring in samples examined by TGA and requiring only small amounts (5–50 mg).

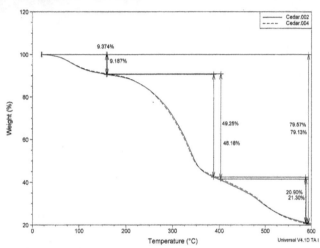

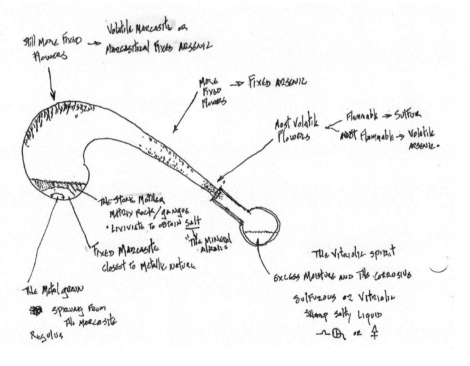

DSC – Differential Scanning Calorimetry

DSC measures the heat flow through a material. Starting at -50 °C, samples are heated at a rate of 20 °C per minute up to 375 °C. Downward curves indicate "Endotherms," that is heat being absorbed indicating changes such as melting, dehydration, crystal habit changes, and decomposition. "Exotherms" are the curves tending upwards from the baseline and indicate release of energy from events such as decomposition, changes of crystal habit, or compound formation.

This information can be used to determine melting points, boiling points, crystal transitions, sublimation and decomposition temperatures. Most of the scans are on compound substances and not single pure materials, so these events can be occurrung to separate compounds within the mixed sample. They do provide "fingerprints" of the sample which can be used to make comparisons to other products within an experiment or with entirely different though related experiments.

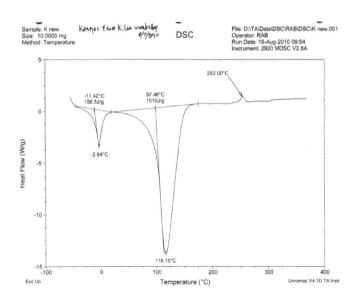

HPLC – High Performance Liquid Chromatography

HPLC provides a method for separating compounds within a mixture and determining their relative rank in concentration. The sample is injected onto a specially prepared column and then pushed through the length of the column with a blended solvent at high pressure. Separation occurs as the sample runs through the column and as each individual compound emerges, it flows past a UV light detector. The position of the peak in the resulting chromatagram and its relative area are recorded in a "Peak Summary Report."

In order to identify each of the peaks, we would have to run hundreds of known standard materials at the same column conditions and create a library for comparison. I didn't have that luxury so the best we can do

is use the scans, again, like fingerprints for comparison. We can see how many components are in a sample and their relative concentrations, as well as some idea as to their complexity based on their position in the chromatogram. Smaller molecules pass through the column fairly quickly whereas larger molecular structures take longer to work their way through. All of this provides guidance for separating compounds from a larger quantity of the sample in the lab by solvent extraction or distillation.

A typical HPLC scan comparing tinctures from antimony and a peak summary table from a different sample. RT refers to the Retention Time, that is, how long it took to get through the column. % Area and Peak Height give indication of the relative concentrations of components within the compound.

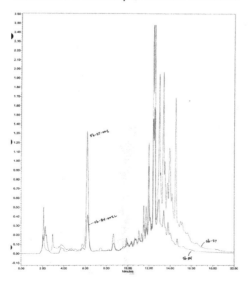

Peak Summary with Statistics

	Sample Name	Inj.	Peak Name	RT (min)	Area (µV*sec)	% Area	Height (µV)	Amount	Units	Vial
1	Sb 84	1		10.531	264540	19.89	17296			1
2	Sb 84	1		12.199	11631	0.87	3121			1
3	Sb 84	1		12.600	66924	5.03	15755			1
4	Sb 84	1		12.793	16251	1.22	4550			1
5	Sb 84	1		12.913	36249	2.73	9738			1
6	Sb 84	1		13.227	184955	13.91	54668			1
7	Sb 84	1		13.336	390098	29.33	107762			1
8	Sb 84	1		13.649	89537	6.73	15644			1
9	Sb 84	1		13.966	73099	5.50	10631			1
10	Sb 84	1		14.583	24919	1.87	3303			1
11	Sb 84	1		15.153	171728	12.91	26751			1
Mean				13.177	120902.815		24476.492			
Std. Dev.				1.236	120514.593		31267.70			
% RSD				9.36	99.68		127.705			

Acquisition Log

Acquired By   RAB
Injection   1
Date Acquired   11/18/2008 9:08:43 AM
Run Time   20.00(min)
Acquisition Method   NTA62359
Injection Volume   15.00(ul)

Sb-84 Tincture sweetened/or

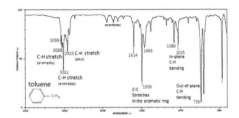

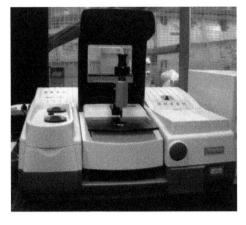

FTIR – Fourier Transform Infrared Spectroscopy

Infrared spectra provide information on molecular structure. The bending and stretching of chemical bonds between atoms in a compound occur at frequencies in the infrared region of the electromagnetic spectrum.

A compound exposed to infrared energy will absorb those frequencies which resonate with the various chemical bonds present. By examination of the frequency ranges absorbed, we can determine the types of chemical bonding present and then deduce a structure of the compound.

The table on the next page presents a simple guide to the frequency ranges for a selection of common atomic bonds.

To the right is the FTIR scan for toluene showing how each part of the molecule absorbs energy of specific wavelengths according to the bonding. These provide "parts of the puzzle" that are arranged to give indication of what the whole molecule must look like.

Remember the scans on most of the products presented here are of compound materials and not pure individual substances, so you will see a blending of peaks generated by the various compounds present and their relative strengths. As for instance, the Fixed Oil of Antimony; there are no commercial libraries for compound comparison that list it, there is nothing to compare it with. You can find something like Oil of Rosemary, it has its own FTIR fingerprint to make comparisons. The scans on various antimony products provide just such fingerprints for comparison and may not exist anywhere else; hopefully they will form the beginnings of a library for future comparisons.

Infrared (IR) Spectroscopy

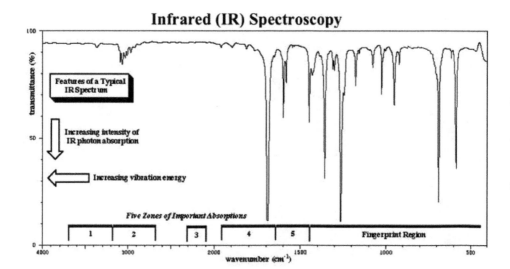

ROBERT ALLEN BARTLETT

Characteristic IR Stretching Frequencies

Functional Group	Bond	Stretching, cm^{-1}	Intensity
Zone 1: 3700 – 3200 cm^{-1}			
alcohol	O-H	3650 – 3200	variable; usually broad
alkyne	≡C-H	~3300	strong
amine, amide	N-H	3500 – 3300	medium, often broad
Zone 2: 3200 – 2700 cm^{-1}			
alkane	sp^3 C-H	2960 – 2850	variable
aryl, vinyl	sp^2 C-H	3100 – 3000	variable
aldehyde	sp^2 C-H	~2900, ~2700	medium, 2 bands
carboxylic acid	O-H	3000 – 2500	strong, broad
Zone 3: 2300 – 2100 cm^{-1}			
alkyne	C≡C	2260 – 2100	variable
nitrile	C≡N	2260 – 2220	variable
Zone 4: 1950 - 1650 cm^{-1}			
aldehyde	C=O	1740 – 1720	strong
amide	C=O	1690 – 1650	strong
aryl ketone	C=O	1700 – 1680	strong
carboxylic acid	C=O	1725 – 1700	strong
ester	C=O	1750 – 1735	strong
ketone	C=O	1750 – 1705	strong
enone (C=C-C=O)	C=O	1685 – 1665	strong
aromatic overtones		1950 – 1750	3 or 4 small humps
Zone 5: 1680 – 1450 cm^{-1}			
alkene	C=C	1680 – 1620	variable
aromatic	C=C	~1600, 1500-1450	variable; 1600 often 2 bands

Fingerprint region: < 1450 cm^{-1}

The functional groups in each zone must be learned. (Do lots of problems!) The exact stretching frequency data for each functional group does not need to be memorized. It will be provided on an exam if needed.

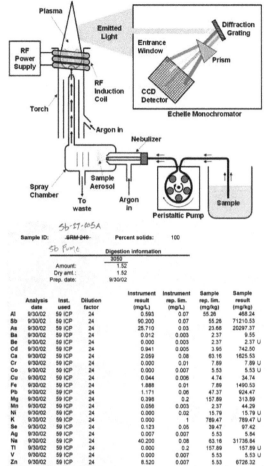

Sb-27-005A

| Sample ID: | ~~SRM 249~~ | | | Percent solids: | 100 |

Sb Fume

			Digestion information	
				3050
Amount:				1.52
Dry amt.:				1.52
Prep. date:				9/30/02

	Analysis date	Inst. used	Dilution factor	Instrument result (mg/L)	Instrument rep. lim. (mg/L)	Sample rep. lim. (mg/kg)	Sample result (mg/kg)
Al	9/30/02	59 ICP	24	0.593	0.07	55.26	468.24
Sb	9/30/02	59 ICP	24	90.200	0.07	55.26	71210.53
As	9/30/02	59 ICP	24	25.710	0.03	23.68	20297.37
Ba	9/30/02	59 ICP	24	0.012	0.003	2.37	9.55
Be	9/30/02	59 ICP	24	0.000	0.003	2.37	2.37 U
Cd	9/30/02	59 ICP	24	0.941	0.005	3.95	742.50
Ca	9/30/02	59 ICP	24	2.059	0.08	63.16	1625.53
Cr	9/30/02	59 ICP	24	0.000	0.01	7.89	7.89 U
Co	9/30/02	59 ICP	24	0.000	0.007	5.53	5.53 U
Cu	9/30/02	59 ICP	24	0.044	0.006	4.74	34.74
Fe	9/30/02	59 ICP	24	1.888	0.01	7.89	1490.53
Pb	9/30/02	59 ICP	24	1.171	0.06	47.37	924.47
Mg	9/30/02	59 ICP	24	0.398	0.2	157.89	313.89
Mn	9/30/02	59 ICP	24	0.056	0.003	2.37	44.29
Ni	9/30/02	59 ICP	24	0.000	0.02	15.79	15.79 U
K	9/30/02	59 ICP	24	0.000	1	789.47	789.47 U
Se	9/30/02	59 ICP	24	0.123	0.05	39.47	97.42
Ag	9/30/02	59 ICP	24	0.007	0.007	5.53	5.84
Na	9/30/02	59 ICP	24	40.200	0.08	63.16	31736.84
Tl	9/30/02	59 ICP	24	0.000	0.2	157.89	157.89 U
V	9/30/02	59 ICP	24	0.000	0.007	5.53	5.53 U
Zn	9/30/02	59 ICP	24	8.520	0.007	5.53	6728.32

Hg 23.5 ppm
By Cold Vapor AA

ICP – Inductively Coupled Argon Plasma Optical Emission Spectroscopy

That's a mouthful that doesn't roll off the tongue easily, but it is a powerful method for determining the presence and concentration of metals in a sample down to the parts per billion with 95% confidence they are accurate.

In this method, the sample in solution is injected into an electrical plasma with a temperature close to 10,000 degrees Celsius. It looks like a flame, but it is a fourth state of matter, an electrical plasma excited by radio frequency and hot as the Sun. The sample is immediately vaporized and excited such that it bursts out glowing with all the light it is able to give out. Each element has its own set of characteristic wavelengths of light that it will emit, and the light is sent through a grating, which, like a prism finely separates the wavelengths, and sends them to a series of detectors. The wavelenghts and their intensities are tallied up by the computer and the concentration for 23 metallic elements is reported. Amazingly, this is all accomplished in 3 or 4 minutes!

ICP report (above): On the far left is the element and on the far right the calculated concentration in the sample. "U" indicates the element below detection levels and thus "Undetected."

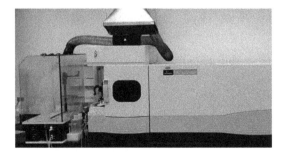

Production of Antimony Tincture at Paralab

With the mineral extractions lab set up, the first priority was to establish a viable method for producing fixed and unfixed tinctures from antimony. Dr. David Schein (mentioned earlier) was the medical consultant for Paralab and directed the research plan for developing the antimony tinctures. David had written his doctoral thesis on "Basil Valentine and his Tinctures from Antimony" in 1978. Frater Albertus teamed us together to establish methodology for fixed and unfixed tinctures starting with antimony fume (of which there many drums stored onsite).

Many of the processes required a bit of time to perform, so David and I would make a plan, then I would carry out the work at Paralab and report the findings. We established a code for processes and products in order to keep track of samples. The code began with the chemical element sign for the parent metal, followed by a numerical code for a product or process, followed by a batch number. For antimony, the numbers you will see ahead read such as; Sb-27-005 meaning, Antimony-Fixed tincture-batch number five or Sb-84-002 meaning Antimony-Unfixed tincture-batch number two. A letter attached to the batch number indicated a sub-sample from the process.

Fixed and Unfixed Antimony Lines

With knowledge of the works already performed for years at the PRS, the methods were already somewhat established; we just needed higher yield, greater purity of product, and reproducibility on a large scale. David and I had both worked with the antimony fume from Paralab in previous years so we were both familiar with what to expect from it. After some exploratory experiments, we were able to isolate the unfixed oil ultimately used in making the tincture. I collected samples of the intermediate compounds and residual impurities that were hidden in the fume. Appended here are the notes from unfixed tincture Sb-84-002 and analyses, over the years, of the various intermediates I had saved. This "dissection" was typical of all the unfixed extractions and the collected analyses have served as "standards" for comparison to future batches even to the present. Flowcharts attached indicate where subsamples were taken. The final production process (shown at the end) was greatly streamlined from this more tedious separation scheme.

PRODUCT: ___UNFIXED ANTIMONY_____   EXP. NUMBER: ___Sb-84-002___

DATE	TIME	PROCEDURE
9/18/79	3:45 p.m.	Placed 4000g Antimony Fume (Sample #Sb-84-002A) into a cotton cloth bag and inserted it into a large reflux apparatus. Over the bag of Antimony Fume was then poured 10 liters of acetone (Sample #Sb-84-002B). A light yellow solution results. The reflux apparatus was then sealed and allowed to macerate.
9/19/79	8:00 a.m.	Heat turned on to 60 Vacuum applied (10" Hg)
	5:00 p.m.	Heat turned off.
9/20/79	8:00 a.m.	Heat turned on to 50, vacuum applied (10" Hg) Reflux continued. The liquid is becoming amber in color.
	5:45 p.m.	Heat turned off.
9/21/79	8:00 a.m.	Heat turned on to 50 and extraction continued.
	5:00 p.m.	Heat turned off.
9/24/79	8:30 a.m.	Heat turned on to 50
	5:30 p.m.	Heat turned off.
9/25/79	8:30 a.m.	Heat turned on and reflux continued The solution is getting dark amber.
	5:30 p.m.	Heat turned off.
9/26/79	8:15 a.m.	Heat turned on 50
	5:30 p.m.	Heat turned off.
9/27/79	8:00 a.m.	Heat turned on 50
	4:40 p.m.	Heat turned off.
9/28/79	8:15 a.m.	Heat turned on 50
	5:00 p.m.	Heat turned off.
10/1/79	8:40 a.m.	Removed the bag of Antimony Fume and let drain in another bucket. The amber colored tincture was then filtered into a large container. After the bag had drained it was returned to the reflux apparatus and all of the liquid obtained was filtered into the container. A sample of Acetone Extract was saved and labeled #Sb-84-002C
	9:30 a.m.	Placed a portion of the acetone extract into a roto-evaporator and began acetone recovery. Heat 25° Vacuum 21" Hg

Total Reflux time=72hrs 25 min

9 Days total Extraction time

NAME: *Robert Allen Bartlett*

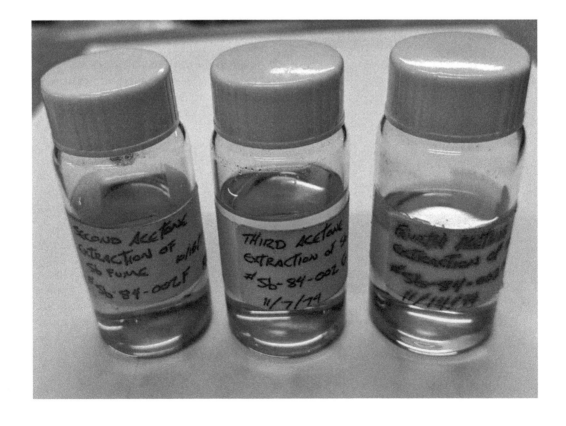

PRODUCT: __UNFIXED ANTIMONY__   EXP. NUMBER: __Sb-84-002__

DATE	TIME	PROCEDURE
10/1/79	10:25 p.m.	Siphoned in another portion of acetone extract and continued the acetone recovery. As the extract concentrates in the roto-evaporator, light colored solids came out of solution. (Sample #Sb-84-002D) The recovered acetone was poured back over the bag of fume in the reflux apparatus to see if more can be extarcted.
	1:15 p.m.	Siphoned another portion of Acetone extract into the roto-evaporator and continued acetone recovery. All recovered acetone was returned to the reflux apparatus.
	2:30 p.m.	Siphoned in the last portion of acetone extract and continued acetone recovery
	3:25 p.m.	Siphoned in 100 ml Ethanol to wash out any remaining acetone and began its recovery. Heat 40°C Vacuum 25" Hg
	4:00 p.m.	Rinsed out the flask containing the oil with several small portions of ether (U.S.P). The liquid was filtered through a fine paper, this produced a dark amber red filtrate and a dark solid filter residue. The dark brown solid residue was removed from the flask and filter paper with acetone, into which it readily dissolved giving a deep amber tincture and a dark grey powdery solid, this was placed in an open dish (Covered with paper) and labeled #Sb-84-002D to dry then placed in a container. The liquid ether extract (Filtrate)was very dark amber and was set aside in a stoppered bottle in refrigerator. A sample of the ether extract was removed and labeled #Sb-84-002E
10/2/79	8:30 a.m.	Turned on the heat for the reflux apparatus and continued the Sb Fume extraction with the recovered acetone.
	6:30 p.m.	Heat turned off on reflux 50
10/3/79	8:00 a.m.	Heat turned on and extraction continued. The acetone has a clear amber tincture.
	5:10 p.m.	Heat turned off.
10/4/79	8:00 a.m.	Heat turned on 50. The acetone extract is getting much darker amber
	5:00 p.m.	Heat turned off.
10/5/79	8:00 a.m.	Heat turned on 50.
	5:30 p.m.	Heat turned off.

NAME: _Robert Allen Bartlett_

PRODUCT: __UNFIXED ANTIMONY__   EXP. NUMBER: __Sb-84-002__

DATE	TIME	PROCEDURE
10/8/79	8:00 a.m.	Heat turned on 50.
	5:30 p.m.	Heat turned off.
10/9/79	8:00 a.m.	Heat turned on 50. Total Reflux Time=63 hrs 40 min
	5:30 p.m.	Heat turned off. Total Extraction Time 16 Days
10/10/79	10:00 a.m.	Heat turned on 50.
	5:00 p.m.	Heat turned off. All to macerate
10/16/79	12:00 a.m.	Removed the bag of Fume and allowed it to drain in a closed bucket. The extract was filtered through fine paper into a large container. A sample of this second acetone extract was removed and labeled #Sb-84-002F
	3:10 p.m.	Siphoned a portion of acetone extract into the roto-evaporator and began acetone recovery.
	4:00 p.m.	Heat turned off.
	6:50 p.m.	Heat turned on and a fresh portion of acetone extract was siphoned into the roto-evaporator. Acetone recovery continued. Heat 25°C Vacuum 24" Hg Acetone recovered was poured back over the bag of Sb Fume.
	7:45 p.m.	Siphoned in the last of the acetone extract and began recovery.
	8:15 p.m.	Heat turned off.
10/18/79	10:15 a.m.	Heat turned on and acetone recovery completed.
	10:30 a.m.	Siphoned 125 ml ethanol into the oily amber residue remaining in the roto-evaporator to wash out any remaining acetone. Began ethanol recovery.
	10:45 a.m.	Removed the roto-evaporator flask and extracted the red amber oily residue with 250 ml of ether in 50 ml portions. This ether extract was filtered and added to the previously obtained ether extract of the first extraction. The residue remaining in the flask was again removed easily with acetone and placed in the container with that obtained in the first extraction labeled #Sb-84-002D.
10/31/79	8:00 a.m.	Heat turned on to 50 and reflux extraction of the Antimony Fume continued using /he recovered acetone plus an additional liter of fresh acetone.
	5:00 p.m.	Heat turned off.

NAME: _Robert Allen Bartlett_

PRODUCT: UNFIXED ANTIMONY   EXP. NUMBER: Sb-84-002

DATE	TIME	PROCEDURE
11/1/79	8:30 a.m.	Placed all of the ether extracted oil obtained into the roto-evaporator and began ether recovery.
	9:00 a.m.	Removed the dark red amber oil from the roto-evaporator and placed it into a small container.
		*14.9g were collected
		The roto-evaporator flask was washed out with alcohol which caused some light colored solids to come out of solution and form a spongy mass. These solids are the same as sample #Sb-84-002D.
		The oil itself is in two fractions a lighter golden amber oil on top and a thick dark amber oil at the bottom.
11/7/79	8:45 a.m.	Removed the bag of Sb Fume from the reflux apparatus and placed it into a container to drain.
		The extract was then filtered into a container.
		A sample of this acetone extract was collected and labeled #Sb-84-002G.
11/8/79	9:45 a.m.	Began acetone recovery of the filtered extract in the roto-evaporator.
	10:15 a.m.	Siphoned in another portion of acetone extract and continued acetone recovery
	10:45 a.m.	Siphoned in another portion of acetone extract and continued acetone recovery
	11:20 a.m.	Siphoned in the last portion of acetone extract and continued acetone recovery
	11:50 a.m.	Heat turned off and acetone recovery stopped.
		All recovered acetone was again poured over the bag of antimony fume in the reflux apparatus, which was then turned on to 50. Vacuum 10" Hg
	11:55 a.m.	Filtered the concentrated acetone extract into a container and stoppered well.
		The ether extracted oil which has been collected 11/5/79 was placed into two centrifuge tubes and placed into a clinical centrifuge spinning at setting #2.
	12:20 p.m.	Centrifuge turned off.
	2:00 p.m.	Removed centrifuge tubes. The oil has separated into two fractions. A dark amber red oil at eh bottom which is the larger of the two fractions and a lighter, golden amber oil on top.
		Removed the light oil fraction and placed it into a container labeled #Sb-84-002H using a suction pipete.
	2:15 p.m.	Placed the centrifuge tubes back into the centrifuge to try and separate the final portions of the light oil fraction.
	3:00 p.m.	Centrifuge turned off. Removed the tubes and again removed the super-

NAME: *Robert Allen Bartlett*

PRODUCT: UNFIXED ANTIMONY   EXP. NUMBER: Sb-84-002

DATE	TIME	PROCEDURE
11/8/79 cont	3:00 p.m.	natant light oil into its container. The heavy oil was then removed and placed into a container labeled #Sb-84-002I.
		The volume ratio of light to heavy oil is approx. 1:3
		A light colored solid has also separated out and rests at the bottom of the centrifuge tubes.
		This solid was collected after washing out the remaining traces of oil with Absolute Ethanol. Teh solid collected was placed in a container labeled #Sb-84-002J.
	5:00 p.m.	Heat turned off on reflux of Sb Fume and recovered acetone.
11/9/79	8:30 a.m.	Heat turned on to 50 and Sb fume reflux continued.
11/11/79	1:30 p.m.	Heat turned off.
11/12/79	8:00 a.m.	Heat turned on.
	5:00 p.m.	Heat turned off.
11/13/79	8:15 a.m.	Heat turned on.
	5:15 p.m.	Heat turned off.
11/14/79	8:30 a.m.	Removed the bag of Sb Fume and allowed to drain in another bucket. The extract was filtered into a large container and a sample was removed and labeled #Sb-84-002K.
	10:00 a.m.	Began acetone recovery from the acetone extract using the roto-evaporator.
	2:30 p.m.	Filtered the concentrated acetone extract into the container which contained the concentrated acetone extract from the third extraction. This was stoppered and set aside.
	3:00 p.m.	Placed all of the recovered acetone back into the reflux apparatus containing the bag of Sb Fume. 2½ liters of fresh acetone were added to bring the volume up to its original mark.
		Heat turned on 55, Vacuum 8" Hg
		Refluxing begun.
	5:00 p.m.	Heat turned off.
11/15/79	8:00 a.m.	Heat turned on 55 and reflux continued.
	5:00 p.m.	Heat turned off.
11/16/79	8:00 a.m.	Heat turned on to 50.
	5:00 p.m.	Heat turned off.

NAME: *Robert Allen Bartlett*

DATE	TIME	PROCEDURE
11/19/79	8:30 a.m 5:00 p.m	Heat turned on to 50 Heat turned off.
11/21/79	8:00 a.m 5:00 p.m	Heat turned on to 50 Heat turned off.
11/26/79	8:00 a.m 5:00 p.m	Heat turned on to 50 Heat turned off.
11/27/79	8:00 a.m 4:00 p.m	Heat turned on 50 Heat turned off.
11/28/79	8:00 a.m 5:00 p.m	Heat turned on 50 Heat turned off.
11/29/79	10:00 a.m	Mixed the light and heavy fractions of oil (#Sb-84-002H and Sb-84-002I), collected previously and diluted with ethanol to give 5 mg oil/ml. A dark solid was precipitated and filtered out before bottling. A sample of the tincture was saved and labeled #Sb-84-002L. The solids remaining on the filter paper were also saved and labeled #Sb-84-002 M.
12/3/79	8:45 a.m	Removed the bag of Sb Fume from the reflux apparatus and filtered the acetone extract into a large container. A sample of the acetone extract was saved and labeled #Sb-84-002N.
12/4/79	8:30 a.m	Began acetone recovery from extract in roto-evaporator. The recovered acetone was again added to the reflux apparatus containing the bag of Sb Fume. The concentrated acetone extract was filtered into the bottle containing the previously collected and concentrated acetone extracts. The solids remaining from the acetone extract, after concentration were collected and washed with two rinsings of acetone. The light cream colored solid has needle like crystals in clumps and was placed into a container labeled #Sb-84-002O.
12/5/79	8:00 a.m 5:00 p.m	Heat turned on reflux of Sb Fume (Heat setting 50) Heat turned off.

NAME: *Robert Allen Bartlett*

PRODUCT: UNFIXED ANTIMONY   EXP. NUMBER: Sb-84-002

DATE	TIME	PROCEDURE
12/6/79	8:00 a.m 5:00 p.m	Heat turned on 50. Heat turned off.
12/7/79	8:00 a.m 4:00 p.m	Heat turned on 50. Heat turned off.
12/10-1/2/80	8:00 a.m	Heat turned on 50 from 8:00 a.m. to 5:00 p.m. on a regular daily basis.
1/2/80	2:00 p.m	Placed all of the concentrated acetone extract obtained to date into the roto-evaporator and removed the acetone. The remaining oily residue was dissolved in a minimum amount of alcohol, then diluted with water. This aqueous solution was extracted with 4-150 ml portions of ether. The ether extracts were filtered giving a deep wine red extract which was placed into the roto-evaporator to remove the ether and washed once with alcohol. *On removal of the alcohol, 5.29g of light & heavy oil remained. No solids or residue. The oil was diluted with ethanol to give 5 mg oil/ml tincture This gave 1058 ml of wine red tincture. This tincture was packed with ice to remove any solids which may be in solution before a final filtration.
1/3-14/80	8:00 a.m 5:00 p.m	Heat turned on reflux continued Heat off.
2/13/80	8:30 a.m 3:00 p.m 4:00 p.m	Filtered the acetone extract of the Sb Fume from the reflux apparatus and began acetone recovery. A sample of the acetone extract was saved and labeled #Sb-84-002P Ethanol washing of the tarry oil remaining. Ether extraction of amber residue with 2 - 200 ml portions. Filtered ether extract is clear amber red.
2/15/80	11:00 a.m 4:00 p.m	Began ether recovery Residue from ether extract taken up into absolute ethanol. Golden amber tincture produced ready for dilution and testing.
2/20/80	9:00 a.m	Reflux of Sb-Fume with recovered acetone continued.

NAME: *Robert Allen Bartlett*

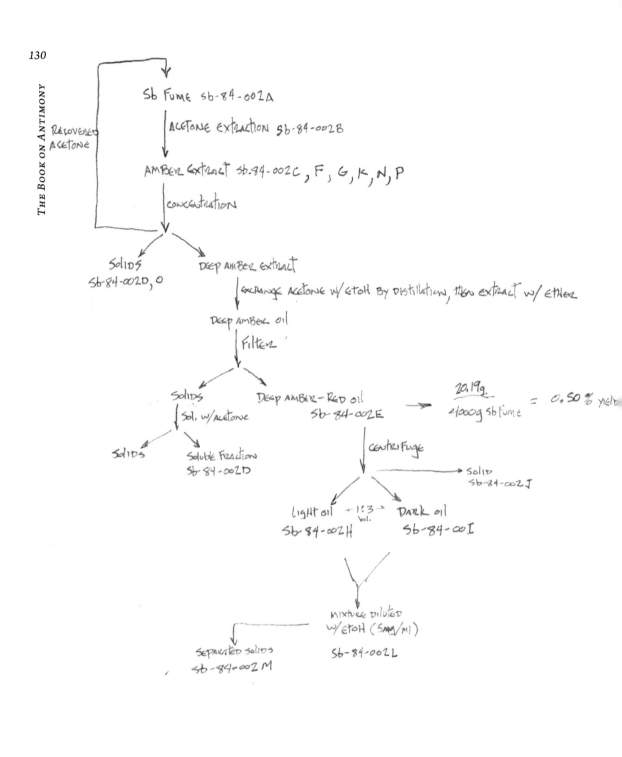

Recovered Acetone

Sb Fume Sb-84-002A

| Acetone Extraction Sb-84-002B

Amber Extract Sb-84-002C, F, G, K, N, P

| Concentration

Solids
Sb-84-002D, O

Deep Amber Extract

| Exchange Acetone w/ EtOH by Distillation, then extract w/ Ether

Deep Amber oil

| Filter

Solids

| Sol. w/Acetone

Solids   Soluble Fraction
             Sb-84-002D

Deep Amber - Red oil
Sb-84-002E

$\dfrac{20.19g.}{4000g \; Sb \; Fume}$ = 0.50% yield

| Centrifuge

Solid
Sb-84-002J

Light oil   ←1:3→   Dark oil
Sb-84-002H   vol.   Sb-84-00I

Mixture Diluted
w/ EtOH (5mg/ml)

Separated solids
Sb-84-002M

Sb-84-002L

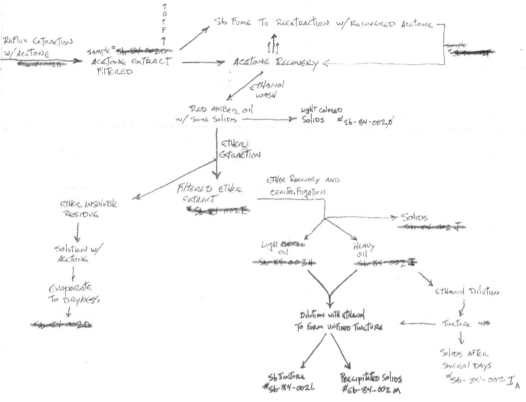

Sb Fume — Reflux Extraction w/ Acetone → Sample "Sb-84-002 Acetone Extract Filtered → Acetone Recovery

Sb Fume To Reextraction w/ Recovered Acetone

T G F

Sample Sb-84-002

Ethanol Wash

Red Amber Oil w/ Some Solids → Light Colored Solids #Sb-84-002 D'

Ether Extraction

Filtered Ether Extract Sb-84-002 E

Ether Recovery and Centrifugation → Solids Sb-84-002 J

Ether Insoluble Residue → Solution w/ Acetone → Evaporate To Dryness → Sb-84-002 D

Light Colored Oil Sb-84-002 H

Heavy Oil Sb-84-002 I

Ethanol Dilution

Dilution with Ethanol To Form Unfixed Tincture ← Tincture

Solids After Several Days #Sb-84-002 I_A

Sb Tincture #Sb-84-002 L

Precipitated Solids #Sb-84-002 M

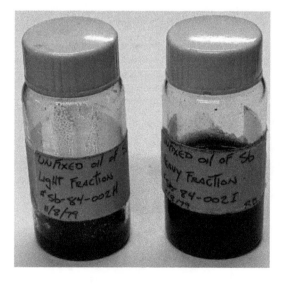

Paralab had limited analytical capabilities; a balance and an old Leitz colorimeter and later I set up an atomic absorbtion spectrometer at the Paracelsus College lab. I was very curious as to what the various products coming from the antimony extractions were chemically. After toying with solubility in various solvents, I began exploring the use of Paper and Thin Layer Chromatography. At the time, this was my best option to at least get a preliminary separation of components in the oils and explore their complexity. It took some trial and error, but I was able to develop several solvent systems that worked quite well. I discovered that there were at least half a dozen compounds in the unfixed oil and several were fluorescent under UV light. Appended below are scans of the actual chromatograms I still have in my notebooks.

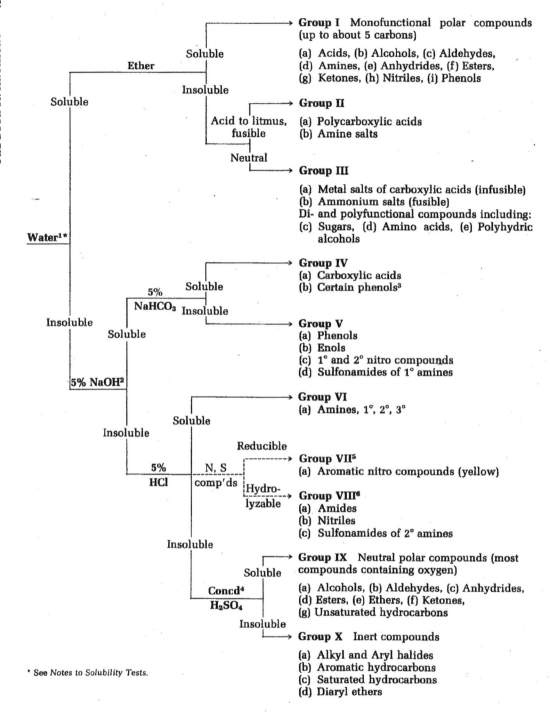

Water[1*]

Soluble

Ether

Soluble → **Group I** Monofunctional polar compounds (up to about 5 carbons)

(a) Acids, (b) Alcohols, (c) Aldehydes, (d) Amines, (e) Anhydrides, (f) Esters, (g) Ketones, (h) Nitriles, (i) Phenols

Insoluble

Acid to litmus, fusible → **Group II**

(a) Polycarboxylic acids
(b) Amine salts

Neutral → **Group III**

(a) Metal salts of carboxylic acids (infusible)
(b) Ammonium salts (fusible)
Di- and polyfunctional compounds including:
(c) Sugars, (d) Amino acids, (e) Polyhydric alcohols

Insoluble

5% NaHCO₃

Soluble

5% NaOH[2]

Soluble → **Group IV**
(a) Carboxylic acids
(b) Certain phenols[3]

Insoluble → **Group V**
(a) Phenols
(b) Enols
(c) 1° and 2° nitro compounds
(d) Sulfonamides of 1° amines

Insoluble

5% HCl

Soluble → **Group VI**
(a) Amines, 1°, 2°, 3°

Insoluble

N, S comp'ds

Reducible → **Group VII[5]**
(a) Aromatic nitro compounds (yellow)

Hydro-lyzable → **Group VIII[6]**
(a) Amides
(b) Nitriles
(c) Sulfonamides of 2° amines

Insoluble

Concd[4] H₂SO₄

Soluble → **Group IX** Neutral polar compounds (most compounds containing oxygen)

(a) Alcohols, (b) Aldehydes, (c) Anhydrides, (d) Esters, (e) Ethers, (f) Ketones, (g) Unsaturated hydrocarbons

Insoluble → **Group X** Inert compounds

(a) Alkyl and Aryl halides
(b) Aromatic hydrocarbons
(c) Saturated hydrocarbons
(d) Diaryl ethers

* See *Notes to Solubility Tests.*

Solvent scheme for identifying compound classes of organic compounds by their solubility

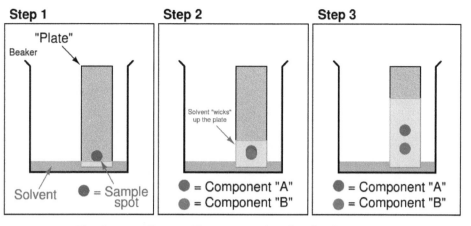

Thin layer and Paper Chromatography of Unfixed Antimony

In the process of Thin Layer or Paper Chromatography, a sample containing multiple components is placed as a concentrated spot on the paper or plate and a mixed solvent is allowed to wick upwards by capillary action carrying the sample components with it. You've seen this before, when you spilled your drink on your papers and suddenly the black ink from the pen you were using starts bleeding out in bands of red, blue, and green. These were pigments blended to create the black ink. Some of the pigments like the solvent better than the paper and so they ride along with the solvent front and move furthest away from their point of origin. Other pigments, like the solvent, but also have an affinity for the paper and move along much slower. The result is that the pigments in the original black ink become separated on the paper as the solvent moves toward the top into a series of spots and each spot is an individual component of the ink.

Using better grade paper and specially prepared plates having a thin layer of powdered silica gel on them, the same process was performed on the various antimony samples. I was able to isolate individual components from the antimony oils by cutting out the spots and washing them off into separate vials. It was frustrating because the amounts were so tiny that I could only proceed with some instrumentation which of course we didn't have nor was it likely that we would for some years to come. So my next recourse was to study microchemical manipulations in hopes that I could identify the small amounts available to work with.

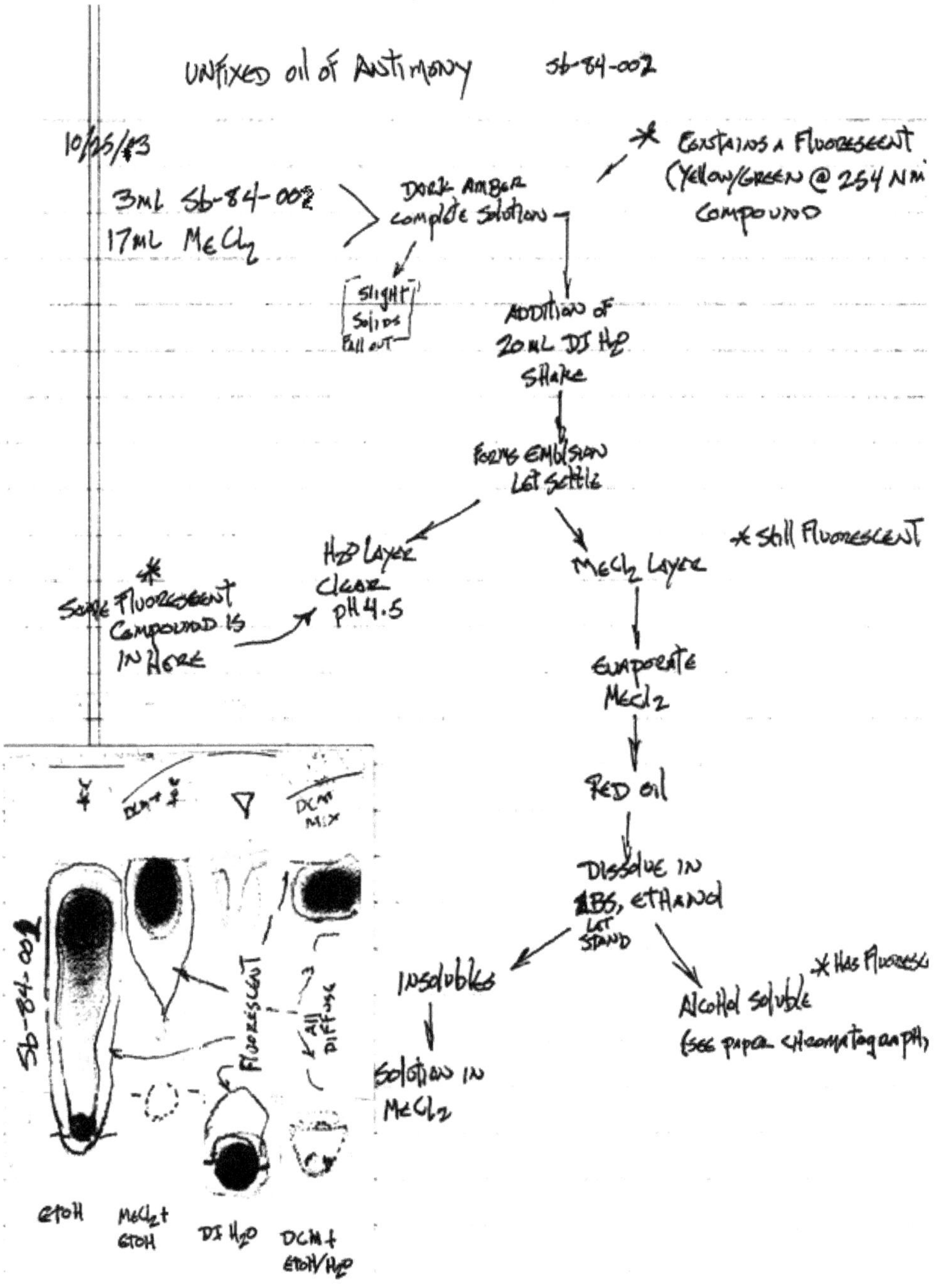

UNFIXED oil of ANTIMONY   Sb-84-002

10/25/83

3mL Sb-84-002
17mL MeCl₂

} DARK AMBER
complete solution

* CONTAINS A FLUORESCENT
(Yellow/Green @ 254 NM
COMPOUND

┌─────────┐
│ SLIGHT │
│ SOLIDS │
│ fall out│
└─────────┘

ADDITION OF
20 mL DI H₂O
SHAKE

FORMS EMULSION
Let settle

H₂O Layer
Clear
pH 4.5

MeCl₂ Layer   * Still FLUORESCENT

*
SOME FLUORESCENT
COMPOUND IS
IN HERE

EVAPORATE
MeCl₂

RED OIL

DISSOLVE IN
ABS. ETHANOL
LET STAND

INSOLUBLES

Solution IN
MeCl₂

Alcohol Soluble   * Has FLUORESC

(see paper chromatography)

Sb-84-002

☿   DCM + ☿   ▽   DCM
                            MIX

FLUORESCENT

ALL
DIFFUSE

EtOH   MeCl₂+   DI H₂O   DCM +
        EtOH   EtOH/H₂O

UNFIXED ANTIMONY OIL

#Sb-84-002

Plates: Silica Gel 60-F-254
(EM Reagents)

Visualized w/ Iodine Vapors

ROBERT ALLEN BARTLETT

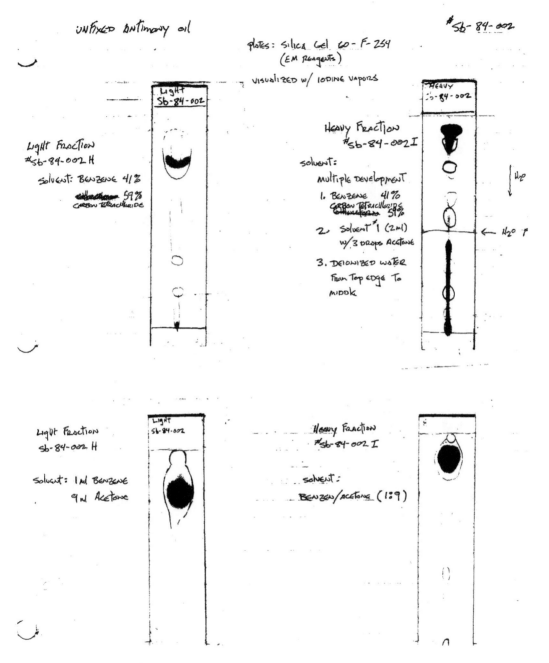

LIGHT FRACTION
#Sb-84-002 H

Solvent: Benzene 41%
~~Ethanol~~ 59%
Carbon Tetrachloride

HEAVY FRACTION
#Sb-84-002 I

Solvent:
Multiple Development

1. Benzene 41%
Carbon Tetrachloride
~~Ethanol~~ 59%

2. Solvent #1 (2ml)
w/ 3 drops Acetone

3. Deionized water
from top edge to
middle

H₂O

← H₂O ↑

LIGHT FRACTION
Sb-84-002 H

Solvent: 1 ml Benzene
9 ml Acetone

HEAVY FRACTION
#Sb-84-002 I

Solvent:
Benzene/Acetone (1:9)

UNFIXED ANTIMONY OIL   #Sb-84-002

plates: Silico gel 60-F-254
visualized w/ IODINE vapors

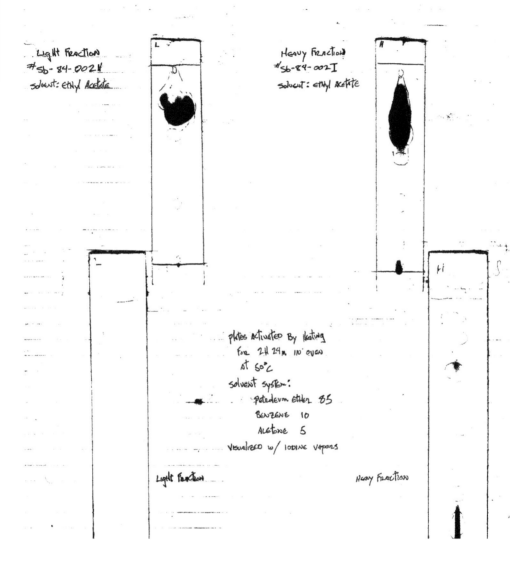

Light Fraction
#Sb-84-002I
solvent: ethyl Acetate

Heavy Fraction
#Sb-84-002I
solvent: ethyl acetate

plates activated by Heating
For 2H 29m in oven
at 60°C
Solvent system:
    petroleum ether 85
    BENZENE 10
    Acetone 5
visualized w/ IODINE vapors

Light Fraction   Heavy Fraction

UNFIXED Sb oil #Sb-84-002

Solvent: BENZENE
Sorbent: Silica gel 60F-254
Visualized with iodine vapors

ETHER extract
#Sb-84-002E

Acetone extract
#Sb-84-002 C

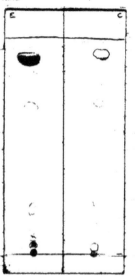

Sb-84-002
Sample: ETHER extracted oil DISSOLVED IN
    ETHANOL THEN DILUTED WITH water.
    Aqueous solution extracted with
    petroleum ETHER (30-60°) THEN CONCENTRATED
Solvent: Petroleum ETHER 80%
    BENZENE 20%
Sorbent: Silica gel 60 F-254
    (EM reagents) .2mm Thickness
    - plate activation By Heating in oven
    At 50°C For 24 Hrs.

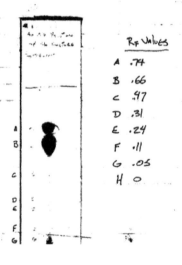

RF Values

A .74
B .66
C .47
D .31
E .24
F .11
G .05
H 0

Sb-84-002 H   Solvent: Petroleum Ether 80%
Silica Gel
Plate 10 × 15.5 cm   Benzene 20%

Double development in same solvent.

Rf:

$$\frac{115}{141} = .82$$

$$\frac{103}{141} = .73$$

$$\frac{96}{141} = .68$$

$$\frac{89}{141} = .63$$

$$\frac{85.5}{141} = .61$$

$$\frac{61}{141} = .43$$

$$\frac{49.5}{141} = .35$$

$$\frac{40.5}{141} = .29$$

$$\frac{19.5}{141} = .14 \qquad \frac{4.5}{141} = .03$$

$$\frac{11}{141} = .08 \qquad \frac{2}{141} = .01$$

$$\frac{8}{141} = .06 \qquad 0$$

ROBERT ALLEN BARTLETT

3/1/79

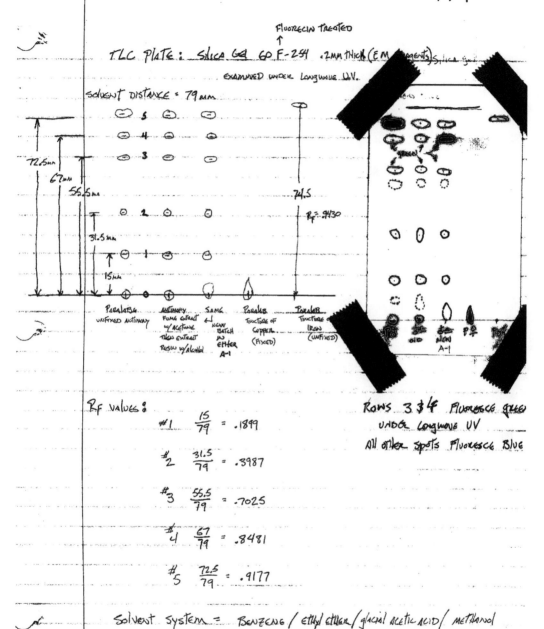

TLC PLATE: SILICA GEL 60 F-254 .2MM THICK (E M REAGENTS)
EXAMINED UNDER LONGWAVE U.V.

FLUORECIN TREATED

SOLVENT DISTANCE = 79 MM

72.5MM
67MM
55.5MM
31.5MM
15MM

74.5

$R_F = .9430$

Row labels (bottom):
PARALAB UNFIXED ANTIMONY | ANTIMONY FUMIG EXTRACT W/ ACETONE THEN EXTRACT RESIN W/ ALCOHOL | SAME NEW BATCH IN ETHER A-1 | PARALAB TINCTURE OF COPPER (FIXED) | PARALAB TINCTURE OF IRON (UNFIXED)

ROWS 3 & 4 FLUORESCE GREEN
UNDER LONGWAVE UV
ALL OTHER SPOTS FLUORESCE BLUE

R$_F$ VALUES:

#1 $\frac{15}{79}$ = .1899

#2 $\frac{31.5}{79}$ = .3987

#3 $\frac{55.5}{79}$ = .7025

#4 $\frac{67}{79}$ = .8481

#5 $\frac{72.5}{79}$ = .9177

SOLVENT SYSTEM = BENZENE / ETHYL ETHER / GLACIAL ACETIC ACID / METHANOL

One of my classmates was Bill Van Doren. He would later go on to help get the French alchemical group, "The Philosophers of Nature" established in the US, but at this time, he would occasionally lend assistance to the work we were doing at Paralab by furnishing some spectrographic analysis on samples sent to him. Bill owned a Spark type Emission Spectrograph, crude by todays standards giving only rough estimates of metals present, but it did give us something to work with. You can see my awe at the development of chemical technology witnessed over time. Below is a report from Bill on samples related to Sb-84-002.

INDUSTRIAL ENGINEERING
PRODUCT DEVELOPMENT
MARKETING RESEARCH

MINING ENGINEERING
ORE PROCESSING EQUIPMENT
MINING PROPERTY DEVELOPMENT

Industrial Development Associates
P. O. BOX 5595 • RIVERSIDE, CALIFORNIA 92517
PHONE (714) 686-8232

January 16, 1980

Paralab
3520 W. 8600 So.
West Jordan, Utah 84084

ATTN: Bob Bartlett

Dear Bob,

I shot your samples a couple of weeks ago and have herein included a brief report of what I found, although I don't know specifically what you are looking for. Unless otherwise stated, elements will be approximately in order of decreasing percentage.

1. Sb fume   Sb-84-002 A
   Major Sb - Na 2-5% - Pb, AS, B, Sn all 1-3%
   Fe Mg Cu Mn Ag Zn Al Cd all less than .2%

2. Sb-84-002D dark red brown oily paste
   Major Na - Cu Ca Zn Mg B all $\frac{1}{2}$ - 3% - Fe Al Sb Cd Pb Ag Mn Sn Si
      all less than .2%

3. Sb-84-002 H & I Dark red brown oil
   Major Na - Ca & Mg minor - Si Cu Zn Al Cd all less than .2%

4. Sb-84-002 IA Solids from heavy oil
   Comparison with #3 above less Cu Na Zn or Na Traces of Si Mg-Sb Trace
      Pb & Ag

5. Sb-84-002J Yellow Powder
   Comparison with #3 above less Mg - more Cu - equal Si Fe Al - No Na - Zn
      Si Trace•Ca Trace

6. Sb-84-002M Black ash or cinder?
   Si major - Cu minor - Mg, Na, Cu, Zn, Pb, Ag, Fe, B, all less than .2%

7. Sb-84-002-0 Resideu from acetone extraction concentrate and filtration
   yellow brown powder
   Si major - Cu minor - Na, Ca B Fe Zn Mg Sb Ag Al Sn all less than .5%

The percentages are given only as rough approximation of order of decreasing quantities. All shots qualitative and with no standards.

Long after Paralab closed, I still had and have samples of our works at Paralab; my continued employment as a chemist, finally allowed access to intsrumentation for their chemical analysis. The following analytical data on the Unfixed Tincture of Antimony Sb-84-002 has been collected over time and by various methodologies.

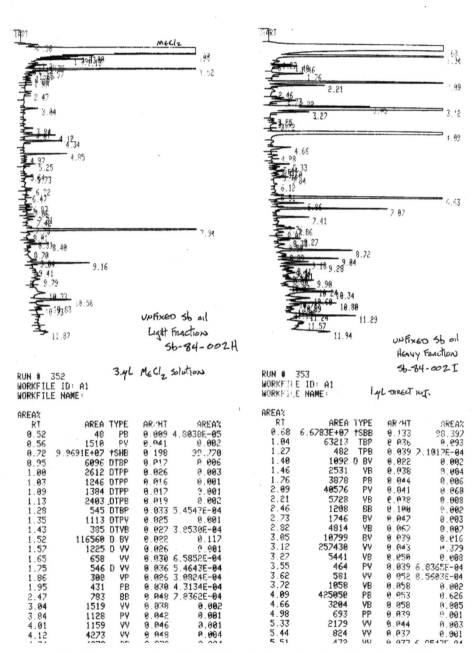

Gas Chromatography of the Light and Heavy fractions of Antimony Oil

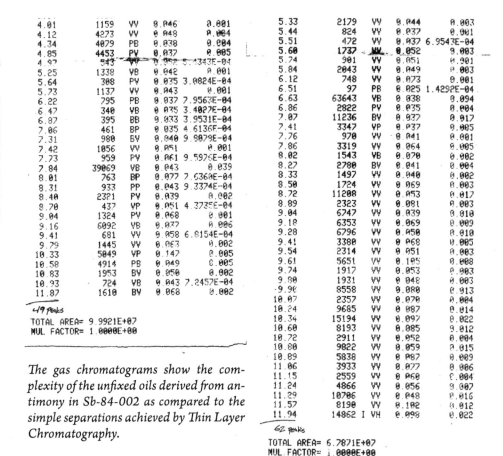

4.01	1159	VV	0.046	0.001	5.33	2179	VV	0.044	0.003
4.12	4273	VV	0.048	0.004	5.44	824	VV	0.037	0.001
4.34	4079	PB	0.038	0.004	5.51	472	VV	0.037	6.9543E-04
4.85	4453	PV	0.032	0.005	5.60	1737	VV	0.052	0.003
4.92	543	VV	0.052	4.1343E-04	5.74	901	VV	0.051	0.001
5.25	1338	VB	0.042	0.001	5.84	2043	VV	0.049	0.003
5.64	308	PV	0.035	3.0824E-04	6.12	748	VV	0.073	0.001
5.73	1137	VV	0.043	0.001	6.51	97	PB	0.025	1.4292E-04
6.22	795	PB	0.037	2.9563E-04	6.63	63643	VB	0.038	0.094
6.47	340	VB	0.035	3.4027E-04	6.86	2822	PV	0.035	0.004
6.87	395	BB	0.033	3.9531E-04	7.07	11236	BV	0.037	0.017
7.06	461	BP	0.035	4.6136E-04	7.41	3347	VP	0.037	0.005
7.31	980	BV	0.040	9.8078E-04	7.76	970	VV	0.041	0.001
7.42	1056	VV	0.051	0.001	7.86	3319	VV	0.064	0.005
7.73	959	PV	0.061	9.5976E-04	8.02	1543	VB	0.070	0.002
7.84	39069	VB	0.043	0.039	8.27	2780	BV	0.041	0.004
8.01	763	BP	0.077	2.6360E-04	8.33	1497	VV	0.040	0.002
8.31	933	PP	0.043	9.3374E-04	8.50	1724	VV	0.069	0.003
8.40	2371	PV	0.039	0.002	8.72	11208	VV	0.053	0.017
8.70	437	VP	0.051	4.3735E-04	8.89	2323	VV	0.081	0.003
9.04	1324	PV	0.068	0.001	9.04	6747	VV	0.039	0.010
9.16	6092	VB	0.037	0.006	9.18	6353	VV	0.069	0.009
9.41	681	VV	0.058	6.8154E-04	9.28	6796	VV	0.050	0.010
9.79	1445	VV	0.063	0.002	9.41	3380	VV	0.068	0.005
10.33	5049	VP	0.142	0.005	9.54	2314	VV	0.051	0.003
10.58	4914	PB	0.049	0.005	9.61	5651	VV	0.105	0.008
10.83	1953	BV	0.050	0.002	9.74	1917	VV	0.053	0.003
10.93	724	VB	0.043	7.2457E-04	9.80	1931	VV	0.048	0.003
11.82	1610	BV	0.068	0.002	9.90	8558	VV	0.080	0.013
					10.07	2357	VV	0.070	0.004
					10.24	9685	VV	0.087	0.014
					10.34	15194	VV	0.097	0.022
					10.60	8193	VV	0.085	0.012
					10.72	2911	VV	0.052	0.004
					10.80	9822	VV	0.059	0.015
					10.89	5838	VV	0.087	0.009
					11.06	3933	VV	0.077	0.006
					11.15	2559	VV	0.060	0.004
					11.24	4866	VV	0.056	0.007
					11.29	10706	VV	0.048	0.016
					11.57	8190	VV	0.102	0.012
					11.94	14862	I VH	0.098	0.022

49 peaks

TOTAL AREA= 9.9921E+07
MUL FACTOR= 1.0000E+00

62 peaks

TOTAL AREA= 6.7871E+07
MUL FACTOR= 1.0000E+00

The gas chromatograms show the complexity of the unfixed oils derived from antimony in Sb-84-002 as compared to the simple separations achieved by Thin Layer Chromatography.

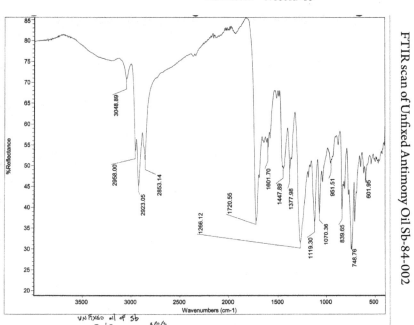

FTIR scan of Unfixed Antimony Oil Sb-84-002

UNFIXED oil of Sb   3/11/11

Remember these scans are on the complete oil and not individual components so they are more like fingerprints than definite identifications. The instrument reports the sample to contain primary and secondary alcohols and carboxylic acids as major components.

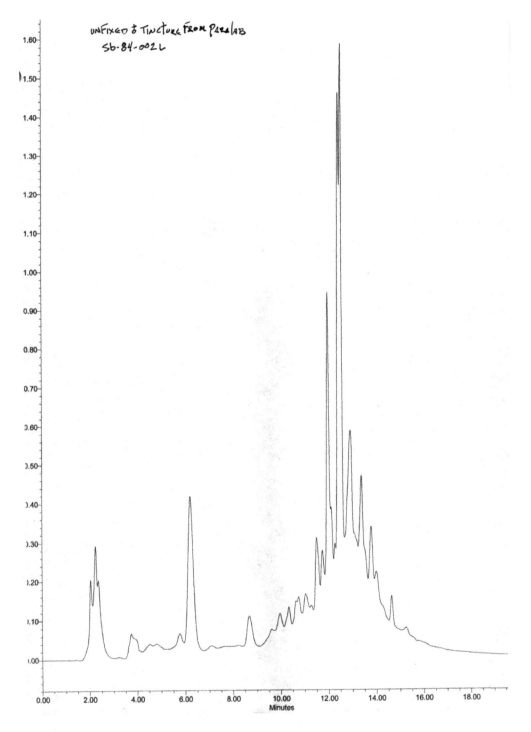

HPLC of the Unfixed Tincture from Antimony Sb-84-002

THE BOOK ON ANTIMONY

Sb-84-002L **Peak Summary with Statistics**

	Sample Name	Inj.	Peak Name	RT (min)	Area (µV*sec)	% Area	Height (µV)	Amount	Units	Vial
1	Sb-27-002L	1		2.038	507900	1.72	107418			1
2	Sb-27-002L	1		2.250	647194	2.20	122559			1
3	Sb-27-002L	1		3.737	1138777	3.87	57293			1
4	Sb-27-002L	1		5.758	320305	1.09	27841			1
5	Sb-27-002L	1		6.219	5829392	19.79	381814			1
6	Sb-27-002L	1		7.048	58017	0.20	5273			1
7	Sb-27-002L	1		8.680	1181345	4.01	78157			1
8	Sb-27-002L	1		9.592	162652	0.55	13522			1
9	Sb-27-002L	1		9.963	383558	1.30	37892			1
10	Sb-27-002L	1		10.341	402439	1.37	45847			1
11	Sb-27-002L	1		10.622	79527	0.27	18032			1
12	Sb-27-002L	1		10.765	131106	0.45	24087			1
13	Sb-27-002L	1		11.032	372130	1.26	41829			1
14	Sb-27-002L	1		11.283	38244	0.13	7681			1
15	Sb-27-002L	1		11.500	1236109	4.20	157393			1
16	Sb-27-002L	1		11.747	459921	1.56	77287			1
17	Sb-27-002L	1		11.985	3674201	12.47	637381			1
18	Sb-27-002L	1		12.137	152763	0.52	44843			1
19	Sb-27-002L	1		12.270	74902	0.25	25044			1
20	Sb-27-002L	1		12.418	2333074	7.92	585701			1
21	Sb-27-002L	1		12.538	2963027	10.06	684735			1
22	Sb-27-002L	1		12.935	3424996	11.63	286336			1
23	Sb-27-002L	1		13.383	1890681	6.42	210651			1
24	Sb-27-002L	1		13.787	1020584	3.46	135548			1
25	Sb-27-002L	1		14.017	311061	1.06	40303			1

HPLC peak summary for Unfixed Tincture Sb-84-002

Looking at the %-area for the peaks, It is likely that the early Thin Layer Chromatograms revealed those with areas around 10% or greater as individual spots.

Analysis by Gas Chromatography/ Mass Spectrometry

In this dual technique, compounds in a sample are separated by gas chromatography and the individual compounds are then injected into a mass spectrometer where they are ionized and passed through a magnetic field. The ionized fragments of the compound are deflected according to their mass and a detector tallies the various fractions then compares them to a library of similarly treated known materials. Peak by peak the results show the computers best guess as to what the individual compound might be and lists several alternatives. A number of internal standards (ISTD) provide known references for retention times. The column marked "Qual" gives a percentage value as to how close the match is. In some cases this match is quite good in others very poor and some even impossible or at least highly unlikely given the reactants involved in their production.

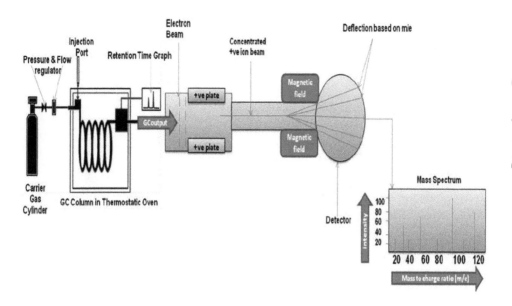

As an example, Peak 5 ,the largest peak with the greatest concentration rating as #1, emerges from the column close to the internal standard 1,4-dichlorobenzene. Based on the mass fragment analysis, the compound library matches it with 4-Hydroxy,-4 -Methyl 2-Pentanone with a 64% match. Also known as Diacetone Alcohol, it is probably a good choice since it could be produced by the catalytic activity of the prepared antimony uniting two molecules of acetone. Additional condensations be-

tween molecules again catalysed by the antimony can also take place. In fact the entire oil is the product of the catalytic activity of the specially prepared antimony. When that material basis is changed through different preparation of the antimony and solvent, different oils can arise.

Although masked by other components, comparing FTIR data of our suspect compound with our oil shows close similarities and the possibility that it is present.

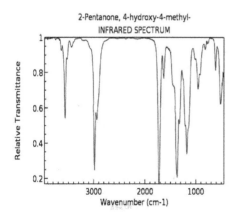

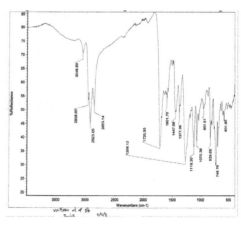

Complete GC-Mass Spec analysis of Antimony Oil Sb-84-002

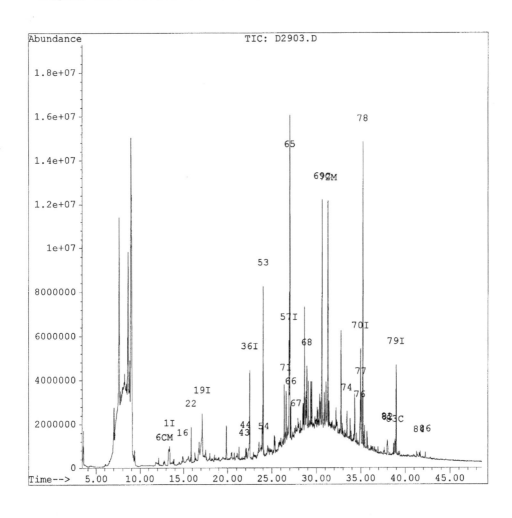

Quantitation Report

Data File : D:\HPCHEM\1\DATA\JUNK\D2903.D   Vial: 3
Acq On   : 29 Apr 103 12:21 pm   Operator: PDC
Sample   : Sb-84-002   Inst   : 5971 - In
Misc   :   Multiplr: 1.00
Quant Time: Apr 29 13:18 19103

Method   : D:\HPCHEM\1\METHODS\SVOA0212.M
Title   : SVOCs by SW-846 Method 8270C
Last Update : Thu Apr 24 12:25:04 2003
Response via : Multiple Level Calibration

```
Data File : D:\HPCHEM\1\DATA\JUNK\D2903.D          Vial: 3
Acq On    : 29 Apr 103  12:21 pm                   Operator: PDC
Sample    : Sb-84-002                              Inst    : 5971 - In
Misc      :                                        Multiplr: 1.00

Method    : D:\HPCHEM\1\METHODS\SVOA0212.M
Title     : SVOCs by SW-846 Method 8270C
Library   : D:\DATABASE\NBS75K.L
```

****
Peak Number 1   Rank in Relative Concentration 3

```
   R.T.   Conc              Area       Relative to ISTD         R.T.
-----------------------------------------------------------------------
   7.05   62.30 ng       27379699     1,4-Dichlorobenzene-d4    13.39
```

Hit# of 20   Tentative ID   Ref#   CAS#   Qual

```
1 2-Pentanone, 4-hydroxy-4-methyl-         64274 000123-42-2   59
2 CH2=CHCH2C(O)OCH3                         1448 003724-55-8   10
3 3-Hydroxy-2-pentanone                     1691 003142-66-3    9
4 Morpholine, 4-methyl-                    63448 000109-02-4    7
5 5-Hexen-2-one                            63205 000109-49-9    7
```

****
Peak Number 2   Rank in Relative Concentration 2

```
   R.T.   Conc              Area       Relative to ISTD         R.T.
-----------------------------------------------------------------------
   7.62  183.29 ng       80560978     1,4-Dichlorobenzene-d4    13.39
```

Hit# of 20   Tentative ID   Ref#   CAS#   Qual

```
1 2-Pentanone, 4-hydroxy-4-methyl-         64275 000123-42-2   72
2 CH2=CHCH2C(O)OCH3                         1448 003724-55-8   10
3 3-Hydroxy-2-pentanone                     1691 003142-66-3    9
4 2-Propanone, 1-cyclopropyl-              1306 004160-75-2    9
5 4-Penten-2-one, 4-methyl-                1244 003744-02-3    9
```

****
Peak Number 3   Rank in Relative Concentration 5

```
   R.T.   Conc              Area       Relative to ISTD         R.T.
-----------------------------------------------------------------------
   8.24   51.77 ng       22753422     1,4-Dichlorobenzene-d4    13.39
```

Hit# of 20   Tentative ID   Ref#   CAS#   Qual

```
1 2-Pentanone, 4-hydroxy-4-methyl-          3245 000123-42-2   64
2 3-Hydroxy-2-pentanone                     1691 003142-66-3    9
3 5-Hexen-2-one                            63205 000109-49-9    9
4 Acetone                                  62326 000067-64-1    7
5 Butane                                      99 000106-97-8    5
```

```
Data File : D:\HPCHEM\1\DATA\JUNK\D2903.D          Vial: 3
Acq On    : 29 Apr 103  12:21 pm                   Operator: PDC
Sample    : Sb-84-002                              Inst   : 5971 - In
Misc      :                                        Multiplr: 1.00

Method    : D:\HPCHEM\1\METHODS\SVOA0212.M
Title     : SVOCs by SW-846 Method 8270C
Library   : D:\DATABASE\NBS75K.L
```

****
Peak Number 4   Rank in Relative Concentration 4

R.T.	Conc	Area	Relative to ISTD	R.T.
8.63	60.21 ng	26465113	1,4-Dichlorobenzene-d4	13.39

Hit# of 20	Tentative ID	Ref#	CAS#	Qual
1 2-Pentanone, 4-hydroxy-4-methyl-		3245	000123-42-2	64
2 3-Hydroxy-2-pentanone		1691	003142-66-3	9
3 CH2=CHCH2C(O)OCH3		1448	003724-55-8	9
4 Acetic acid, 2-methylpropyl ester		64298	000110-19-0	9
5 5-Hexen-2-one		63205	000109-49-9	7

****
Peak Number 5   Rank in Relative Concentration 1

R.T.	Conc	Area	Relative to ISTD	R.T.
8.95	249.75 ng	109771122	1,4-Dichlorobenzene-d4	13.39

Hit# of 20	Tentative ID	Ref#	CAS#	Qual
1 2-Pentanone, 4-hydroxy-4-methyl-		64274	000123-42-2	64
2 Propane, 2-methyl-2-(1-methylethoxy		3378	017348-59-3	28
3 tert-Butyl Hydroperoxide		922	000075-91-2	25
4 Acetic acid, cyano-, 1,1-dimethylet		7666	001116-98-9	17
5 Butane, 1-ethoxy-		63550	000628-81-9	9

****
Peak Number 6   Rank in Relative Concentration 8

R.T.	Conc	Area	Relative to ISTD	R.T.
9.35	8.50 ng	3737284	1,4-Dichlorobenzene-d4	13.39

Hit# of 20	Tentative ID	Ref#	CAS#	Qual
1 2-Pentanone, 4-hydroxy-4-methyl-		3245	000123-42-2	40
2 Formamide, N,N-diethyl-		1629	000617-84-5	9
3 Acetic acid, 2-methylpropyl ester		64298	000110-19-0	9
4 Acetic acid, 1,1-dimethylethyl este		3292	000540-88-5	9
5 CH2=CHCH2C(O)OCH3		1448	003724-55-8	8

```
Data File : D:\HPCHEM\1\DATA\JUNK\D2903.D            Vial: 3
Acq On    : 29 Apr 103  12:21 pm                     Operator: PDC
Sample    : Sb-84-002                                Inst    : 5971 - In
Misc      :                                          Multiplr: 1.00

Method    : D:\HPCHEM\1\METHODS\SVOA0212.M
Title     : SVOCs by SW-846 Method 8270C
Library   : D:\DATABASE\NBS75K.L
```

****
Peak Number 7   Rank in Relative Concentration 16

R.T.	Conc	Area	Relative to ISTD	R.T.
11.80	4.80 ng	2109631	1,4-Dichlorobenzene-d4	13.39

Hit# of 20	Tentative ID	Ref#	CAS#	Qual
1	2-Butanamine, N,N-dimethyl-	1656	000921-04-0	59
2	Butanal, 2-ethyl-	63381	000097-96-1	50
3	Acetaldehyde, methylhydrazone	256	017167-73-6	40
4	1-Butanamine, N-(1-methylethyl)-	64243	039099-23-5	40
5	2-Propanol, 1-[(1-methylethyl)amino	71852	006452-71-7	36

****
Peak Number 8   Rank in Relative Concentration 21

R.T.	Conc	Area	Relative to ISTD	R.T.
12.14	4.41 ng	1936517	1,4-Dichlorobenzene-d4	13.39

Hit# of 20	Tentative ID	Ref#	CAS#	Qual
1	Propane, 2-ethoxy-2-methyl-	1790	000637-92-3	38
2	2-Butanol, 2,3-dimethyl-	63571	000594-60-5	37
3	1-Propanol, 3-[3-(1-methylethoxy)pr	16653	054518-03-5	33
4	Acetic acid, 1,1-dimethylethyl este	3292	000540-88-5	10
5	1,3-Dioxane, 2-methyl-	1731	000626-68-6	9

****
Peak Number 9   Rank in Relative Concentration 22

R.T.	Conc	Area	Relative to ISTD	R.T.
13.88	4.40 ng	1931894	1,4-Dichlorobenzene-d4	13.39

Hit# of 20	Tentative ID	Ref#	CAS#	Qual
1	3-Penten-2-one, semicarbazone	7641	016983-59-8	52
2	1H-Imidazol-2-amine, sulfate (2:1)	510	001450-93-7	50
3	1,1-Hexylenedioxybutane	15761	000000-00-0	42
4	2-Pyrazoline-1-carboxamide, 3,5-dim	7640	017014-31-2	42
5	4,4-Dimethyl-2-imidazoline	1225	002305-59-1	33

Library Search Compound Report

```
Data File : D:\HPCHEM\1\DATA\JUNK\D2903.D          Vial: 3
Acq On    : 29 Apr 103  12:21 pm                   Operator: PDC
Sample    : Sb-84-002                              Inst    : 5971 - In
Misc      :                                        Multiplr: 1.00

Method    : D:\HPCHEM\1\METHODS\SVOA0212.M
Title     : SVOCs by SW-846 Method 8270C
Library   : D:\DATABASE\NBS75K.L
```

```
**********************************************************************
Peak Number 10                    Rank in Relative Concentration 18

  R.T.   Conc           Area      Relative to ISTD          R.T.
----------------------------------------------------------------------
 15.55   4.52 ng      3177682     Naphthalene-d8            17.15

Hit# of 20             Tentative ID           Ref#   CAS#     Qual
----------------------------------------------------------------------
 1 2-Cyclohexen-1-one, 3,5,5-trimethyl       65921 000078-59-1   49
 2 2-Cyclohexen-1-one, 3-methyl-             63863 001193-18-6   23
 3 Histamine Dihydrochloride                 63897 000051-45-6   23
 4 n-Heptadecylcyclohexane                   45915 019781-73-8   23
 5 Hexanoic acid, 3-hexenyl ester, (Z)       22400 031501-11-8   23

**********************************************************************
Peak Number 11                    Rank in Relative Concentration 20

  R.T.   Conc           Area      Relative to ISTD          R.T.
----------------------------------------------------------------------
 16.29   4.44 ng      3118750     Naphthalene-d8            17.15

Hit# of 20             Tentative ID           Ref#   CAS#     Qual
----------------------------------------------------------------------
 1 1-Methyl-1H-1,2,4-triazole                  507 006086-21-1   47
 2 2-Butenoic acid, 3-methyl-, ethyl e        4944 000638-10-8   42
 3 2-Aminoimidazole                            506 000000-00-0   40
 4 Propanedinitrile, dicyclohexyl-           30028 074764-28-6   38
 5 2,6-Dimethyl-6-nitro-2-hepten-4-one       19157 073583-56-9   38

**********************************************************************
Peak Number 12                    Rank in Relative Concentration 10

  R.T.   Conc           Area      Relative to ISTD          R.T.
----------------------------------------------------------------------
 16.78   7.64 ng      5371447     Naphthalene-d8            17.15

Hit# of 20             Tentative ID           Ref#   CAS#     Qual
----------------------------------------------------------------------
 1 Benzoic Acid                              64647 000065-85-0   92
 2 Benzoic acid, ammonium salt                7152 001863-63-4   49
 3 Benzoic acid, silver(1+) salt             29712 000532-31-0   49
 4 Histamine, N-benzoyl-2-cyano-             31918 000000-00-0   43
 5 Hydrazine, 1-methyl-1-phenyl-              3927 000618-40-6   38
```

Library Search Compound Report

```
Data File : D:\HPCHEM\1\DATA\JUNK\D2903.D          Vial: 3
Acq On    : 29 Apr 103  12:21 pm                   Operator: PDC
Sample    : Sb-84-002                              Inst   : 5971 - In
Misc      :                                        Multiplr: 1.00

Method    : D:\HPCHEM\1\METHODS\SVOA0212.M
Title     : SVOCs by SW-846 Method 8270C
Library   : D:\DATABASE\NBS75K.L
```

****
Peak Number 13   Rank in Relative Concentration 14

R.T.	Conc	Area	Relative to ISTD	R.T.
17.55	5.01 ng	3519461	Naphthalene-d8	17.15

Hit# of 20	Tentative ID	Ref#	CAS#	Qual
1	Hexanoic acid, anhydride	26310	002051-49-2	53
2	Glycocyanidine	1373	000503-86-6	53
3	Hexanethioic acid, S-heptyl ester	29963	002432-80-6	45
4	4-Methylthiazole	63277	000693-95-8	42
5	1,3,2-Dioxaborolane, 2,4-diethyl-	4896	057633-63-3	38

****
Peak Number 14   Rank in Relative Concentration 23

R.T.	Conc	Area	Relative to ISTD	R.T.
19.47	4.27 ng	2997782	Naphthalene-d8	17.15

Hit# of 20	Tentative ID	Ref#	CAS#	Qual
1	Benzaldehyde, 4-hydroxy-	64655	000123-08-0	83
2	Benzaldehyde, 2-hydroxy-4-methoxy-	10175	000673-22-3	50
3	Methylparaben	10173	000099-76-3	46
4	Benzaldehyde, 2-hydroxy-	64652	000090-02-8	42
5	Benzoic acid, 2-hydroxy-, hydrazide	10124	000936-02-7	35

****
Peak Number 15   Rank in Relative Concentration 13

R.T.	Conc	Area	Relative to ISTD	R.T.
19.86	5.43 ng	3929530	Acenaphthene-d10	22.48

Hit# of 20	Tentative ID	Ref#	CAS#	Qual
1	Benzaldehyde, 2-hydroxy-4-methoxy-	66912	000673-22-3	97
2	Benzaldehyde, 3-hydroxy-4-methoxy-	66889	000621-59-0	80
3	Benzaldehyde, 2,4-dihydroxy-6-methy	10148	000487-69-4	64
4	Vanillin	66917	000121-33-5	50
5	Benzaldehyde, 4-(methylthio)-	10139	003446-89-7	32

THE BOOK ON ANTIMONY

Library Search Compound Report

```
Data File : D:\HPCHEM\1\DATA\JUNK\D2903.D          Vial: 3
Acq On    : 29 Apr 103  12:21 pm                   Operator: PDC
Sample    : Sb-84-002                              Inst    : 5971 - In
Misc      :                                        Multiplr: 1.00

Method    : D:\HPCHEM\1\METHODS\SVOA0212.M
Title     : SVOCs by SW-846 Method 8270C
Library   : D:\DATABASE\NBS75K.L
```

****
Peak Number 16   Rank in Relative Concentration 9

R.T.	Conc	Area	Relative to ISTD	R.T.
23.52	7.99 ng	5780024	Acenaphthene-d10	22.48

Hit# of 20	Tentative ID	Ref#	CAS#	Qual
1 Diethyl Phthalate		28064	000084-66-2	30
2 Benzene, 4-ethyl-1,2-dimethyl-		65569	000934-80-5	30
3 Benzenebutanoic acid, 2,5-dimethyl-		20735	001453-06-1	30
4 Benzene, 2-ethyl-1,3-dimethyl-		65533	002870-04-4	30
5 Benzene, 1-ethyl-2,3-dimethyl-		65556	000933-98-2	27

****
Peak Number 17   Rank in Relative Concentration 12

R.T.	Conc	Area	Relative to ISTD	R.T.
24.53	5.78 ng	4182913	Acenaphthene-d10	22.48

Hit# of 20	Tentative ID	Ref#	CAS#	Qual
1 Ethanone, 1-naphthalenyl-		15330	001333-52-4	87
2 Ethanone, 1-(1-Naphthalenyl)-		15335	000941-98-0	86
3 2-Naphthyl methyl ketone		15334	000093-08-3	64
4 Thiazole, 4-butyl-2,5-dimethyl-		14906	041981-77-5	38
5 Chlorzoxazone		68144	000095-25-0	25

****
Peak Number 18   Rank in Relative Concentration 11

R.T.	Conc	Area	Relative to ISTD	R.T.
28.66	6.14 ng	18096603	Phenanthrene-d10	26.92

Hit# of 20	Tentative ID	Ref#	CAS#	Qual
1 1H-Phenalen-1-one		68767	000548-39-0	96
2 Biphenylene		67016	000259-79-0	93
3 Benzo[c]cinnoline		68760	000230-17-1	91
4 Acenaphthylene		67014	000208-96-8	91
5 9H-Fluoren-9-one		68768	000486-25-9	68

Library Search Compound Report

```
Data File : D:\HPCHEM\1\DATA\JUNK\D2903.D          Vial: 3
Acq On    : 29 Apr 103  12:21 pm              Operator: PDC
Sample    : Sb-84-002                         Inst   : 5971 - In
Misc      :                                   Multiplr: 1.00


Method    : D:\HPCHEM\1\METHODS\SVOA0212.M
Title     : SVOCs by SW-846 Method 8270C
Library   : D:\DATABASE\NBS75K.L
```

****
Peak Number 19   Rank in Relative Concentration 19

R.T.	Conc	Area	Relative to ISTD	R.T.
31.07	4.45 ng	4007440	Chrysene-d12	34.97

Hit# of 20	Tentative ID	Ref#	CAS#	Qual
1	Naphthalene, 1,2,3,4-tetrahydro-1-p	70124	003018-20-0	64
2	1,8-Anthracenediamine	24949	000000-00-0	50
3	2,4,7-Pteridinetriol, 6-ethyl-	24724	031053-47-1	42
4	Thiourea, N-(2-methylpropyl)-N'-phe	24826	016275-53-9	40
5	Dibenzo[a,c]cyclooctene, 5,6,7,8-te	25017	001082-12-8	40

****
Peak Number 20   Rank in Relative Concentration 17

R.T.	Conc	Area	Relative to ISTD	R.T.
31.42	4.72 ng	4246430	Chrysene-d12	34.97

Hit# of 20	Tentative ID	Ref#	CAS#	Qual
1	Octadecanoic acid, ethyl ester	73051	000111-61-5	99
2	Tetradecanoic acid, ethyl ester	71611	000124-06-1	74
3	Hexadecanoic acid, ethyl ester	72375	000628-97-7	72
4	Dodecanoic acid, ethyl ester	70839	000106-33-2	64
5	Octadecanoic acid, 2-methyl-, methy	73047	002490-22-4	62

****
Peak Number 21   Rank in Relative Concentration 24

R.T.	Conc	Area	Relative to ISTD	R.T.
32.19	4.21 ng	3789028	Chrysene-d12	34.97

Hit# of 20	Tentative ID	Ref#	CAS#	Qual
1	Undecanone, 2-methyl oxime	22652	000000-00-0	42
2	Uridine, 2'-O-methyl-	35425	002140-76-3	38
3	2-Nonadecanone, O-methyloxime	44382	036379-39-2	36
4	1,3-Dioxolane, 4-methyl-2-pentadecy	42498	054950-56-0	28
5	Pentanamide, N-ethyl-	5248	054007-33-9	17

Library Search Compound Report

```
Data File : D:\HPCHEM\1\DATA\JUNK\D2903.D        Vial: 3
Acq On    : 29 Apr 103  12:21 pm                 Operator: PDC
Sample    : Sb-84-002                            Inst    : 5971 - In
Misc      :                                      Multiplr: 1.00

Method    : D:\HPCHEM\1\METHODS\SVOA0212.M
Title     : SVOCs by SW-846 Method 8270C
Library   : D:\DATABASE\NBS75K.L
```

****
Peak Number 22   Rank in Relative Concentration 6

R.T.	Conc	Area	Relative to ISTD	R.T.
32.76	15.80 ng	14219077	Chrysene-d12	34.97

Hit# of 20	Tentative ID	Ref#	CAS#	Qual
1	Benzofuran, 2,3-dihydro-2-methyl-7-	25468	054965-08-1	64
2	Benzene, 1-methoxy-2-(2-phenylethen	25459	052805-92-2	64
3	4(3H)-Quinazolinone, 3-(o-hydroxyph	31501	003977-51-3	39
4	1,1'-Biphenyl, 3,3',4,4'-tetramethy	25496	004920-95-0	39
5	Benzofuran, 2,3-dihydro-2-methyl-5-	25466	054965-07-0	9

****
Peak Number 23   Rank in Relative Concentration 15

R.T.	Conc	Area	Relative to ISTD	R.T.
33.79	4.93 ng	4435533	Chrysene-d12	34.97

Hit# of 20	Tentative ID	Ref#	CAS#	Qual
1	2,5-Hexanediol	64444	002935-44-6	25
2	Ethanol, 2-butoxy-, phosphate (3:1)	53673	000078-51-3	17
3	2-Propanone, ethylhydrazone	1488	007422-99-3	14
4	Butane, 1,4-dibutoxy-	23384	004161-40-4	14
5	Butane, 1-(1-methylpropoxy)-	5557	000999-65-5	12

****
Peak Number 24   Rank in Relative Concentration 7

R.T.	Conc	Area	Relative to ISTD	R.T.
34.31	14.04 ng	12636396	Chrysene-d12	34.97

Hit# of 20	Tentative ID	Ref#	CAS#	Qual
1	1,3-Dioxolane, 4-methyl-2-pentadecy	42498	054950-56-0	47
2	(Carboxyacetamido)sulfur pentafluor	29701	000000-00-0	38
3	Pentanamide, N-ethyl-	5248	054007-33-9	36
4	Uridine, 2'-O-methyl-	35425	002140-76-3	36
5	2-Nonadecanone, O-methyloxime	44382	036379-39-2	36

```
Data File : D:\HPCHEM\1\DATA\JUNK\D2903.D              Vial: 3
Acq On    : 29 Apr 103  12:21 pm                       Operator: PDC
Sample    : Sb-84-002                                  Inst    : 5971 - In
Misc      :                                            Multiplr: 1.00

Method    : D:\HPCHEM\1\METHODS\SVOA0212.M
Title     : SVOCs by SW-846 Method 8270C
Library   : D:\DATABASE\NBS75K.L
```

****

Peak Number 25   Rank in Relative Concentration 25

R.T.	Conc	Area	Relative to ISTD	R.T.
35.70	4.01 ng	3612831	Chrysene-d12	34.97

Hit# of 20	Tentative ID	Ref#	CAS#	Qual
1	Benzo(a)carbazole	26997	000239-01-0	89
2	3-Fluoranthenamine	26996	002693-46-1	87
3	Benzo(c)carbazole	26998	034777-33-8	62
4	1-Aminopyrene	26994	001606-67-3	59
5	4-Dimethylamino-2-(3-fluorophenyl)p	26931	076144-35-9	42

Soil Sample Report

Sample ID:	Sb-84-002	**Percent solids:**	0.24

Digestion information

	3050
Amount:	1.2486
Dry amt.:	0.00
Prep. date:	5/1/03

	Analysis date	Inst. used	Dilution factor	Instrument result (mg/L)	Instrument rep. lim. (mg/L)	Sample rep. lim. (mg/kg)	Sample result (mg/kg)
Al	5/1/03	59 ICP	1	0.000	0.07	1167.97	1167.97 U
Sb	5/1/03	59 ICP	1	0.000	0.07	1167.97	1167.97 U
As	5/1/03	59 ICP	1	0.070	0.03	500.56	1167.97
Ba	5/1/03	59 ICP	1	0.000	0.003	50.06	50.06 U
Be	5/1/03	59 ICP	1	0.000	0.003	50.06	50.06 U
Cd	5/1/03	59 ICP	1	0.207	0.005	83.43	3453.87
Ca	5/1/03	59 ICP	1	0.000	0.08	1334.83	1334.83 U
Cr	5/1/03	59 ICP	1	0.000	0.01	166.85	166.85 U
Co	5/1/03	59 ICP	1	0.000	0.007	116.80	116.80 U
Cu	5/1/03	59 ICP	1	0.025	0.006	100.11	417.13
Fe	5/1/03	59 ICP	1	0.000	0.01	166.85	166.85 U
Pb	5/1/03	59 ICP	1	0.000	0.06	1001.12	1001.12 U
Mg	5/1/03	59 ICP	1	1.240	0.2	3337.07	20689.84
Mn	5/1/03	59 ICP	1	0.000	0.003	50.06	50.06 U
Ni	5/1/03	59 ICP	1	0.000	0.02	333.71	333.71 U
K	5/1/03	59 ICP	1	2.420	1	16685.35	40378.56
Se	5/1/03	59 ICP	1	1.180	0.05	834.27	19688.72
Ag	5/1/03	59 ICP	1	0.000	0.007	116.80	116.80 U
Na	5/1/03	59 ICP	1	3.960	0.08	1334.83	66074.00
Tl	5/1/03	59 ICP	1	0.000	0.2	3337.07	3337.07 U
V	5/1/03	59 ICP	1	0.000	0.007	116.80	116.80 U
Zn	5/1/03	59 ICP	1	4.000	0.007	116.80	66741.42

ICP analysis of metals present in the Unfixed Oil of Antimony Sb-84-002

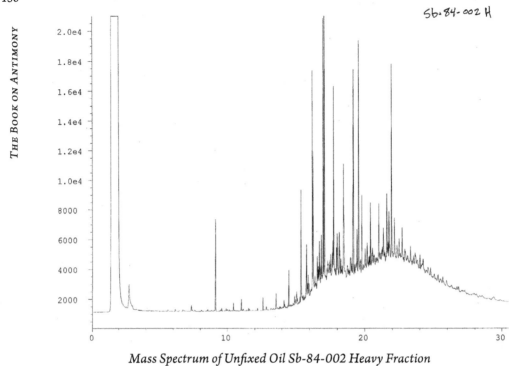

Mass Spectrum of Unfixed Oil Sb-84-002 Heavy Fraction

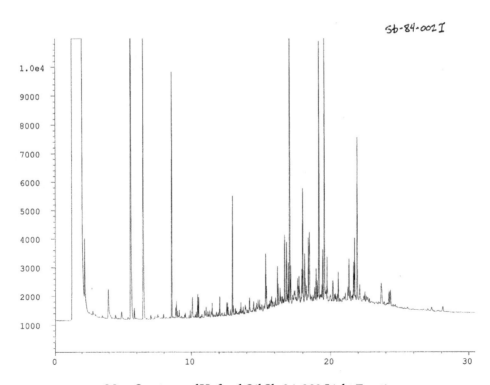

Mass Spectrum of Unfixed Oil Sb-84-002 Light Fraction

Sample ID: Sb-84-002

Digestion information   *Final Tinctures*

Method	3010
Initial Volume	1.50
Final Volume	50.00
Prep. Date	5/1/03

	Analysis date	Inst. used	Dilution factor	Instrument result (ug/ml)	Instrument rep. lim. (ug/ml)	Sample result (mg/L)	
Al	5/1/03	59 ICP	1	0.000	0.07	0.070	U
Sb	5/1/03	59 ICP	1	0	0.07	0.070	U
As	5/1/03	59 ICP	1	0.070	0.03	0.070	
Ba	5/1/03	59 ICP	1	0.000	0.003	0.003	U
Be	5/1/03	59 ICP	1	0.000	0.003	0.003	U
Cd	5/1/03	59 ICP	1	0.207	0.005	0.207	
Ca	5/1/03	59 ICP	1	0.000	0.08	0.080	U
Cr	5/1/03	59 ICP	1	0.000	0.01	0.010	U
Co	5/1/03	59 ICP	1	0.0000	0.007	0.007	U
Cu	5/1/03	59 ICP	1	0.025	0.006	0.025	
Fe	5/1/03	59 ICP	1	0.000	0.01	0.010	U
Pb	5/1/03	59 ICP	1	0.000	0.06	0.060	U
Mg	5/1/03	59 ICP	1	1.240	0.1	1.240	
Mn	5/1/03	59 ICP	1	0.000	0.003	0.003	U
Ni	5/1/03	59 ICP	1	0.000	0.02	0.020	U
K	5/1/03	59 ICP	1	2.420	1	2.420	
Se	5/1/03	59 ICP	1	1.180	0.05	1.180	
Ag	5/1/03	59 ICP	1	0.000	0.007	0.007	U
Na	5/1/03	59 ICP	1	3.960	0.08	3.960	
Tl	5/1/03	59 ICP	1	0.000	0.2	0.200	U
V	5/1/03	59 ICP	1	0.000	0.007	0.007	U
Zn	5/1/03	59 ICP	1	4.000	0.007	4.000	

ICP analysis of metals in final tincture Sb-84-002

ROBERT ALLEN BARTLETT

The presence of Arsenic and Cadmium were of concern so these metals were analyzed by Graphite Furnace Atomic Absorption Spectroscopy (GFAA). Using this more accurate method focused on one element, indicated Arsenic at 30 parts per billion and Cadmium at less than 10 parts per billion.

The volatile metal Zinc is present at 4 parts per million, a small amount of copper and alkali metals none of which are toxic, especially at the intended dosages. This is probably true for the Arsenic as well.

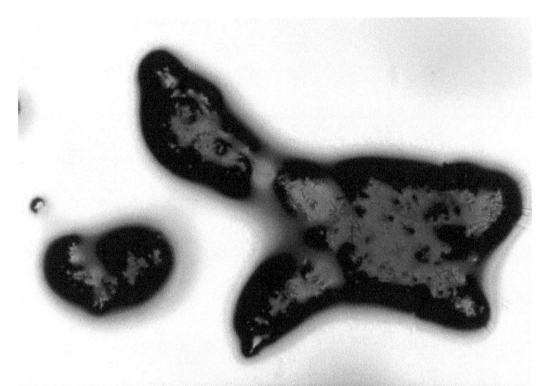

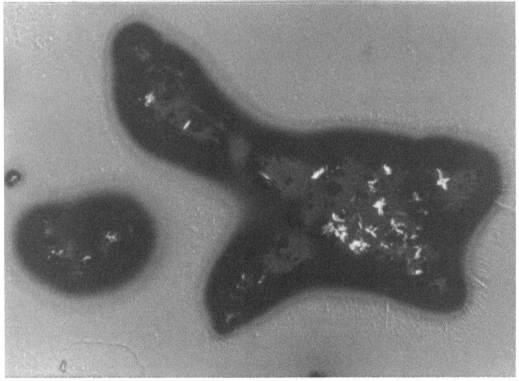

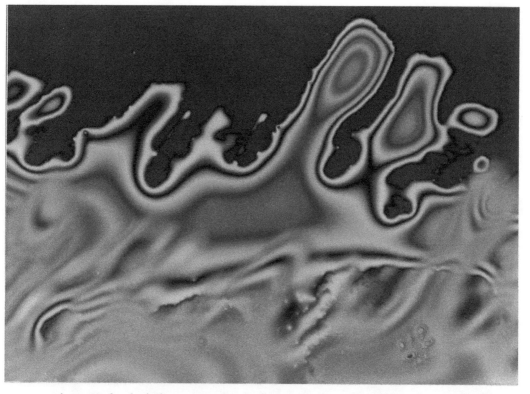

Above: Unfixed oil Sb-84-002 after final wash; Facing page: Photos of Unfixed Oil under polarized light showing crystalline contaminant prior to final washing

Other methods for producing the unfixed tincture were also explored, such as the following:

Sb-84-003

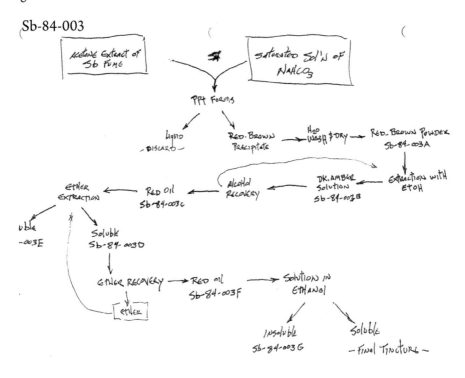

PRODUCT:	UNFIXED ANTIMONY	EXP. NUMBER: Sb-84-003

DATE	TIME	PROCEDURE
'79	10:00 a.m.	Placed 1180g of red-brown precipitate (washed), obtained by treating an Sb Fume/acetone extract with a saturated solution of sodium bicarbonate, into a cloth bag and inserted it into a large soxhlet extractor. 3800 ml ethanol was placed into the lower flask and extraction was begun under vacuum. A sample of the precipitate was saved and labeled #Sb-84-003A
	5:15 p.m.	Heat turned off.
'79	8:30 a.m.	Heat turned on and extraction continued. The ethanol extract is deep amber in color.
	5:00 p.m.	Heat turned off.
12/17/79	8:00 a.m.	Heat turned on (water bath 65°C) for 8 hours a day 11 days during that time.
'79	9:00 a.m.	Removed the dark amber extract and placed it into a large flask. Refilled the extractor with fresh ethanol and continued extraction.
1/3/80	8:00 a.m.	Heat turned on (65°C) for 8 hours an day 7 times during that time span.
)	10:30 a.m.	Placed a portion of the dark amber extract into the roto-evaporator and began alcohol recovery. A sample of extract was saved and labeled #Sb-84-003B.
)	9:00 a.m.	Continued extraction of Sb precipitate with recovered alcohol. Heat 65°C 20" Hg vacuum.
	10:00 a.m.	Began ether extraction of the concentrate produced from the ethanol extract on 1/4/80. A sample of the concentrate was saved and labeled #Sb-84-003C. Placed filtered ether extract into freezer.
	5:00 p.m.	Heat on extractor turned off.
)	8:00 a.m.	Heat on reflux 65°C extraction continued.
	9:00 a.m.	Removed the ether extract from the freezer and filtered into a roto-evaporator. A sample of ether extract was saved and labeled is #Sb-84-003D. A sample of the ether extracted residue was also saved and labeled #Sb-84-003E.
	9:20 a.m.	Began roto-evaporation of ether from the extract.

NAME:

PRODUCT: UNFIXED ANTIMONY   EXP. NUMBER: Sb-84-003

DATE	TIME	PROCEDURE
) cont	9:40 a.m.	Flask removed from roto-evaporator. A dark red amber oil remains. 54.4g total oil collected. A lighter almost clear oil separates and floats to the top while the dark red oil forms a layer at the bottom. A sample of the oil was saved and labeled #Sb-84-003F.
	4:30 p.m.	The remaining portion of ether extracted residue, (Sample #Sb-84-003E) was placed in a flask and covered with acetone, and sealed. A deep amber red extract was produced.
)	8:00 a.m.	Heat turned on, extraction continued of Sb ppt with ethanol
	5:00 p.m.	Heat turned off.
30	8:00 a.m.	Heat on 65°C
	9:00 a.m.	The residue #Sb-84-003E, extracting with acetone was filtered, concentrated, then diluted with water. A cloudy brown mixture resulted. This aqueous mixture was extracted with several portions of ether. The ether layers were collected and filtered. This gave a clear amber red extract which was concentrated in the roto-evaporator. On removal of the ether, a brown solid remained which was fairly soluble in alcohol. No oil was obtained.
	2:00 p.m.	Dissolved 25g of the dark red Sb oil in 5000 ml absolute ethanol. A golden orange tincture results and also a residue of thick very dark resiny oil which rests at the bottom. This was stoppered and allowed to sit, shaking occassionally. This will be the unfixed tincture of Sb at 5 mg oil/mg tincture.
	5:00 p.m.	Heat turned off on extractor.
.6/80	8:00 a.m.	Heat on for 8 hours a day four times during this period.
30	9:00 a.m.	Drained the extract from the extractor and placed into a large container
30	4:00 p.m.	The thick resiny oil which rested on the bottom of the flask when the oil was diluted with alcohol for the unfixed tincture (1/10/80) has turned into a light brown solid mass. This substance was collected and labeled #Sb-84-003G.
)	2:20 p.m.	Filtered the alochol extract of Sb precipitate, collected on 1/22/80, into the roto-evaporator and began alcohol recovery.
	5:00 p.m.	Heat off. NAME: *Robert Allen Bartlett*

PRODUCT: UNFIXED ANTIMONY   EXP. NUMBER: Sb-84-003

DATE	TIME	PROCEDURE
	8:30 a.m.	Alcohol recovery continued.
	2:00 p.m.	Heat turned off. A brown solid residue remains.
	9:00 a.m.	Began ether extraction of the brown residue and filtration of the amber red extract.
	11:00 a.m.	Alcohol recovered from the extract was placed back into the extractor and extraction of the Sb precipitate was continued.
	5:00 p.m.	Heat off on extractor.
/80	8:00 a.m.	Heat on extraction for 8 hours 6 times.
0	11:00 a.m.	Ether recovery begun on extract produced 2/6/80.
	11:20 a.m.	Added alcohol to the residue remaining in the roto-evaporator and allowed it to reflux extract.
	2:00 p.m.	Removed the golden amber alcohol extract from the roto-evaporator flask and rinsed the flask with 2 - 300 ml portions of alcohol. The extracts were combined in a flask for later dilution into the unfixed tincture.
	2:30 p.m.	Weighed out 11.77g of the dark amber oil obtained on 1/8/80 and dissolved it into 2354 ml absolute alcohol. A golden amber tincture was produced and also a thick tar-like substance which remained on the bottom.
0	8:00 a.m.	Extraction of Sb precipitate with ethanol continued daily.
	5:00 p.m.	Heat off.
0	8:00 a.m.	Heat on.
	5:00 p.m.	Heat off.
	1:00 p.m.	Evaporation of a sample of the unfixed tincture prepared on 2/15/80, left 5mg oil per ml of tincture sample.
0	10:15 a.m.	Removed the ethanol extract from the extractor containing the Sb precipitate, and began recovery in roto-evaporator.

NAME: *Robert Allen Bartlett*

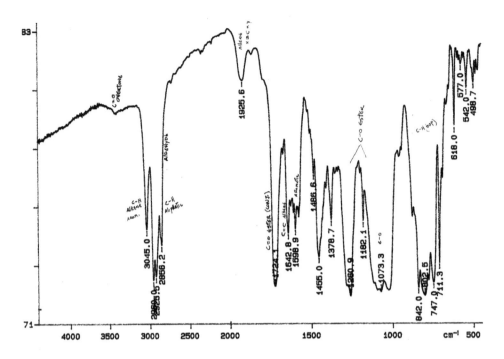

FTIR scan of the Unfixed Oil Sb-84-003

Sb-84-003

VIAL

← Pale Golden Light Fraction

← Dark Amber Red (Heavy Fraction)

Facing page: FTIR scan of Light fraction from Sb-84-003 (above); FTIR scan of the Heavy Fraction from Unfixed Oil Sb-84-003 (below)

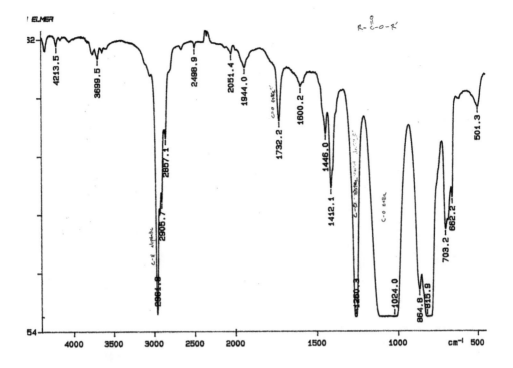

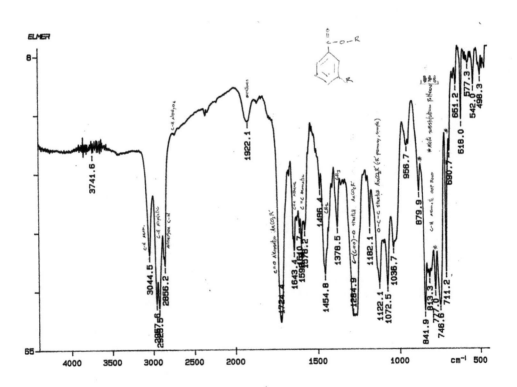

```
                    Unfixed Tincture of Antimony Production


    Apparatus:                              Materials:

    large soxhlet or reflux                 Sb fume
    roto-evaporator                         acetone
                                            ethanol



    Procedure:


    1. Extract fume with acetone.


    2. Roto-evaporate acetone to obtain oil.


    3. Wash oil with two portions of ethanol. Recover ethanol wash.


    4. Extract oil with three small portions of diethyl ether and filter.
       Evaporate the ether and wash the resulting oil with ethanol.


    5. Dilute the oil with a small amount of ethanol and then filter.


    6. Make up tincture to weight of fume used by addition of ethanol. Filter
       again if needed.
```

Final production process for the Unfixed Tincture from Antimony adopted by Paralab.

Fixed Tincture of Antimony

Parallel to the Unfixed Antimony line, a separate process line for the Fixed Tincture was started. In the same way as the Unfixed line, a few preliminary experiments established a viable method for production. The most complete set of samples I have are from Sb-27-005, a preparation of the Fixed tincture showing the various intermediated stages and impurities removed, These have provided a standard of reference for future extractions. As with the Unfixed Tincture, this "dissection" of the material was greatly streamlined for production.

PRODUCT: <u>FIXED TINCTURE OF ANTIMONY</u>   EXP. NUMBER: <u>Sb-27-005</u>

DATE	TIME	PROCEDURE
1/14/80	4:00 pm	Placed 3892 grams of antimony fume (sample #Sb-27-005A) into a 5 gallon plastic bucket and covered with 5 gallons of acetic acid recovered from previous Sb fume extractions. (Acetic acid, sample #Sb-27-005B) The bucket was sealed and allowed to macerate in a warm area.
1/22/80	10:00 am	Siphoned the amber extract produced into another 5 gallon container and sealed. 3 gallons extract obtained. A sample of the extract was saved and labeled Sb-27-005C.
1/24/80	2:15 pm	Began recovery of the acetic acid from the extract in the roto-evaporator.
	5:00 pm	Roto-evaporator turned off.
1/25/80	8:30 am	Acetic acid recovery continued.
	5:00 pm	Heat turned off.
1/28/80	8:30 am	Acetic acid recovery continued.
	10:00 am	Acetic acid recovery complete. A brown solid residue remains. Siphoned in 250 ml. deionized water to wash the residue and began its recovery. The recovered acetic acid was poured back over the Sb fume in the bucket and sealed.
	11:00 am	Removed the thick brown residue from the roto-evaporator and placed in a crystallizing dish to dry in the oven. (50°c)
2/4/80	2:30 pm	Removed the dish from the oven. The substance was amber and partly crystalline, partly brown residue. The gummy brown residue sits at the bottom, while the crystalline layer forms at the top. A syrupy liquid also remains. A representative sample of this substance (residue, crystals & liquid) was taken and labeled #Sb-27-005D. The dish was rinsed with deionized water and the contents placed in a beaker with about 200 ml. deionized water. This was set on a hot plate and heated slowly. When the solution was just under boiling, it was filtered under vacuum. The clear filtrate was golden amber. There remained in the beaker, a large amount (@50 grams) of a dark sticky tar-like residue which balled up easily into a mass. The residue was labeled Sb-27-005E. The filtrate was placed in a dish in the oven at 50°c and labeled Sb-27-005F.

NAME: _Robert Allen Bartlett_

PRODUCT: <u>FIXED TINCTURE OF ANTIMONY</u>   EXP. NUMBER: <u>Sb-27-005</u>

DATE	TIME	PROCEDURE
2/6/80	2:30 pm	Placed 44 grams of the dark gum Sb-27-005E into a flask and covered it with 350 ml. ABS. ethanol. Sealed the flask and shook well. Light golden amber extract is formed. Most of the gum sits on the bottom in lumps.
2/7/80	9:00 am	Decanted the amber tincture from the remaining gum. Added 300 ml. of fresh ABS ethanol to the gum and shook well. Repeated the decantation/extraction of the gum with fresh ethanol until 2000 ml. of amber tincture was obtained.
	1:45 pm	Filtered the amber alcohol tincture into the roto-evaporator and began ethanol recovery. A sample of the ethanol extract was saved and labeled as #Sb-27-005G. A sample of the residue was labeled Sb-27-005H.
2/8/80	3:00 pm	The brown residue (Sb-27-005H) was extracted with acetone by washing the filter paper which contained it in acetone. A deep amber tincture is produced. This extract was filtered and a sample removed, labeled Sb-27-005I.
	3:20 pm	The water soluble crystalline mush (Sb-27-005F) was placed in a flask and extracted with ethanol. A light golden yellow extract is produced. This was filtered and the residue extracted with a fresh portion of ethanol.
	4:40 pm	Heat turned off on roto-evaporator containing Sb-27-005G. A dark amber red oily residue remains. This residue was removed with ether and filtered into a container then sealed. A sample of this ether extract was saved and labeled as #Sb-27-005J. The insoluble brown residue remaining was collected and labeled #Sb-27-005K.
2/11/80	10:00 am	Placed the filtered acetone extract (Sb-27-005I) into the roto-evaporator and began acetone recovery.
	10:30 am	Bringing the extract just to dryness, there remains a thick red tarry residue. This residue was extracted with several portions of ether and filtered. A sample of this extract was saved and labeled as #Sb-27-005L. The remaining brown residue was labeled #Sb-27-005M.

NAME: _Robert Allen Bartlett_

PRODUCT: __FIXED TINCTURE OF ANTIMONY__   EXP. NUMBER: __Sb-27-005__

DATE	TIME	PROCEDURE
2/11/80	2:00 pm	Placed the filtered ethanol extract of the crystalline fraction #Sb-27-005F into the roto-evaporator and began ethanol recovery. A sample of the extract was saved aside and labeled #Sb-27-005N. The insoluble crystalline residue was saved for recrystallization and identification labeled #Sb-27-005Ø.
	3:30 pm	Removed the flask from the roto-evaporator. A golden-orange crystalline mass which is fluid while warm remains. On cooling it is solid. A sample of this substance was saved and labeled #Sb-27-005P. Ether was added to this crystalline mass and shaken well. A white crystalline powder separates from the gummy residue as the ether takes on a very light golden tincture. This extract was filtered and the white crystalline powder labeled #Sb-27-005Q. The gum remaining was dissolved in a small amount of water which produced a golden clear solution. This solution was placed into a separatory funnel and the ether extract (previously filtered off) was poured back over it and shaken well. A sample was taken and labeled #Sb-27-005R.
2/12/80	8:00 am	Poured together the three ether extracts, #Sb-27-005J, Sb-27-005L, and Sb-27-005R into the roto-evaporator. A clear red amber solution results. Began recovery of the ether.
	10:00 am	Washed =he residue remaining in the roto-evaporator out with alcohol. A deep amber extract is produced and a brown tarry residue remains undissolved.
2/13/80	9:00 am	Began extracting the tarry residue with 100 ml. portions of ethanol allowing it to macerate for 30-45 minutes before each decantation of tincture. The tarry residue slowly became more powdery in appearance as the extractions proceeded. 1800 ml. tincture obtained.
2/14/80	10:00 am	Continued extraction of the tarry residue with 100 ml. portions of ethanol.
	2:30 pm	E xtraction stopped. 2200 ml. tincture obtained. Collected the brown residue remaining after the ethanol extractions and labeled #Sb-27-005S.
2/18/80	3:00 pm	Diluted tincture to 4000 ml. with ethanol. Using colorimeter (Lietz), the tincture was compared to fixed tincture #Sb-27-004 and the values agreed fairly well.

NAME: _Robert Allen Bartlett_

Page 4

PRODUCT: __FIXED TINCTURE OF ANTIMONY__   EXP. NUMBER: __Sb-27-005__

DATE	TIME	PROCEDURE
2/20/80	10:00 am	Two 5 ml. portions of the fixed tincture were placed in small tarred dishes and evaporated to dryness at 50°c. Weights were recorded at 1.8 mg. oil/ml and 2.2 mg. oil/ml giving an average weight of 2 mg/ml. This is now ready to be filtered a final time before bottling

NAME: _Robert Allen Bartlett_

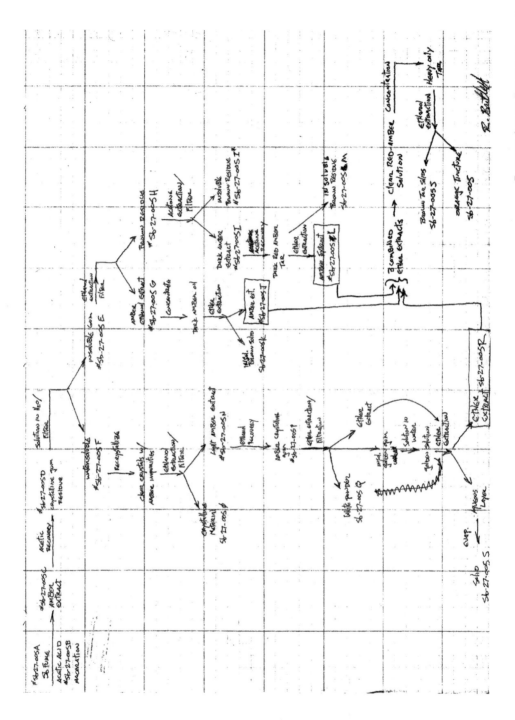

Process flowchart indicating sampling points

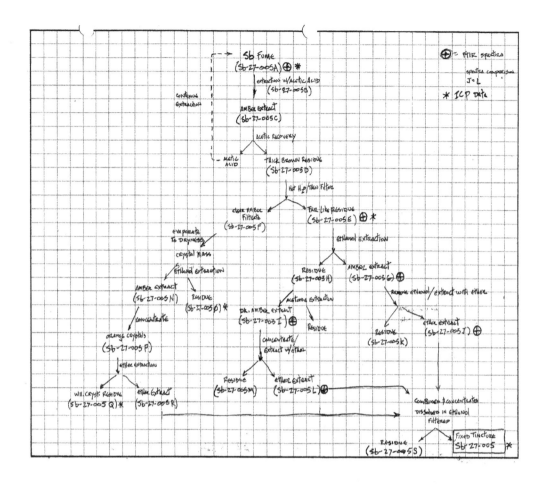

I spread out the samples on a large flow-chart on the lab bench when Frater was coming for a progress check one day. I showed him the Chromatograms I had been making and some of the preliminary analyses on the various intermediates. He was quite excited and said this was as far as they had ever gotten; then he looked at me and said, "keep gathering as much analytical information on all of these things as you can because it doesn't exist anywhere else and such information is critical before they will ever be taken into medical consideration." I took up the charge and have pursued gathering analytical data on as many alchemical products as I could over the years by any methodologies that came my way.

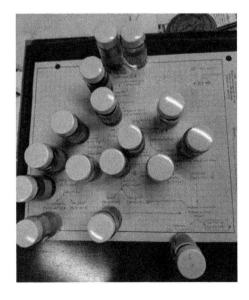

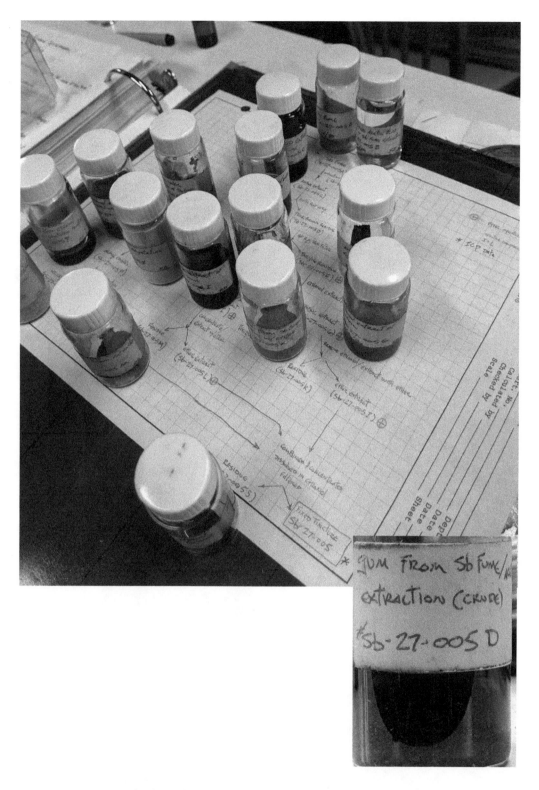

Samples from Sb-27-005 and the flowchart showing points of collection

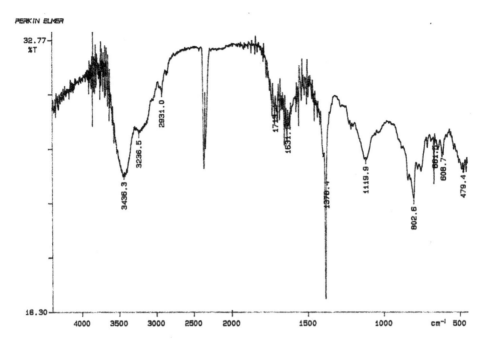

PERKIN ELMER

90/02/04 12:39
Z: 4 scans, 4.0cm-1, flat
sb_27_005e (sb gum)

FTIR scan of the extracted gummy resin from Fume Sb-27-005E

Sample ID: Sb-27-005 E   **Percent solids:**   100

ROBERT ALLEN BARTLETT

	Digestion information
	3050
Amount:	0.3216
Dry amt.:	0.32 0.3216g
Prep. date:	4/24/03

	Analysis date	Inst. used	Dilution factor	Instrument result (mg/L)	Instrument rep. lim. (mg/L)	Sample rep. lim. (mg/kg)	Sample result (mg/kg)
Al	4/24/03	59 ICP	8	0.000	0.07	87.06	87.06 U
Sb	4/24/03	59 ICP	8	5.427	0.07	87.06	6750.00
As	4/24/03	59 ICP	8	153.650	0.03	37.31	191106.97
Ba	4/24/03	59 ICP	8	0.000	0.003	3.73	3.73 U
Be	4/24/03	59 ICP	8	0.000	0.003	3.73	3.73 U
Cd	4/24/03	59 ICP	8	1.302	0.005	6.22	1619.40
Ca	4/24/03	59 ICP	8	0.000	0.08	99.50	99.50 U
Cr	4/24/03	59 ICP	8	0.000	0.01	12.44	12.44 U
Co	4/24/03	59 ICP	8	0.000	0.007	8.71	8.71 U
Cu	4/24/03	59 ICP	8	0.036	0.006	7.46	44.78
Fe	4/24/03	59 ICP	8	0.000	0.01	12.44	12.44 U
Pb	4/24/03	59 ICP	8	0.000	0.06	74.63	74.63 U
Mg	4/24/03	59 ICP	8	0.000	0.2	248.76	248.76 U
Mn	4/24/03	59 ICP	8	0.000	0.003	3.73	3.73 U
Ni	4/24/03	59 ICP	8	0.000	0.02	24.88	24.88 U
K	4/24/03	59 ICP	8	0.000	1	1243.78	1243.78 U
Se	4/24/03	59 ICP	8	1.110	0.05	62.19	1380.60
Ag	4/24/03	59 ICP	8	0.000	0.007	8.71	8.71 U
Na	4/24/03	59 ICP	8	96.860	0.08	99.50	120472.64
Tl	4/24/03	59 ICP	8	0.000	0.2	248.76	248.76 U
V	4/24/03	59 ICP	8	0.000	0.007	8.71	8.71 U
Zn	4/24/03	59 ICP	8	111.350	0.007	8.71	138495.02

Digestion: 6mL conc. HNO₃ @ 120°C 10 min
ADD 5mL H₂O₂ Heat to 120°C 10 min
ADD 3mL HCl " " " "

Dilute to 50mL w/ DI water

Sample appears Largely undissolved (Dark insol. Residue)

Little to No ppt on dilution

Water soluble fraction of the Gum that has been recrystallized.

Sb-27-005F

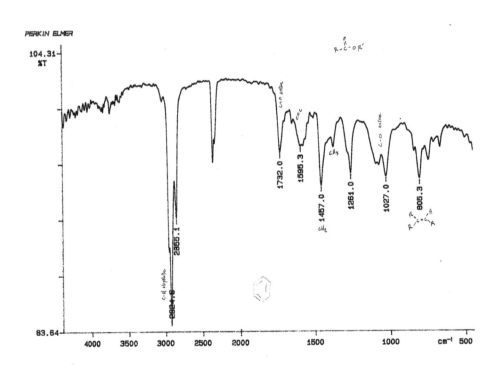

Facing page: *FTIR scan of Fixed Oil Sb-27-005J in 1991 (above); FTIR of Fixed Oil Sb-27-005J in 2008 (below).*

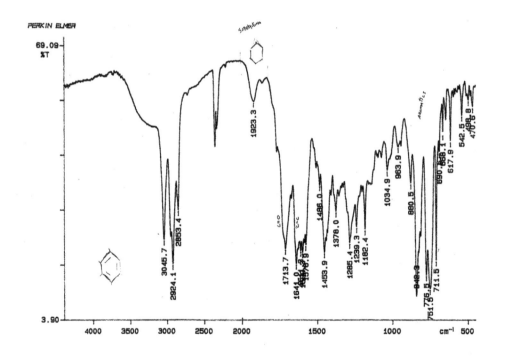

FTIR scan of Fixed Oil Sb-27-005J in 1990

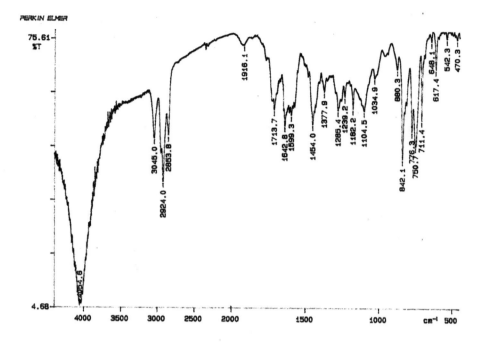

91/12/31 11:36 pacific laboratories
Y: 4 scans, 4.0cm-1
Sb-27-005J   ether sol. oil

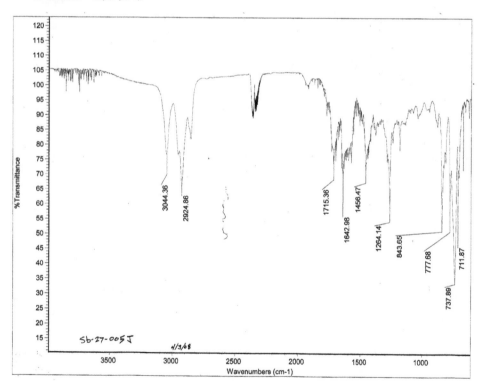

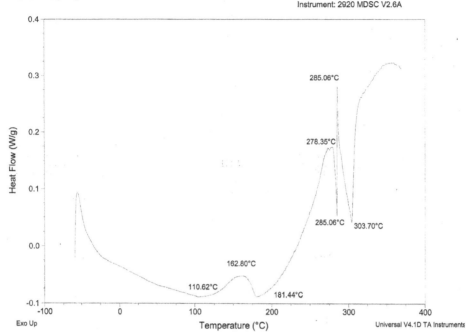

Sample: Sb-27-005J
Size: 6.0000 mg
Method: Ramp 20°C/min

DSC

File: N:...\Thermal\DSC\Data\Sb-27-005J.001
Operator: JM
Run Date: 04-Apr-2008 08:28
Instrument: 2920 MDSC V2.6A

DSC scan of Fixed Oil Sb-27-005J

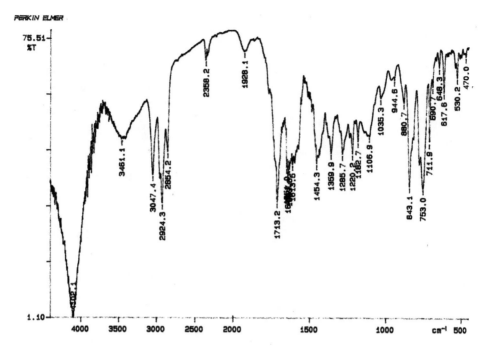

91/12/31 11:48 pacific laboratories
X: 4 scans, 4.0cm-1
Sb-27-005L

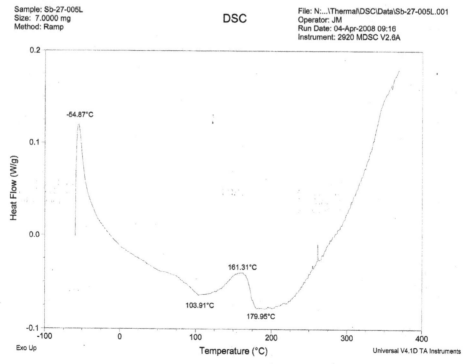

Sample: Sb-27-005L
Size: 7.0000 mg
Method: Ramp

DSC

File: N:...\Thermal\DSC\Data\Sb-27-005L.001
Operator: JM
Run Date: 04-Apr-2008 09:16
Instrument: 2920 MDSC V2.6A

Above: FTIR scan of Unfixed Oil Sb-27-005L
Below: DSC scan of Fixed Oil Sb-27-005L

Sample ID: Sb-27-005 O   **Percent solids:** 100

	Digestion information
	3050
Amount:	0.7792
Dry amt.:	0.78
Prep. date:	4/25/03

	Analysis date	Inst. used	Dilution factor	Instrument result (mg/L)	Instrument rep. lim. (mg/L)	Sample rep. lim. (mg/kg)	Sample result (mg/kg)
Al	4/28/03	59 ICP	8	0.126	0.07	35.93	64.58
Sb	4/28/03	59 ICP	8	4.946	0.07	35.93	2539.01
As	4/28/03	59 ICP	8	10.170	0.03	15.40	5220.74
Ba	4/28/03	59 ICP	8	0.000	0.003	1.54	1.54 U
Be	4/28/03	59 ICP	8	0.000	0.003	1.54	1.54 U
Cd	4/28/03	59 ICP	8	4.143	0.005	2.57	2126.80
Ca	4/28/03	59 ICP	8	0.000	0.08	41.07	41.07 U
Cr	4/28/03	59 ICP	8	0.000	0.01	5.13	5.13 U
Co	4/28/03	59 ICP	8	0.000	0.007	3.59	3.59 U
Cu	4/28/03	59 ICP	8	0.009	0.006	3.08	4.41
Fe	4/28/03	59 ICP	8	0.000	0.01	5.13	5.13 U
Pb	4/28/03	59 ICP	8	0.096	0.06	30.80	49.38
Mg	4/28/03	59 ICP	8	0.000	0.2	102.67	102.67 U
Mn	4/28/03	59 ICP	8	0.000	0.003	1.54	1.54 U
Ni	4/28/03	59 ICP	8	0.000	0.02	10.27	10.27 U
K	4/28/03	59 ICP	8	3.936	1	513.35	2020.53
Se	4/28/03	59 ICP	8	0.000	0.05	25.67	25.67 U
Ag	4/28/03	59 ICP	8	0.023	0.007	3.59	11.60
Na	4/28/03	59 ICP	8	838.400	0.08	41.07	430390.14
Tl	4/28/03	59 ICP	8	0.000	0.2	102.67	102.67 U
V	4/28/03	59 ICP	8	0.000	0.007	3.59	3.59 U
Zn	4/28/03	59 ICP	8	7.810	0.007	3.59	4009.24

Sample ID: Sb-27-005 Q   **Percent solids:**   100

	Digestion information	
	3050	
Amount:	0.1551	
Dry amt.:	0.16	
Prep. date:	4/25/03	

	Analysis date	Inst. used	Dilution factor	Instrument result (mg/L)	Instrument rep. lim. (mg/L)	Sample rep. lim. (mg/kg)	Sample result (mg/kg)
Al	4/28/03	59 ICP	2	0.091	0.07	45.13	58.67
Sb	4/28/03	59 ICP	2	0.359	0.07	45.13	231.53
As	4/28/03	59 ICP	2	7.300	0.03	19.34	4706.64
Ba	4/28/03	59 ICP	2	0.000	0.003	1.93	1.93 U
Be	4/28/03	59 ICP	2	0.000	0.003	1.93	1.93 U
Cd	4/28/03	59 ICP	2	0.405	0.005	3.22	261.38
Ca	4/28/03	59 ICP	2	0.000	0.08	51.58	51.58 U
Cr	4/28/03	59 ICP	2	0.000	0.01	6.45	6.45 U
Co	4/28/03	59 ICP	2	0.000	0.007	4.51	4.51 U
Cu	4/28/03	59 ICP	2	0.000	0.006	3.87	3.87 U
Fe	4/28/03	59 ICP	2	0.000	0.01	6.45	6.45 U
Pb	4/28/03	59 ICP	2	0.000	0.06	38.68	38.68 U
Mg	4/28/03	59 ICP	2	0.000	0.2	128.95	128.95 U
Mn	4/28/03	59 ICP	2	0.000	0.003	1.93	1.93 U
Ni	4/28/03	59 ICP	2	0.000	0.02	12.89	12.89 U
K	4/28/03	59 ICP	2	31.760	1	644.75	20477.11
Se	4/28/03	59 ICP	2	0.113	0.05	32.24	72.60
Ag	4/28/03	59 ICP	2	0.000	0.007	4.51	4.51 U
Na	4/28/03	59 ICP	2	295.400	0.08	51.58	190457.77
Tl	4/28/03	59 ICP	2	0.000	0.2	128.95	128.95 U
V	4/28/03	59 ICP	2	0.000	0.007	4.51	4.51 U
Zn	4/28/03	59 ICP	2	35.590	0.007	4.51	22946.49

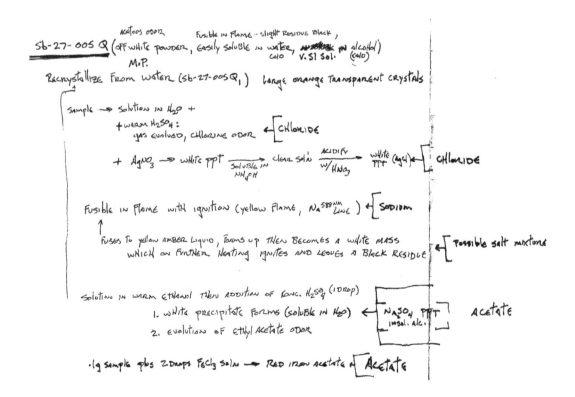

ACETOUS ODOR   FUSIBLE IN FLAME - SLIGHT RESIDUE BLACK,

Sb-27-005 Q (OFF WHITE POWDER, EASILY SOLUBLE IN WATER, ~~INSOLUBLE~~ IN ALCOHOL)
                                            COLD   V. SL SOL. (COLD)
                M.P.

Recrystallize From water (Sb-27-005Q₁)   Large orange Transparent crystals

Sample → Solution in H₂O +

        + WARM H₂SO₄ :
          GAS EVOLVED, CHLORINE ODOR ← [CHLORIDE

     + AgNO₃ → WHITE PPT ――――――→ CLEAR SOL'N ――ACIDIFY―→ WHITE ← [CHLORIDE
                          SOLUBLE IN   W/ HNO₃   PPT (AgCl)
                          NH₄OH

   Fusible in Flame with ignition (yellow Flame, Na 588ᴺᴹ LINE) ← [SODIUM

     ↑
     FUSES TO YELLOW AMBER LIQUID, FOAMS UP THEN BECOMES A WHITE MASS
     WHICH ON FURTHER HEATING IGNITES AND LEAVES A BLACK RESIDUE ← [Possible salt mixture

   Solution in WARM ETHANOL THEN ADDITION OF CONC. H₂SO₄ (1 DROP)
           1. WHITE PRECIPITATE FORMS (SOLUBLE IN H₂O) ← [Na₂SO₄ PPT   Acetate
           2. EVOLUTION OF ETHYL ACETATE ODOR   INSOL. ALC.

   .1g SAMPLE PLUS 2 DROPS FeCl₃ SOL'N → RED IRON ACETATE A [ACETATE

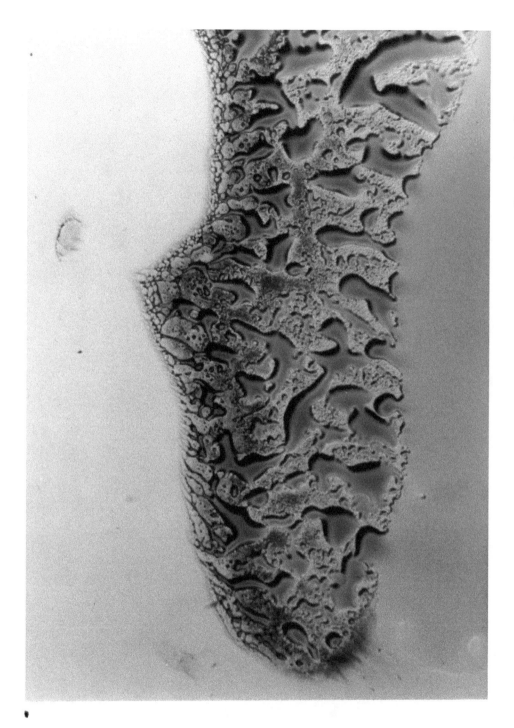

Fixed Oil of Antimony under a microscope

Final Unfixed Tincture from Antimony Sb-84-002 containing 5mg of oil per milliliter (5000 ppm).

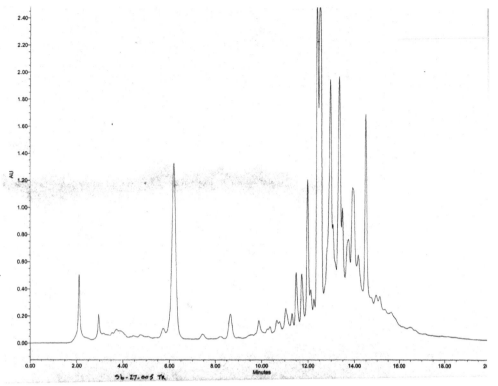

HPLC of final Fixed Tincture of Antimony Sb-27-005

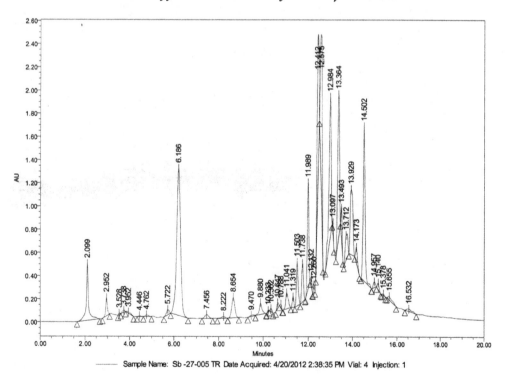

Sample Name: Sb -27-005 TR Date Acquired: 4/20/2012 2:38:35 PM Vial: 4 Injection: 1

Details of HPLC analysis of final Fixed Tincture of Antimony Sb-27-00

Peak Summary with Statistics

	Sample Name	Inj.	Peak Name	RT (min)	Area (µV*sec)	% Area	Height (µV)	Amount	Units	Vial
1	Sb -27-005 TR	1		2.099	3612375	4.40	492483			4
2	Sb -27-005 TR	1		2.952	811278	0.99	160278			4
3	Sb -27-005 TR	1		3.528	42493	0.05	11162			4
4	Sb -27-005 TR	1		3.738	132164	0.16	18679			4
5	Sb -27-005 TR	1		3.952	153565	0.19	11306			4
6	Sb -27-005 TR	1		4.446	53496	0.07	7474			4
7	Sb -27-005 TR	1		4.762	138495	0.17	14952			4
8	Sb -27-005 TR	1		5.722	391704	0.48	45790			4
9	Sb -27-005 TR	1		6.186	15580229	18.99	1269434			4
10	Sb -27-005 TR	1		7.456	397552	0.48	34366			4
11	Sb -27-005 TR	1		8.222	165597	0.20	15109			4
12	Sb -27-005 TR	1		8.654	1821984	2.22	176969			4
13	Sb -27-005 TR	1		9.470	114268	0.14	9097			4
14	Sb -27-005 TR	1		9.880	870374	1.06	101311			4
15	Sb -27-005 TR	1		10.233	40381	0.05	10739			4
16	Sb -27-005 TR	1		10.362	148214	0.18	30059			4
17	Sb -27-005 TR	1		10.647	228021	0.28	48646			4
18	Sb -27-005 TR	1		10.788	123039	0.15	28711			4
19	Sb -27-005 TR	1		11.041	1086913	1.32	139122			4
20	Sb -27-005 TR	1		11.319	424070	0.52	87871			4
21	Sb -27-005 TR	1		11.503	2086374	2.54	377549			4
22	Sb -27-005 TR	1		11.738	1850492	2.26	333071			4
23	Sb -27-005 TR	1		11.989	4306677	5.25	917505			4
24	Sb -27-005 TR	1		12.132	293928	0.36	82672			4
25	Sb -27-005 TR	1		12.260	211542	0.26	65679			4
26	Sb -27-005 TR	1		12.412	6412289	7.82	1356497			4
27	Sb -27-005 TR	1		12.575	7794825	9.50	1404764			4
28	Sb -27-005 TR	1		12.984	7840707	9.56	1208285			4
29	Sb -27-005 TR	1		13.097	270412	0.33	104151			4
30	Sb -27-005 TR	1		13.364	7157466	8.72	1236051			4
31	Sb -27-005 TR	1		13.493	923244	1.13	265247			4
32	Sb -27-005 TR	1		13.712	1689293	2.06	210886			4
33	Sb -27-005 TR	1		13.929	4705628	5.74	559948			4
34	Sb -27-005 TR	1		14.173	773553	0.94	136998			4
35	Sb -27-005 TR	1		14.502	7952424	9.69	1329652			4
36	Sb -27-005 TR	1		14.957	320587	0.39	50253			4
37	Sb -27-005 TR	1		15.140	321930	0.39	56968			4
38	Sb -27-005 TR	1		15.378	68955	0.08	12388			4
39	Sb -27-005 TR	1		15.655	387544	0.47	29194			4
40	Sb -27-005 TR	1		16.532	344121	0.42	20313			4
Mean				10.425	2051205.037		311790.819			
Std. Dev.				4.001	3302599.021		458797.29			
% RSD				38.38	161.01		147.149			

Acquisition Log

Acquired By   RAB   Injection Volume   15.00(ul)
Injection   1
Date Acquired   4/20/2012 2:38:35 PM
Run Time   20.00(min)
Acquisition Method   NTA62359

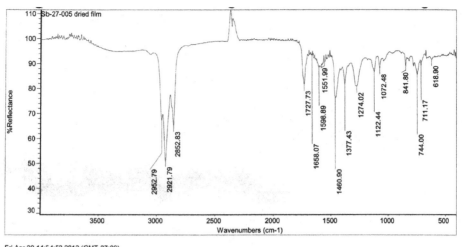

Fri Apr 20 14:54:53 2012 (GMT-07:00)
FIND PEAKS:
    Spectrum: Sb-27-005 dried film
    Region: 3999.70   400.00
    Absolute threshold: 95.297
    Sensitivity: 50
    Peak list:
                       Position: 618.90   Intensity: 91.627
                       Position: 711.17   Intensity: 89.068
                       Position: 744.00   Intensity: 85.566
                       Position: 841.80   Intensity: 88.971
                       Position: 1072.48   Intensity: 88.277
                       Position: 1122.44   Intensity: 86.933
                       Position: 1274.02   Intensity: 80.887
                       Position: 1377.43   Intensity: 81.562

                       Position: 1460.90   Intensity: 75.836
                       Position: 1551.99   Intensity: 90.760
                       Position: 1598.89   Intensity: 88.490
                       Position: 1658.07   Intensity: 93.049
                       Position: 1727.73   Intensity: 81.640
                       Position: 2852.83   Intensity: 65.218
                       Position: 2921.79   Intensity: 50.934
                       Position: 2952.79   Intensity: 67.292

FTIR of final Fixed Tincture of Antimony Sb-27-005

Quantitation Report

Data File : D:\HPCHEM\1\DATA\JUNK\D2902.D   Vial: 2
Acq On   : 29 Apr 103 11:18 am   Operator: PDC
Sample   : Sb-27-005 Final Tincture   Inst   : 5971 - In
Misc   :   Multiplr: 1.00
Quant Time: Apr 29 12:14 19103

Method   : D:\HPCHEM\1\METHODS\SVOA0212.M
Title   : SVOCs by SW-846 Method 8270C
Last Update : Thu Apr 24 12:25:04 2003
Response via : Multiple Level Calibration

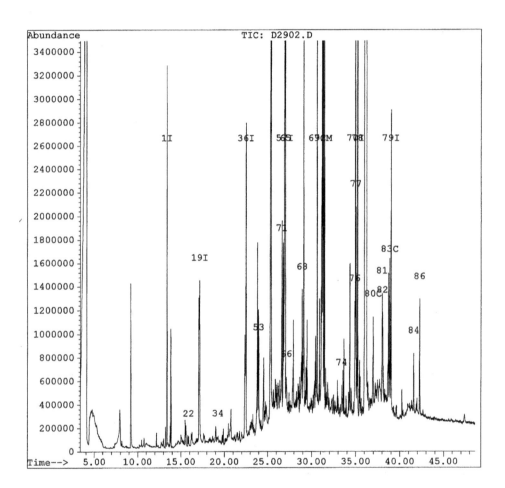

GC-Mass Spec analysis of final Fixed Tincture of Antimony Sb-27-005

```
Data File : D:\HPCHEM\1\DATA\JUNK\D2902.D          Vial: 2
Acq On    : 29 Apr 103  11:18 am                   Operator: PDC
Sample    : Sb-27-005                              Inst   : 5971 - In
Misc      :                                        Multiplr: 1.00

Method    : D:\HPCHEM\1\METHODS\SVQA0212.M
Title     : SVOCs by SW-846 Method 8270C
Library   : D:\DATABASE\NBS75K.L
```

****

Peak Number 1   Rank in Relative Concentration 2

R.T.	Conc	Area	Relative to ISTD	R.T.
4.08	297.68 ng	117679854	1,4-Dichlorobenzene-d4	13.39

Hit# of 20	Tentative ID	Ref#	CAS#	Qual
1	Acetic acid	62351	000064-19-7	90
2	Hydrazine, ethyl-, ethanedioate (1:	9559	006629-60-3	9
3	Methyl formate	62350	000107-31-3	5
4	Thiirane	117	000420-12-2	5
5	Carbonyl sulfide	62347	000463-58-1	5

****

Peak Number 2   Rank in Relative Concentration 3

R.T.	Conc	Area	Relative to ISTD	R.T.
4.77	45.15 ng	17847849	1,4-Dichlorobenzene-d4	13.39

Hit# of 20	Tentative ID	Ref#	CAS#	Qual
1	Ethane, 1,1-diethoxy-	64434	000105-57-7	83
2	Butane, 2-ethoxy-	63540	002679-87-0	9
3	Propanoic acid, 2-hydroxy-, ethyl e	64418	000097-64-3	9
4	1,3-Dioxolane-4-methanol	1874	086687-05-0	9
5	Acetic acid, methoxy-, methyl ester	1873	006290-49-9	9

****

Peak Number 3   Rank in Relative Concentration 9

R.T.	Conc	Area	Relative to ISTD	R.T.
7.94	10.71 ng	4233041	1,4-Dichlorobenzene-d4	13.39

Hit# of 20	Tentative ID	Ref#	CAS#	Qual
1	3-Penten-2-one, 4-methyl-	63216	000141-79-7	94
2	2-Pentene, 3,4-dimethyl-, (Z)-	63266	004914-91-4	86
3	2-Pentene, 3,4-dimethyl-, (E)-	1362	004914-92-5	86
4	3-Penten-2-one, 3-methyl-	1269	000565-62-8	60
5	1H-Pyrazole, 4,5-dihydro-1,5-dimeth	1226	005775-96-2	59

THE BOOK ON ANTIMONY

Library Search Compound Report

```
Data File : D:\HPCHEM\1\DATA\JUNK\D2902.D          Vial: 2
Acq On    : 29 Apr 103  11:18 am                   Operator: PDC
Sample    : Sb-27-005                              Inst   : 5971 - In
Misc      :                                        Multiplr: 1.00

Method    : D:\HPCHEM\1\METHODS\SVOA0212.M
Title     : SVOCs by SW-846 Method 8270C
Library   : D:\DATABASE\NBS75K.L
```

****
Peak Number 4   Rank in Relative Concentration 10

R.T.	Conc	Area	Relative to ISTD	R.T.
9.18	10.44 ng	4127225	1,4-Dichlorobenzene-d4	13.39

Hit# of 20	Tentative ID	Ref#	CAS#	Qual
1	2-Pentanone, 4-hydroxy-4-methyl-	3245	000123-42-2	78
2	CH2=CHCH2C(O)OCH3	1448	003724-55-8	10
3	5-Hexen-2-one	63205	000109-49-9	9
4	3-Hydroxy-2-pentanone	1691	003142-66-3	9
5	Formamide, N,N-diethyl-	1629	000617-84-5	7

****
Peak Number 5   Rank in Relative Concentration 11

R.T.	Conc	Area	Relative to ISTD	R.T.
13.83	8.70 ng	3437854	1,4-Dichlorobenzene-d4	13.39

Hit# of 20	Tentative ID	Ref#	CAS#	Qual
1	1H-Pyrazole, 4,5-dihydro-1,5-dimeth	1226	005775-96-2	37
2	1-Methyl-1H-1,2,4-triazole	62695	006086-21-1	37
3	Cyclohexanone, 3,3,5-trimethyl-	66047	000873-94-9	23
4	3-Penten-2-one, semicarbazone	7641	016983-59-8	10
5	1-Pentanol, 2,3-dimethyl-	3343	010143-23-4	10

****
Peak Number 6   Rank in Relative Concentration 15

R.T.	Conc	Area	Relative to ISTD	R.T.
14.68	3.26 ng	1290010	1,4-Dichlorobenzene-d4	13.39

Hit# of 20	Tentative ID	Ref#	CAS#	Qual
1	Acetaldehyde, dimethylhydrazone	681	007422-90-4	37
2	Clofexamide	40091	001223-36-5	17
3	Propane, 1,1-diethoxy-	65388	004744-08-5	12
4	N,N-Diisopropylformamide	5242	002700-30-3	9
5	Butylamine, N-methyl-N-propyl-	5278	024551-99-3	9

```
Data File : D:\HPCHEM\1\DATA\JUNK\D2902.D          Vial: 2
Acq On    : 29 Apr 103  11:18 am               Operator: PDC
Sample    : Sb-27-005                          Inst    : 5971 - In
Misc      :                                    Multiplr: 1.00

Method    : D:\HPCHEM\1\METHODS\SVOA0212.M
Title     : SVOCs by SW-846 Method 8270C
Library   : D:\DATABASE\NBS75K.L
```

****

Peak Number 7   Rank in Relative Concentration 21

R.T.	Conc	Area	Relative to ISTD	R.T.
20.74	2.19 ng	1395476	Acenaphthene-d10	22.48

Hit# of 20	Tentative ID	Ref#	CAS#	Qual
1 Tetradecane		69658	000629-59-4	89
2 Tridecane		69020	000629-50-5	64
3 Heptadecane		71191	000629-78-7	58
4 Hexadecane		70789	000544-76-3	58
5 Pentadecane		70274	000629-62-9	52

****

Peak Number 8   Rank in Relative Concentration 16

R.T.	Conc	Area	Relative to ISTD	R.T.
23.21	3.07 ng	1951026	Acenaphthene-d10	22.48

Hit# of 20	Tentative ID	Ref#	CAS#	Qual
1 Naphthalene, 2,3,6-trimethyl-		15375	000829-26-5	90
2 Naphthalene, 1,3,6-trimethyl-		15373	003031-08-1	86
3 Naphthalene, 1,4,6-trimethyl-		68270	002131-42-2	76
4 Naphthalene, 1,6,7-trimethyl-		68264	002245-38-7	70
5 1H,3H-Thieno[3,4-c]thiophene, 4,6-d		15073	015441-54-0	50

****

Peak Number 9   Rank in Relative Concentration 6

R.T.	Conc	Area	Relative to ISTD	R.T.
23.85	11.06 ng	7037579	Acenaphthene-d10	22.48

Hit# of 20	Tentative ID	Ref#	CAS#	Qual
1 Hexadecane		70787	000544-76-3	96
2 Heptadecane		71191	000629-78-7	62
3 Pentadecane		70274	000629-62-9	62
4 Eicosane		72324	000112-95-8	58
5 Tetradecane		69661	000629-59-4	58

Library Search Compound Report

```
Data File : D:\HPCHEM\1\DATA\JUNK\D2902.D          Vial: 2
Acq On    : 29 Apr 103  11:18 am                  Operator: PDC
Sample    : Sb-27-005                             Inst   : 5971 - In
Misc      :                                       Multiplr: 1.00

Method    : D:\HPCHEM\1\METHODS\SVOA0212.M
Title     : SVOCs by SW-846 Method 8270C
Library   : D:\DATABASE\NBS75K.L
```

```
**********************************************************************
Peak Number 10                    Rank in Relative Concentration 14

  R.T.    Conc           Area       Relative to ISTD          R.T.
-----------------------------------------------------------------------
 24.55    3.49 ng      2217427     Acenaphthene-d10           22.48

Hit# of 20           Tentative ID            Ref#    CAS#      Qual
-----------------------------------------------------------------------
 1 Undecane, 5-ethyl-                       19036 017453-94-0   72
 2 Undecane, 2,5-dimethyl-                  69031 017301-22-3   68
 3 Undecane, 3,5-dimethyl-                  19003 017312-81-1   64
 4 Heptadecane, 2,6,10,15-tetramethyl-      42196 054833-48-6   64
 5 Pentadecane                              70274 000629-62-9   59
```

```
**********************************************************************
Peak Number 11                    Rank in Relative Concentration 5

  R.T.    Conc           Area       Relative to ISTD          R.T.
-----------------------------------------------------------------------
 25.38    22.89 ng    58589825     Phenanthrene-d10           26.92

Hit# of 20           Tentative ID            Ref#    CAS#      Qual
-----------------------------------------------------------------------
 1 Pentadecane, 2,6,10,14-tetramethyl-      71951 001921-70-6   97
 2 Heptadecane, 2,6-dimethyl-               37466 054105-67-8   93
 3 Dodecane, 2,6,11-trimethyl-              70271 031295-56-4   90
 4 Hexadecane, 2,6,10,14-tetramethyl-       72328 000638-36-8   90
 5 Dodecane, 2,7,10-trimethyl-              26005 074645-98-0   86
```

```
**********************************************************************
Peak Number 12                    Rank in Relative Concentration 12

  R.T.    Conc           Area       Relative to ISTD          R.T.
-----------------------------------------------------------------------
 29.11    6.89 ng     17647537     Phenanthrene-d10           26.92

Hit# of 20           Tentative ID            Ref#    CAS#      Qual
-----------------------------------------------------------------------
 1 Hexadecanoic acid, ethyl ester          72375 000628-97-7   91
 2 Tetradecanoic acid, ethyl ester         71611 000124-06-1   91
 3 Pentadecanoic acid, ethyl ester         37809 041114-00-5   91
 4 Dodecanoic acid, ethyl ester            70839 000106-33-2   86
 5 Decanoic acid, ethyl ester              22936 000110-38-3   78
```

```
Data File : D:\HPCHEM\1\DATA\JUNK\D2902.D          Vial: 2
Acq On    : 29 Apr 103  11:18 am                  Operator: PDC
Sample    : Sb-27-005                             Inst   : 5971 - In
Misc      :                                       Multiplr: 1.00

Method    : D:\HPCHEM\1\METHODS\SVOA0212.M
Title     : SVOCs by SW-846 Method 8270C
Library   : D:\DATABASE\NBS75K.L
```

****
Peak Number 13   Rank in Relative Concentration 4

R.T.	Conc	Area	Relative to ISTD	R.T.
31.16	33.29 ng	25664666	Chrysene-d12	34.96

Hit# of 20	Tentative ID	Ref#	CAS#	Qual
1 Ethyl Oleate		72984	000111-62-6	99
2 Ethyl 9-hexadecanoate		39817	000000-00-0	91
3 9-Octadecenoic acid (Z)-, methyl es		72673	000112-62-9	53
4 Cyclopentadecanone, 2-hydroxy-		32022	004727-18-8	47
5 1-Undecanol		68375	000112-42-5	35

****
Peak Number 14   Rank in Relative Concentration 8

R.T.	Conc	Area	Relative to ISTD	R.T.
31.42	10.95 ng	8437535	Chrysene-d12	34.96

Hit# of 20	Tentative ID	Ref#	CAS#	Qual
1 Octadecanoic acid, ethyl ester		73051	000111-61-5	98
2 Hexadecanoic acid, ethyl ester		72375	000628-97-7	93
3 Tetradecanoic acid, ethyl ester		71613	000124-06-1	86
4 Dodecanoic acid, ethyl ester		70837	000106-33-2	72
5 Octadecanoic acid, 2-methyl-, methy		73047	002490-22-4	70

****
Peak Number 15   Rank in Relative Concentration 22

R.T.	Conc	Area	Relative to ISTD	R.T.
31.81	2.16 ng	1661740	Chrysene-d12	34.96

Hit# of 20	Tentative ID	Ref#	CAS#	Qual
1 p-Terphenyl-d14		32805	001718-51-0	78
2 [1,1'-Biphenyl]-4,4'-diamine, 3,3'-		32735	000119-90-4	45
3 1,1':3',1''-Terphenyl, 5'-methyl-		32819	000000-00-0	38
4 Pentadecane		70273	000629-62-9	20
5 Hexadecane		70790	000544-76-3	20

```
Data File : D:\HPCHEM\1\DATA\JUNK\D2902.D          Vial: 2
Acq On    : 29 Apr 103  11:18 am                   Operator: PDC
Sample    : Sb-27-005                              Inst   : 5971 - In
Misc      :                                        Multiplr: 1.00

Method    : D:\HPCHEM\1\METHODS\SVOA0212.M
Title     : SVOCs by SW-846 Method 8270C
Library   : D:\DATABASE\NBS75K.L
```

****
Peak Number 16   Rank in Relative Concentration 17

R.T.	Conc	Area	Relative to ISTD	R.T.
33.63	2.75 ng	2117626	Chrysene-d12	34.96

Hit# of 20	Tentative ID	Ref#	CAS#	Qual
1 Hexanedioic acid, bis(2-ethylhexyl)		73987	000103-23-1	83
2 Hexanedioic acid, dioctyl ester		51386	000123-79-5	49
3 Hexanedioic acid, bis(1,3-dimethylb		44807	055125-22-9	38
4 Hexanedioic acid, mono(2-ethylhexyl		35514	004337-65-9	38
5 Hexanedioic acid, dihexyl ester		44802	000110-33-8	37

****
Peak Number 17   Rank in Relative Concentration 13

R.T.	Conc	Area	Relative to ISTD	R.T.
34.34	6.10 ng	4705775	Chrysene-d12	34.96

Hit# of 20	Tentative ID	Ref#	CAS#	Qual
1 Benzo[ghi]fluoranthene		29274	000203-12-3	90
2 Cyclopenta[cd]pyrene		29275	027208-37-3	89
3 .beta.-Carboline, 7-methoxy-1,2-dim		29168	000000-00-0	50
4 9H-Xanthen-9-one, 3-methoxy-		29157	003722-52-9	37
5 9H-Thioxanthen-9-one, 2-methyl-		29151	015774-82-0	9

****
Peak Number 18   Rank in Relative Concentration 19

R.T.	Conc	Area	Relative to ISTD	R.T.
35.43	2.69 ng	2069971	Chrysene-d12	34.96

Hit# of 20	Tentative ID	Ref#	CAS#	Qual
1 7H-Benz[de]anthracen-7-one		30040	000082-05-3	95
2 1-Pyrene-carboxaldehyde		30041	003029-19-4	59
3 Benzonitrile, 4,4'-(1,2-ethenediyl)		30032	006292-62-2	25
4 m-Terphenyl		70906	000092-06-8	9
5 o-Terphenyl		70909	000084-15-1	9

```
Data File : D:\HPCHEM\1\DATA\JUNK\D2902.D          Vial: 2
Acq On    : 29 Apr 103  11:18 am                   Operator: PDC
Sample    : Sb-27-005                              Inst    : 5971 - In
Misc      :                                        Multiplr: 1.00

Method    : D:\HPCHEM\1\METHODS\SVOA0212.M
Title     : SVOCs by SW-846 Method 8270C
Library   : D:\DATABASE\NBS75K.L
```

****
Peak Number 19   Rank in Relative Concentration 1

R.T.	Conc	Area	Relative to ISTD	R.T.
36.10	317.29 ng	244592094	Chrysene-d12	34.96

Hit# of 20	Tentative ID	Ref#	CAS#	Qual
1 Pentadecane, 2,6,10,14-tetramethyl-		71951	001921-70-6	93
2 Nonadecane, 2,6,10,14-tetramethyl-		46163	055124-80-6	93
3 Docosane, 7-hexyl-		53458	055373-86-9	87
4 Eicosane, 3-methyl-		42195	006418-46-8	87
5 Eicosane, 2-methyl-		72682	001560-84-5	83

****
Peak Number 20   Rank in Relative Concentration 18

R.T.	Conc	Area	Relative to ISTD	R.T.
37.22	2.74 ng	980992	Perylene-d12	38.99

Hit# of 20	Tentative ID	Ref#	CAS#	Qual
1 1,2-Benzenedicarboxylic acid, dipen		43719	000131-18-0	43
2 Cyclopropanenonanoic acid, 2-[(2-bu		45907	010152-69-9	43
3 Benzothiazole, 2-methyl-		66648	000120-75-2	38
4 1,2-Benzenedicarboxylic acid, bis(2		47478	007299-89-0	32
5 Di-n-octyl phthalate		53129	000117-84-0	32

****
Peak Number 21   Rank in Relative Concentration 23

R.T.	Conc	Area	Relative to ISTD	R.T.
37.47	2.06 ng	735604	Perylene-d12	38.99

Hit# of 20	Tentative ID	Ref#	CAS#	Qual
1 1,2-Benzenedicarboxylic acid, diiso		55245	028553-12-0	27
2 1,2-Benzenedicarboxylic acid, butyl		43452	000084-64-0	27
3 Bis(2-ethylhexyl) phthalate		74171	000117-81-7	17
4 1,2-Benzenedicarboxylic acid, butyl		50567	000089-18-9	17
5 1,2-Benzenedicarboxylic acid, bis(4		47481	000146-50-9	16

Library Search Compound Report

```
Data File : D:\HPCHEM\1\DATA\JUNK\D2902.D          Vial: 2
Acq On    : 29 Apr 103  11:18 am               Operator: PDC
Sample    : Sb-27-005                          Inst    : 5971 - In
Misc      :                                    Multiplr: 1.00

Method    : D:\HPCHEM\1\METHODS\SVOA0212.M
Title     : SVOCs by SW-846 Method 8270C
Library   : D:\DATABASE\NBS75K.L
```

****
Peak Number 22   Rank in Relative Concentration 7

R.T.	Conc	Area	Relative to ISTD	R.T.
38.71	10.96 ng	3919065	Perylene-d12	38.99

Hit# of 20	Tentative ID	Ref#	CAS#	Qual
1 Benzo[j]fluoranthene		34435	000205-82-3	98
2 Benzo[k]fluoranthene		71510	000207-08-9	96
3 Benz[e]acephenanthrylene		34432	000205-99-2	96
4 Benzo[e]pyrene		71509	000192-97-2	96
5 Perylene		71507	000198-55-0	95

****
Peak Number 23   Rank in Relative Concentration 20

R.T.	Conc	Area	Relative to ISTD	R.T.
47.39	2.21 ng	789285	Perylene-d12	38.99

Hit# of 20	Tentative ID	Ref#	CAS#	Qual
1 Coronene		42869	000191-07-1	93
2 Clobazam		42736	022316-47-8	25
3 5.alpha.-Pregnan-20-one, 12.beta.-h		50386	003002-93-5	10
4 2,4,6-Trimethyl-1,3-phenylenediamin		9766	003102-70-3	10
5 Benzaldehyde, 2-methyl-, (2,4-dinit		42702	001773-44-0	9

Analysis of both the Fixed and Unfixed Tinctures of Antimony using Graphite Furnace Atomic Absorbtion Spectroscopy for Arsenic content revealed low levels do pass through the process. Fixed Tincture shows a lesser amount at about 7 ppb (parts per billion) while the Unfixed was close to 30 ppb. Of course with the doseage of tincture usually taken, these numbers would drop 10- or even 100-fold.

Metal	**As**		

Sequence # **6230429-1**   Analyst/Date   RAB 4/29/03

Instrument Comments: Flame _____   Furnace   X   Cold Vapor _____

Standard Concentrations: Standard 1   5   Standard 2   10   Standard 3   25   Standard 4 _____
units: mg/L   ug/L

Standard Absorbance: Standard 1   5   Standard 2   10   Standard 3   25   Standard 4 _____

Sample ID		mean concentration	Dilution factor	Dry wt. g	Sample Concentration mg/Kg mg/L (ug/L)	QC % Recovery	Comments
ICB		0.00			< 5.0		
ICV(20)		22.32			22.32	112	
MB 4/29/02		1.57			< 5.0		
BS(20)		18.48			18.48	92	
BSD(20)		20.86			20.86	104	
Final Tincture Sb-27-005	TOT	6.92			6.92		
Final Tincture Sb-84-002	TOT	29.05			29.05		
CCB		1.48			< 5.0		
CCV(20)		17.67			17.67	88	

Perkin Elmer 4100 ZL

Zeeman Background Correction

Graphite Furnace AA

Note: Solids assume digestate vol. of 50 mL.
Liquids 50 mL to 50 mL.

As sheet.XLS

Page 1 of 1

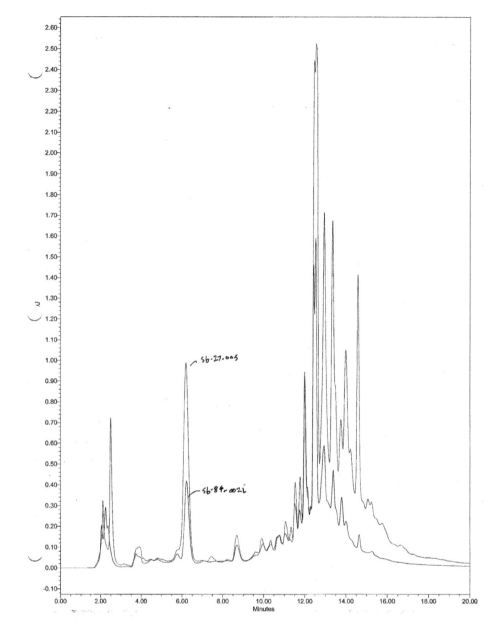

Comparison of Fixed and Unfixed Tinctures of Antimony by HPLC; They look so similar here and yet they are quite different in odor, taste, and effect.

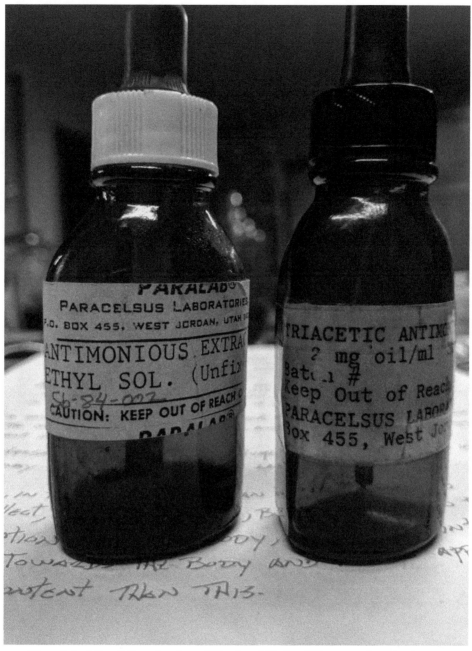

The original Paralab packaging of Fixed and Unfixed Tinctures from Antimony.

Fixed Tincture of Antimony Production

Apparatus: Materials

large reflux apparatus   Sb fume
large soxhlet   glacial acetic acid
crystallizing trays   ethanol

Procedure:

1. Reflux cloth bag full of Sb fume with acetic acid.

2. Filter acetic extract.

3. Recover most of the acetic by roto-evaporator.

4. Pour thickened extract into evaporating dishes and cover with cheesecloth. Allow extract to crystallize.

5. Wash crystallized substance with deionized water in evaporating dish to dissolve acetate. Filter solution and allow recrystallization of liquid.

6. Wash crystals obtained with deionized water and filter again if necessary. Let solution crystallize. All acetic acid odor should be removed.

7. Grind the Sb acetate crystals and place into dried soxhlet thimble.

8. Soxhlet extraction of acetate using ethanol as solvent.

9. After obtaining the tincture, remove the ethanol and extract the solid remaining with several portions of diethyl ether.

10. Filter ~~with vacuum and sintered glass frit.~~

11. Remove the ether and extract residue with ethanol.

(Con't)

The final production process for Fixed Tincture of Antimony adopted by Paralab.

12. Filter tincture produced and dilute to original ~~fume~~ weight using ethanol, (1:1 tincture). Filter again if required before bottling.

Production Notes

1. Keep one batch in each of the three major steps at all times. Keep one batch in the acetic reflux stage, one batch crystallizing, and one batch in the soxhlet extracting, ready for bottling.

2. Extract twice in both cases with fresh or recovered solvent.

3. Keep notes on weights used and label materials in containers and apparatus, including date, batch number, and initials.

4. Take samples of finished product.

Miscellaneous Experiments on Antimony at Paralab

In addition to the Fixed and Unfixed Antimony lines, there were many other experiments seeking to derive medicinal virtues from the Antimony Fume and from other sources of Antimony as well. An example is the following extraction of oil from antimony glass that had been prepared and supplied by Karl Lee, another student and fellow classmate at the PRS living in Big Sur, California. Karl was a goldsmith and lapidary with a large furnace in which he produced several batches of Antimony Glass for research at Paralab.

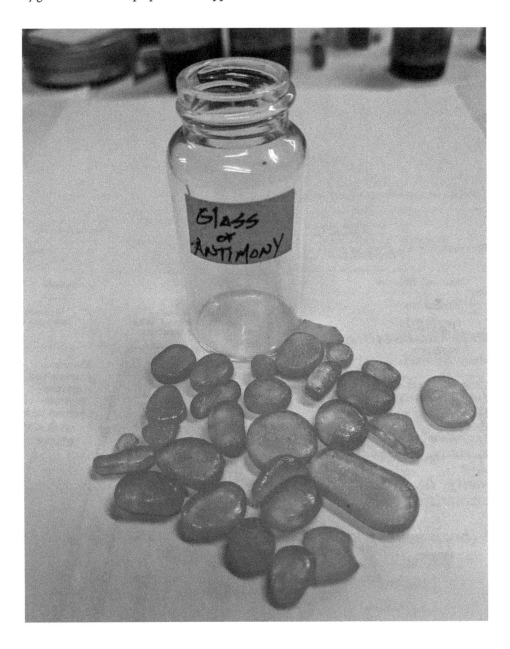

Antimony (Fixed oil)   Sb 26-000

Antimony Trioxide, (Harshaw Chemical Co. #670-004-22 Lot# J513
Type KR) sample # Sb-26-000A was fused in a porcelin
crucible at about 1300°C in a pottery kiln then poured
out into a thin layer on a steel sheet. This produced
a clear golden yellow glass on cooling (sample #Sb-26-000B)
(Note: This operation was carried out by Karl Lee in Big Sur, Calif.)

11/25/80 2:30pm Placed 950 g of the yellow glass (#Sb-26-000B) into
a small Ball mill and added 350 ml of water.
Closed the Ball mill jar tightly then began its grinding cycle.

11/26/80 8:30 AM Turned Ball mill off and opened jar.
A thick white mush of ground glass covered the
in side. 500 ml more DI water was added
and the jar agitated well then the liquid
was poured into a Beaker.
The liquid was thick and white like cream.
Small bits of glass remained in the jar so
500 ml of DI H₂O was added and grinding
continued.

5:00pm grinding stopped

12/2/80 5:00pm Continued grinding the glass in the Ball mill.

12/3/80 9:00 AM grinding stopped.

12/4/80 8:40 AM Agitated the Ball mill jar well then poured the
entire contents into a Large Flat dish.
Added the previously collected slurry of antimony glass
to the dish then set it in an oven at 60°C

Sb-26-000

12/8/80 9:30 AM Placed all of the ~~glass~~ non dry antimony glass powder into the Ball Mill Jar and added 750 ml of glacial acetic acid and 190 ml deionized water.
Sealed the Jar and Began the grinding cycle (1 hr twice a day)
Sample of ground glass labeled Sb-26-000 C

12/30/80 1:30 pm using acetic acid (glacial), the ground glass/acid mixture was ~~poured~~ rinsed into a 6000 ml flask (about 250 ml D.I. H₂O was also used for rinsing).
Total volume = 3500 ml
Closed the container and set aside in a warm place (45°C) with occasional shaking.

2/3/81 10:20 AM Removed the container of glass/acetic acid from the incubator and let cool to room temperature a pale golden colored extract now covers the white ground glass.

2/4/81 10:30 AM Filtered the golden acetic acid extract off of the ground glass through a fine paper (VWR #613)

1:40 pm Began concentrating the acetic acid extract in the Roto-evaporator. Temp 70°C vacuum 18" Hg

4:30 pm concentration stopped.

2/5/81 10:45 AM Continued concentrating the acetic acid extract of glass.

12:00 pm concentration stopped. Poured the concentrate into a container and sealed. The recovered acetic acid was poured back over the antimony glass. Digestion 40°C.

Antimony (Fixed oil)   Sb-26-000

2/23/81 10⁰⁰ AM Removed the Flask of glass/acetic acid From
        Digestion and Filtered the contents through a Fine
        paper Filter (Whatman 2") into a Roto-evaporator Flask.
        The Filtrate was clear and pale golden ~~~~ in color.

        3:30pm Began concentrating the Filtered extract in the
        Roto-evaporator. Temp 70°C 18"Hg Vacuum.

        4:40pm Removed the concentrated extract From the Roto-evaporator
        and placed it with that obtained Previously.
        The Recovered Acetic Acid was placed over the
        ground glass again and placed into a Digestive
        Heat (40°C)

3/30/81 12:00pm Filtered the Acetic Acid extract off of the Antimony
        glass (tincture is very pale yellow in color) into a Flask.

        2:00pm Began concentrating the Filtered Acetic Acid
        extract in the roto evaporator (70°C 28"Hg Vacuum)

        3:00pm Added all of the previously obtained concentrated
        acetic acid extract to the Roto-evaporator and
        continued concentration.

        3:30pm Removed the thick Light Brown concentrate From
        the Roto-evaporator Flask By Rinsing with about 10ml
        of Deionized water into a 6" porcelin evaporating
        Dish. The Dish was then placed into an oven
        at 60°C to Dry.

Sb-26-000

3/31/81 8:00 AM Removed the dish of now dried residue from the oven. The substance was light brown in color with a faint "earthy" odor and slightly gummy in consistency.

10:42 AM Scraped the residue (sample# Sb-26-000C) from the dish and placed it into a 300 ml Erlenmeyer flask with ground glass stopper (90.5g total). Poured 150 ml of absolute ethanol over the residue then sealed the flask. A golden yellow tincture was produced immediately and the gummy residue became fluffy in consistency.

4/3/81 9:30 AM Filtered off the ethanol extract from the residue. The extract was deep golden yellow in color and crystal clear. The residue was light tan and had a jelly-like consistency. (Residue labeled Sb-26-000D)

2:50 PM Placed the ethanol extract into a roto-evaporator and began concentrating. Temp 55°C 15"Hg vacuum.

3:15 PM Concentration complete. Removed the concentrated extract from the roto-evaporator (15 ml total) and placed it into a container labeled #Sb-26-000E

4/6/81, 10:30 AM Filtered off the deep red amber liquid from the solids which had separated from the cooled concentrate (Sb-26-000E) and further concentrated the filtrate in the roto-evaporator.

11:00 AM Concentration complete. A deep red amber oil remains which was placed into a container labeled Sb-26-000F, 3.5g total

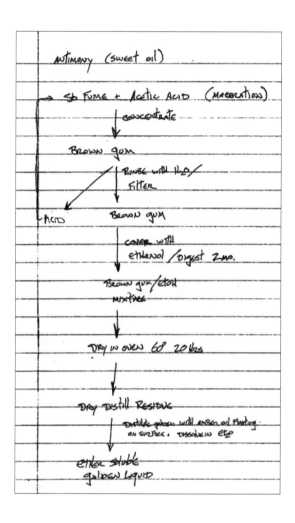

ANTIMONY (SWEET OIL)

→ Sb FUME + ACETIC ACID   (MACERATION)
  ↓ CONCENTRATE

BROWN GUM
  ↓ RINSE WITH H₂O
    FILTER

ACID   BROWN GUM
                ↓ COVER WITH
                  ETHANOL / DIGEST 2 MO.

            BROWN GUM / EtOH
            MIXTURE
                ↓

        DRY IN OVEN 60° 20 hrs
                ↓

        DRY DISTILL RESIDUE
                ↓ DISTILLS GOLDEN WITH AMBER OIL FLOATING
                  ON SURFACE. DISSOLVE IN ETₑ

        ETHER SOLUBLE
        GOLDEN LIQUID

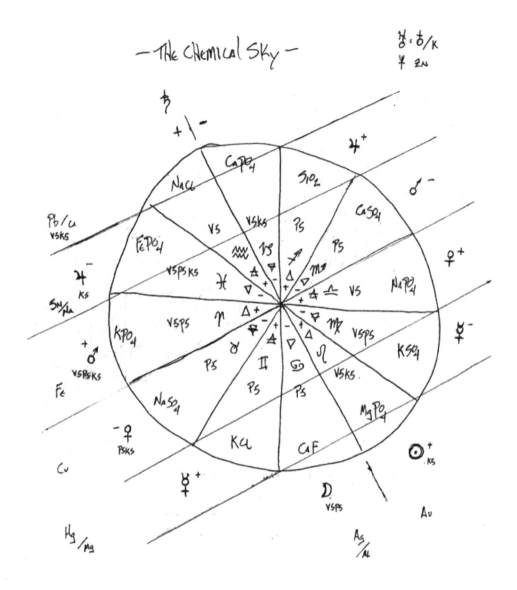

Another important line developed at Paralab was the "Mineral Salts in Solution" line, which addressed the twelve Schuessler Biochemic cell salts and their zodiacal associations.

Antimony was also available as a homeopathic preparation. A full line of 21 mineral salts were developed for homeopathic use and the Golden Sulfide of Antimony was among them. In each case, the purified alchemical Sulfur and Mercury of the parent metal was imbibed and digested with the proper homeopathic salt as the body. Once matured, these were subjected to the standard homeopathic attenuation process.

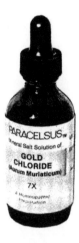
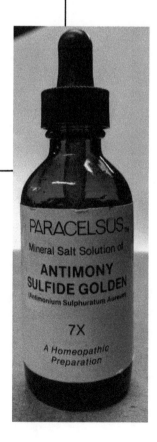

In the following experiment, solid stibnite was triturated with dextrose to produce a solid form of the homeopathic remedy. Here stibnite was imbibed with the Fixed oil of Antimony into a solid stone which was then attenuated homeopathically.

ANTIMONY SULFIDE TRITURATION   Sb - TRIT. - 000

1/15/81 8:30 AM FINELY GROUND A SMALL PIECE OF ANTIMONY SULFIDE (STIBNITE ORE
FROM NEUMANA MINE, ATLANTA, IDAHO; SEE ATTACHED SPECTROGRAPHIC ANALYSIS; SAMPLE
#Sb-TRIT.-000A) IN A PORCELIN MORTAR THEN INSERTED IT INTO AN
OVEN AT 60°C TO DRY.

10:00 AM REMOVED THE GROUND STIBNITE FROM THE OVEN THEN WEIGHED OUT
1.00g INTO A CLEAN, DRY WEIGHING BOTTLE.

10:30 AM ADDED 80mg OF OIL FROM ANTIMONY (FIXED) DERIVED FROM
TINCTURE #Sb-27-007.

10:45 AM ADDED 80mg OF ABS. ETHANOL (STAMP# 272654 ID# BTC-80B-08)
SEALED THE WEIGHING BOTTLE AND PLACED IN AN OVEN AT 60°C.

11:15 AM REMOVED THE BOTTLE FROM THE OVEN AND LET COOL.
THE SUBSTANCE APPEARS AS A SATURATED DARK GREY MASS.

1:30 pm WEIGHED OUT 3.0 grams DEXTROSE (
INTO A SMALL DISH THEN ADDED TO IT 1gram OF THE DIGESTED ANTIMONY
SULFIDE. THIS MIXTURE WAS THEN PLACED INTO A CLEAN DRY
UNGLAZED PORCELIN MORTAR AND MIXED WITH AN
UNGLAZED SPATULA OF PORCELIN, GROUND FORCEFULLY 6MIN, SCRAPED
DOWN FROM THE MORTAR SIDES WITH THE SPATULA 4MIN, REGROUND
6MIN, SCRAPED 4MIN.

2:05 pm REPEATED THE MIXING/GRINDING PROCEDURE WITH 3.0 grams
FRESH DEXTROSE ADDED.

3:00 pm REPEATED MIXING/GRINDING PROCEDURE WITH 3.0 grams FRESH
DEXTROSE ADDED

(CONT)
1/15/80 3:50 COLLECTED THE TRITURATED STIBNITE (9.38g TOTAL COLLECTED) AND
PLACED IT INTO A CONTAINER LABELED AS #Sb-TRIT-000 1:10

In 1982 Frater Albertus announced the proposed organization of Phameres (Pharmaceutical and Medical Research) a separate research division with ties to the College and Paralab. I was invited to become one of the Directors of Research. My immediate duties would be to continue with the analysis of the various spagyric and alchemical products under way at Paralab.

Paracelsus College

UTAH INSTITUTE OF PARACHEMISTRY

P.O. BOX 6006 • SALT LAKE CITY, UTAH U.S.A. 84106 • Tel. Area Code 801 486-6730 - 487-7178

May 19th 1982

Robert Bartlett
455 East 1st Ave #3
Salt Lake City UT 84103

Dear Bob,

This letter is to inform you in writing of the proposed names for the Reorganization of Phameres, as was discussed at the meeting called by the President of the College on May 14th, 1982.

Please confirm on the lower part of this letter your acceptance of the position as Director of Research. We need this written confirmation for our records to comply with the College regulations.

Detailed instructions concerning individual assignments will be discussed at the next meeting.

Looking forward with great anticipation to our joint efforts in behalf of Phameres

I am gratefully,

Dr. Albert Riedel
Pres. Paracelsus College

I, Robert Bartlett, herewith accept the position as Director of Research with Phameres.

Signed: _____

Date _____

The Spagyric Way

*of Preparing Medicine
in Relationship to
Parachemistry*

By

Albert Richard Riedel, Ph.D.

©

PHAMERES

Pharmaceutical Medical Research Foundation

A Division of Paracelsus College

Salt Lake City, Utah, U.S.A.

Phameres was short lived with the death of Frater Albertus in 1984, and the college closed its doors. Paralab struggled on for awhile before also closing its doors.

And thus closed another chapter in my journey with a dragon. I kept up the charge Frater had given me, to collect as much analytical data as I could on the various experimental products, up to the present time. This *Book on Antimony* is one such collection; there are more to come in future writings.

The Spagyric Method of Preparing Substances

By ROBERT BARTLETT

This is intended as a brief overview of the process known as the spagyric method of preparing substances of value, whether they are used in conventional health care schemes toward alleviating a specific disorder or as normal dietary supplements in a preventive health care program.

The term "spagyric" is derived from the greek spao, to separate, and ageiro, to reunite, (i.e. to separate and reunite); and first appears in the early chemical tracts of the 1600's. Although the term spagyric is of relatively recent origin, the origins of the technique it describes dates much earlier, to the dim beginnings of chemical thought.

The obscurity of the spagyric method among contemporary methods of pharmaceutical preparation is a typical example where ancient doctrines have been passed over or prematurely rejected, without in-depth research, for more recent "sophisticated" methods. Another example of this kind is the recent revival of interest and research in the ancient method known as acupuncture. The spagyric method is at this time entertaining a revival of interest as well among serious professionals and students in many countries, where the underlying goal is to determine whether or not superior medications are to be found in the system as claimed by the ancient authors and practitioners of this science.

The basic theory and process of the spagyric method is threefold in nature. First there is a separation step where the active principles, according to this system's theory, are separated in crude form from the substance. These essentials, as they are called, appear in the form of three sub-groups, a clear volatile fraction, an oily fraction, and a mineral residue.

Secondly, there is a purification step where each fraction is subjected to purification methods within certain guidelines, based on the nature of the particular fraction. The purification methods generally involve distillation, calcination, sublimation and recrystallization.

Once these essential active fractions have been separated and purified, the third and final step in the spagyric method is that of recombining the three fractions as one substance again. Since spagyric products are derived from all natural sources (herbs and minerals), one major dispute is the determination of what exactly is essential in the substance and of therapeutic value. In the medical profession, there are those who use the whole crude drug, those who use only a tincture or extract from the drug, and those who prefer to use only the mineral components of the substance. The unique approach of the spagyric practitioners is grounded in ancient concepts of matter and life which serve as the basis of the whole method. Only certain key ideas can be outlined here to show why spagyric preparations are made as they are.

A few anecdotes on the use of Antimony tinctures during this period of time stand out in memory. Over time, I had personally tasted the tinctures many times and never with any sign of ill effect, but I was young and healthy; how would it affect someone really ill, I wondered. Past successes with the tinctures bolstered my confidence that they had great healing potential.

A friend approached me one day and told me her close friend (a real cat lady) had a cat with feline leukemia. The vet told her the cat was going to die very soon and recommended euthanasia. That was unthinkable to the owner, and she was desperately reaching out for some way to save her favorite cat. My friend described the black cat as looking emaciated, weak with a dull matted coat. Right there in my home lab I compounded my old favorite, Stinging Nettles spagyric with Fixed Antimony and a dash of Gold tincture then gave it to my friend with instructions for her friend's cat.

A month had passed when I heard from my friend again. She told me that her friend's cat had made an amazing recovery and was now filled out with a beautiful shining coat; "she looks better that all of her other cats now." The vet told her the cat was in total remission; in fact, it was difficult to tell if she had leukemia at all. Pets are interesting subjects: There is no placebo effect; it either works or it doesn't. My own dog was always getting banged up, and I treated him internally and externally with Antimony tinctures many times always with amazing success. He was gored by a goat, and the external application of Fixed Tincture sealed it up overnight without pain, swelling, or inflammation; internally, it also cured his pancreatitis. He lived to 130 dog years, which is long for a Sheppard-Wolf mix.

Another use anecdote from this time took much longer to have the results revealed. One evening we had visitors and one, a young lady and I, stayed up late into the night talking about alchemy and magick.

We had never met before but I could sense that there was something wrong with her; her color was "off" somehow, but she didn't mention anything. On parting I gave her some of the Fixed Tincture of Antimony, and we never crossed paths again. Some 20 years later through the miracle of the internet, I received an email from that same lady asking if I remembered her; describing the night we sat up talking. I said I did but under her maiden name, to which she was highly impressed that I would remember that and even spelled it correctly. She told me that she had cancer the night she visited and later started taking the Antimony Tincture I had given her, and it cured her of the cancer entirely.

This next anecdote is epic. Hans Nintzel, founder of RAMS (Restorers of Alchemical Manuscripts Society), was my classmate at PRS and became a long time friend. Hans would always send me a copy of the latest RAMS production gratis, and we kept in touch through the mail. One day I received the following letter from him:

"Great Work has been sent today. What else did you want?

733 Melrose Drive
Richardson, TX. 75080
Sept. 30, 1982

Dear Bob:

I just talked to Dr. Israel Regardie.
As you may know, Doc caught a little dose
of Mercury fumes (or was it Antimony?)
and it messed up his lungs. He goes on
a breathing machine every night.

He told me that before he "kicked the
bucket" he wanted to take some gold
tincture, some potable gold. I told him
you had made some up. He does not wish
to kick the bucket before he finishes
"his work". So, would like some of the
liquid sol.

Now. I would like you to do one of two
things. And I will PAY (I insist) for
this, ---either send him a portion directly, or send me some extra so I can
send it to Doc. If YOU send it, you make
a valuable "connection" (Leverage!) I
leave the choice to you. He needs it real
soon, so if you have any around, I would
like HIS needs cared for first. Doc is a
great soul and we want to try and keep
him with us as long as we can and as long
as he is willing.Right now, he is hurting
in the chest, but willing.

On the reverse side, I print his address.
If you DO send it direct, advise and I DO
want to reimburse you. If you send it to
me, ditto. But Bob, PLEASE, hurry. O.K.?

Peace.
In L.V.X.

Hans

I immediately compounded the oil pre-pared from Gold with Unfixed Antimony I had on hand and sent it off the next day gratis. Though it didn't fix his burned lungs or previous asthmatic condition, it did bring some relief for which he was very appreciative.

Such testimonials inspired me to keep searching out the mysteries of Antimony.

FRANCIS I. REGARDIE
P.O. Box 844
Sedona, Arizona 86336

15 Oct. 82

Dear Bob,

Thank you for your letter of a few days ago, and for the bottle of the tincture. It was very generous and gracious of you to send it, at the suggestion of our mutual friend Hans. I was deeply touched by the sentiments in your letter; thank you.

When you state 6 drops in water, I presume that is once per day? That is the procedure I am following. If it should be taken more than once, do let me know; I'd be most grateful. In time, I will let you know of its effects on me, and then we can discuss another supply of it for which I would like to reimburse you. One of my personal idiosyncracies is that I don't like to accept anything for nothing. So do humor an old man.

If your friend's pussycat responds to this incture, so should I -- for I am a cat man.

Thanks for your kind comments about my writing.

All the very best to you, and my deepest thanks,

Sincerely

Regardie

Part Six: Post Paralab through the 90s

The period after closure of the College and Paralab was very unsettled. People slowly drifted apart. Sometime in1985 I was called back to Paralab. Paralab had subcontracts with several companies for the preparation of their product. The CEO of one of those companies asked if I would act as a consultant and teach some of their employees how to operate equipment and prepare their products. I jumped at the opportunity to revisit Paralab and agreed. It was like a ghost town, everything pretty much the way it was but strangely empty. I had heard that many materials and documents from Paralab had been rashly disposed of. There had been several attempts to sell the place but they all fell through. The cosmetics company that had now hired me, leased the property and equipment for an undetermined amount of time. We spent about two months training until all felt comfortable, during which time I noticed many of my samples sitting on the shelf where I had left them. Since I was the only one who knew what they were and had the only complete set of notes on them, they were certain to be relinquished to the garbage. So, as I took my leave from the cosmetics company, I took the samples along with me; this, in part, is the tale of what became of them.

I changed residence a number of times, taking chemist jobs with companies involved in materials testing. This exposed me to a variety of instruments for testing and collection of new data on samples.

During this time and through the efforts of two classmates (mentioned above), Hans Nintzel and Bill Van Doren, the French alchemical group, "The Philosophers of Nature," (PON) established an American Chapter. The PON material closely mirrored the class material of the PRS but with quite a bit of new material based on the research findings of groups within the PON

Above: Infrared spectroscopy and gas chromatography provided many new insights on the nature of Antimony oils and process intermediates during the early 90s.

working on specific problems. The PON Mineral Alchemy lessons contain a wealth of information on antimony works and are highly recommended.

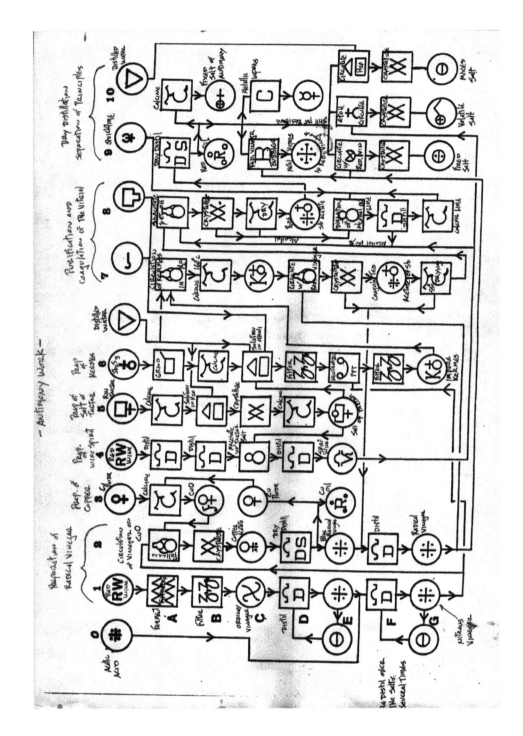

Flow chart of Antimony Works developed by the PON

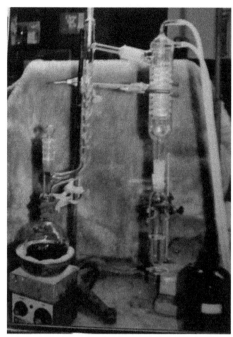 

Fractionating oils by distillation for analysis of their components

Anecdotes on Uses

Always curious as to the effectiveness of the Antimony Tinctures I tried them myself on numerous occasions. Two stand out in memory during this time. It was flu season, and it was rapidly spreading around at work one year. I felt it coming on one evening and took a large dose of Fixed Tincture (10 or 15 drops) and went to bed. I woke up at about 3:00 a.m. drenched in sweat, and the bed sheet soaked with sweat, and yet it felt really good. After a quick rinse in the shower, I felt absolutely "glowing" without a trace of flu. The Fixed Tincture of Antimony really does purge toxins through perspiration, as Basil Valentine indicates.

On another occasion I had broken a tooth, and it had become infected. During the day when I was up and about, it didn't cause much pain, but as soon as I would lie down, there was a relentless pounding of pain in my jaw which made sleep impossible. After a

sleepless night and uncomfortable day I decided to try the Fixed Antimony. My tooth was pounding with pain as I let a single drop land on it. To my astonishment and pleasure, the pain immediately stopped and was replaced by a penetrating warmth that filled my jaw, that subtle fire hidden in Antimony. The pain never came back and it was nearly a month before the dentist removed it. Some twenty years later, a neighbor called late one night. Her son had broken a tooth and was in great pain. They tried various pain relievers to no avail. The boy had been unable to sleep for a couple of days and was becoming delirious; the mother was frantic and asked if there was something we could try. I told her to bring him down, and within 10 minutes they were at our door. Once again a single drop of Fixed tincture on the tooth, and the pain evaporated. They went home, and he immediately fell asleep.

"The Lab," hidden away in a large trailer, soon became a classroom

I began teaching classes on alchemy in 2003 at a local wellness center and later out of our home with a small lab set up in a trailer in the yard.

As the classes gained popularity, we were invited to give presentations at numerous locations in the US and Europe which in turn allowed the expansion of classes and curriculum into a formal school, The Spagyricus Institute, with classes running each year.

Above: corner of the lab at Spagyricus Institute where students receive hands-on training in some difficult alchemical operations including the works on antimony (below). Facing page: Setting up a furnace in Germany to demonstrate preparation of glass and regulus of antimony.

Part Seven: Into the 21ˢᵗ Century

Anecdotes on Uses

By this time, I had great confidence in the healing properties of the antimony tinctures. As people heard the stories in class about successful uses of the tinctures, more and more wanted to try it for themselves and so we began making it available for research purposes. Over time the responses have piled up, and they have always been positive.

A student wrote that his dog had suffered a stroke and half of his face was paralyzed. The vet told him it was likely a permanent effect. He started giving the dog some of the Fixed Tincture of Antimony he obtained while in class, and within two weeks he saw 70 to 80% recovery with continuing improvement each day.

Another told me he suffered from genital herpes quite frequently and started taking the Fixed Tincture internally and applying it directly to the lesions. The problem cleared up almost immediately, though he kept taking the tincture for a month. He told me later that he has never had a flare-up since, and it has been over ten years now.

My wife's pet rabbit contracted Pasturella, a respiratory infection which is not treatable and usually a death sentence for a rabbit. She treated him with Fixed Tincture in his drinking water, and soon his breathing was clear. The vet retested the rabbit and he showed no signs of Pastorella. My wife excitedly posted the news to her fellow rabbit enthusiasts online and the moderator cut her off the site for making impossible claims. The rabbit is still with us and one of the happiest and healthiest we have. My wife had already become a true believer in the power of antimony when some years earlier one of the horses had an infected insect bite. The vet had been treating the horse for several weeks with antibiotics to no avail; the side of the horses face was very swollen with a festering sore in the midst. She asked if I had some-thing to try and so I gave her Fixed Tincture which she applied to the sore directly. Within hours the swelling had noticeably reduced and by morning it was completely normal. The sore had scabbed over and was well on its way to healing.

Dr. Theodor Kerkring, who, in his 1678 translation and commentary to Basil Valentine's, *Triumphal Chariot of Antimony*, describes the medicinal activity of these preparations and cautions us to perform a general purge and cleansing of the body prior to using the alchemical remedy in order to elicit its maximum effect; he writes:

These Medicaments, which perform their operations, not by sensible forces, as cathartics, emetics, diaphoretics, and the like are wont to operate, but insensibly uniting their own more pure Universal Spirit unto our Spirits, amend Nature and restore health, are not to be used, unless where the Body hath first been cleansed from the impurities of pecant humors, otherwise you cast pearls into a dunghill, where (overwhelmed with filths) they cannot shine and manifest their virtues.

During a class in early 2010, one of the students mentioned that he was attending a workshop on antimony that summer. When I inquired for details, I found it was being hosted by my old friend Karl Lee, PRS classmate and source of several large batches of antimony glass at Paralab. We had lost contact for the past 30 years and so I invited myself to join in.

Our group spent three days preparing sufficient kermes, glass, and regulus for all to take a portion of each to work with later in their own laboratories. The flowchart on the next page indicates the work done at Karl's and after.

K. Lee

Antimony Workshop

Location: Southern Oregon (near Coos Bay) Presenter: Sir Charles, worked with Frater Albertus from 1972 - 1984   Date: August 6th-9th 2010
Accommodations: Hotels in Bandon, and Port Orford, or using tents at nearby campground.
Supplies for work: (can be brought be participants or provided by us)
Iron pipe (mortar and pestle to crush antimony ore, 3 or 4 pound charge per crucible) Could also be pre-ground, with small samples being used for demonstration)
Acetic Acid (white distilled vinegar)
Argol (potassium tartrate) crude tartar
Sodium Hydroxide
Antimony Trisulfide (50 lbs) (will be provided)
Borosilicate Beakers 1000 ml
Melting furnace (will be provided)
Respirators
Asbestos gloves
Iron (nails not galvanized, or iron bailing wire)
Safety glasses

Necessities:
Port a Potty
Canopy (in case it rains)
Video Camera
Extra batteries, extra film for Camera
 Camera to record process and not participants

Misc:
Reach out to the Newton Project
Footage to be donated to Newton Project or an interested academy\university

Objective:
To Bond group together first before commencing in the work.
To provide a workshop and networking opportunity for practicing alchemists
To provide hands on workshop. This can be a huge opportunity for folks that don't have an appropriate setup for this process.
To work with Antimony, create the Kermes, make glass with the kermes (which can be used to make the star Regulus - time permitting)

Prerequisites:
Work within the Vegetable Realm. Knowledge of the classics including but not limited to the works of Basil Valentine, Mariănus, Eirenaeus Philalethes, Christofle Glaser, Michael Sendivogius and\or Isaac Newton.

    With the notes and photographs I had already collected and now with fresh material on hand to work with, I decided to combine previous works I had performed with those documenting the current raw materials and their processing, into a compendium of works on antimony.

Karl Lee Workshop 2010 Group Photo

Stibnite → ground to powder in Ball Mill by Paul Bretschler

Glass

Sb_2S_3

calcination

MIX
Various Proportions

Sb_2O_3 (commercial)
Borax
Raw Stibnite

Glass MIX

Fusion/
Maturation

et Knali's

[Pour Glass]

CRUSH Glass & Place
IN Ball mill w/MEDIA
AND Water

GRIND 12Hrs

Pour out Slurry
To Dry

ADD Fresh Water To
Remaining glass In Jar

[DRY Washed Glass of $\circ$]

200g For
Extraction with
Acetic Acid

Kermes

Sb_2S_3 Slurry/V

ADD NaOH

Color Changes
& clears

Let settle

Decant &
Save Liquid

ADD Vinegar
To Liquid

Red Brown
Kermes ppt

Decant

Liquo

[Solid Slurry]   At Knali's

Wash w/water
settle & Decant

Liquid

evaporated

NaOAc
Crystals

Solid Slurry

Pour out on Kraft
Paper To Dry

Washed & Dried

[Kermes]

Regulus

Sb_2S_3
Iron Nails
K_2CO_3
KNO_3

Blood

ADD To Hot crucible
spoon By spoon

Fusions

Pour into Iron cone

et Knali's

[Regulus]   Scoria

Photo of some of the treasures produced at Karl's workshop.

The compendium documents the preparation of raw materials beginning with stibnite liquation for high-grade ores and Kermes for lower-grade ores. Presented next are details concerning the preparation of Glass of Antimony and the metallic Regulus of Antimony. Once these working materials are prepared, the spagyric operations to separate the Alchemical Sulfur, Salt, and Mercury from Antimony are explored from different approaches. Finally, some of the traditional methods of Alchemical works on antimony are detailed such as the "Wet" and "Dry" ways, along with some "Particulars" of antimony and some works finding contemporary interest.

Our first concern is to obtain a supply of pure antimony, generally as the sulfide ore, Stibnite. It rarely occurs totally pure in nature so requires some cleaning and concentrating. The two main methods are the liquation process and the Kermes process.

Part Eight: A Compendium of Works

Liquation Process

This is a method for purifying and concentrating stibnite ores which contain 50% or more antimony sulfide by taking advantage of its relatively low melting point of 550 ºC. Lower grade ores are purified by different processes, one of which we will look at next.

The crushed ore is placed into special crucibles that have an opening at the bottom connected to a tube that runs out of the furnace, or to a cooler region at the bottom of the furnace. The furnace is heated using gas, coal, or even wood. As the crucible of ore heats up, the stibnite melts and flows out of the tube at the bottom into a catch vessel. Sometimes the catch vessel is filled with water so that as the molten stibnite hits the water, it cools and is shattered into finer particles. This makes grinding it later much easier. The residue of the ore remaining in the crucible consists mainly of the matrix rock, such as silica, which contained the stibnite, along with some of the stibnite that didn't melt out. It is saved for processing as a low grade ore.

The material that did melt out is often well over 95% pure antimony trisulfide and suitable for use in alchemical works; it forms especially nice glass and regulus.

We can use simple materials to perform this type of concentration easily.

For the crucible, an unglazed earthenware flowerpot with a hole at the bottom works well. You can find these at any garden supply in a range of sizes to fit your needs. The secret is to slowly bake the flower pot in an oven raising the temperature to maximum for about an hour prior to use. This will drive out any moisture from the pot and prevent it from breaking when loaded into the furnace pit.

Use firebricks to construct a simple fire pit with a supporting metal can, having both ends cut out, placed in the center. Three or four nails poked in through the side of the

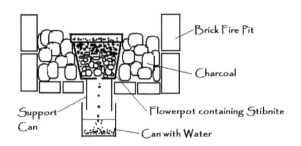

Liquation of Stibnite

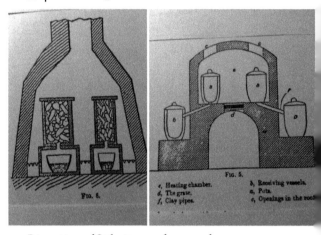

Liquation of Stibnite on a large scale

can will hold it in place an inch or two from the furnace bottom. Below this can is placed a second larger can, such as a coffee can partly filled with water, to act as a catch vessel.

Fill the flowerpot with crushed stibnite, placing larger fragments at the bottom and finer portions at the top. You can cover the pot with a piece of steel screen to keep ashes out and also keep heat in. Heating is provided with charcoal packed all around the flowerpot as shown in the diagram above.

Collect all of the material that falls into the catch vessel as your purified stibnite, and be sure to save the residue remaining in the flowerpot, as it can be processed further by the Kermes method described below. Also, save the water from the catch vessel, as it can be used for preparing Vinegar of Antimony.

Kermes Mineral

Stibnite is easily soluble in strong alkaline solutions, forming alkali antimonates.

By taking advantage of this property it is possible to purify Stibnite, even low-grade ores, with a chemical process. The result of this purification is a red-brown powder called "Kermes Mineral," named after a dye of this color made from insects. Chemically it is known as Antimony Oxysulfide.

The preparation is easy but involves using a strong caustic solution and it produces a foul-smelling odor like rotten eggs (hydrogen sulfide), which is quite toxic to breathe, so this is best performed outside or in a fume hood.

Start by grinding the ore or the residue from the liquation process to a fine powder, and then set it aside until we need it.

Now prepare a strong alkali solution by dissolving Lye (sodium hydroxide) into rainwater. A 20 to 30% solution works well; this will get very hot as the lye dissolves, so add it slowly to avoid boiling; also wear eye and hand protection. You can find lye in most hardware stores or even supermarkets; it is used to unclog plumbing. Be sure to buy the solid lye flakes or pellets and not the liquid mixtures which contain other soaps and surfactants.

Start adding the powdered stibnite to the still hot lye solution with stirring by a non-metal rod. The amount of ore added depends on its quality, but it is better to add it in excess to the weight of lye used; we can do this alkaline leaching several times to pull out all of the antimony. The solution can even be heated to near boiling to hasten the dissolution of the stibnite.

After an hour of digestion, let the solution settle a bit, then decant the clear solution or filter it through a wad of glass wool. This solution is very caustic and will eat right through paper filters; you can find glass wool at aquarium suppliers. You will see the undissolved rock and sand as a residue stripped of its antimony.

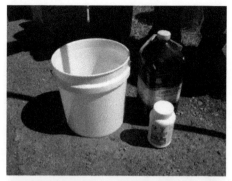

Robert Allen Bartlett

The resulting solution will be of a deep golden yellow color (above left and right). Slowly pour into a 10 to 30% solution of acetic acid until the solution pH is 7 or neutral. Distilled white vinegar which has been concentrated by freezing and thawing once or twice works well.

Be cautious at this point a lot of hydrogen sulfide is released. Remember, this is toxic, so definitely be outside and upwind, if not using a fume hood.

As the acetic acid is added, you will begin to see a red-brown solid form and fall to the bottom; this is the Kermes Mineral (below left and right).

Allow the solids to settle, and then decant the clear liquid from the top and save it aside. This liquid contains mostly sodium acetate which can be recovered for use in the acetate work. Its previous association with antimony makes it even more valuable.

Sodium Acetate recovered from the Kermes neutralization filtrate.

The still-moist Kermes is washed several times with rainwater by covering it with 10 to 20 times its volume of water and letting it settle, then decant and repeat.

Place the wet solid into a dish to dry, or you can line a shallow cardboard box with craft paper and pour the kermes slurry into it. The paper will wick out the liquid and the kermes will dry into a cake. If the dried powder has a white crystalline crust, it means the sodium acetate was not washed out completely, and you will have to repeat the water washing again to remove it.

The resulting red-brown powder, the Kermes, is now cleansed of many impurities that are associated with antimony ores, including lead, mercury, and the alumina and silica matrix. Chemically the powder represents a complex mixture of antimony trisulfide and antimony trioxide.

Other alkalis will also work to dissolve the stibnite, such as potassium hydroxide, salt of tartar, even liquid ammonia. By altering the concentrations and the order of mixing the acid and alkali solutions, the powder can be made to take on shades of canary yellow to brilliant orange to crimson red, as the particle size varies.

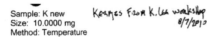

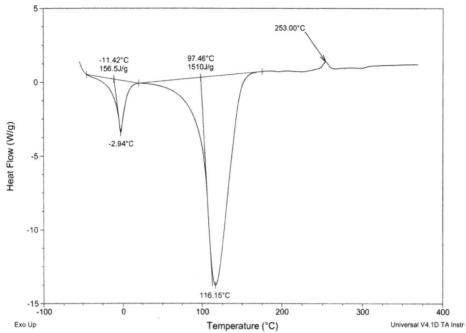

Sample: K new   *Kermes from K. Lee workshop*   **DSC**   File: D:\TA\Data\DSC\RAB\DSC\K new.001
Size: 10.0000 mg   *8/7/2010*   Operator: RAB
Method: Temperature   Run Date: 16-Aug-2010 09:54
Instrument: 2920 MDSC V2.6A

Above: DSC of Kermes from Karl Lee workshop

Below: DSC of powdered Antimony Glass from Karl Lee workshop for comparison

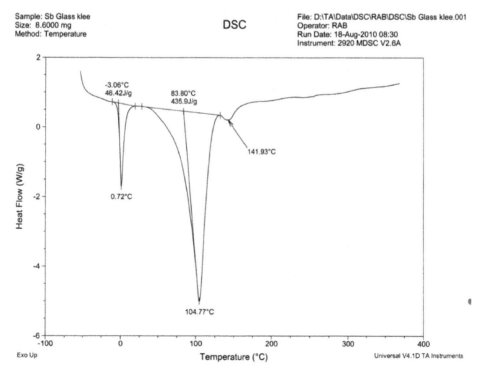

Sample: Sb Glass klee   **DSC**   File: D:\TA\Data\DSC\RAB\DSC\Sb Glass klee.001
Size: 8.6000 mg   Operator: RAB
Method: Temperature   Run Date: 18-Aug-2010 08:30
Instrument: 2920 MDSC V2.6A

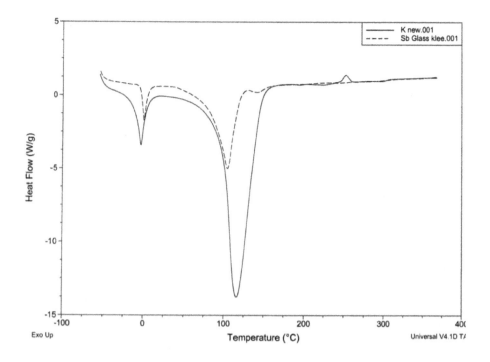

Above: DSC overlay of Kermes and Antimony Glass

Below: Differential Thermogravimetric Analysis of Kermes; The lower curve shows how quickly the upper curve is changing; allowing a more precise selection of events.

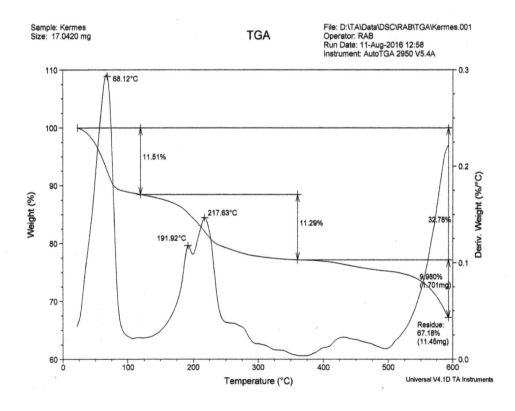

Purifying Kermes by *Solve et Coagula*

Once prepared, the Kermes can be additionally purified by redissolving in strong alkali and precipitating it again, or even multiple times.

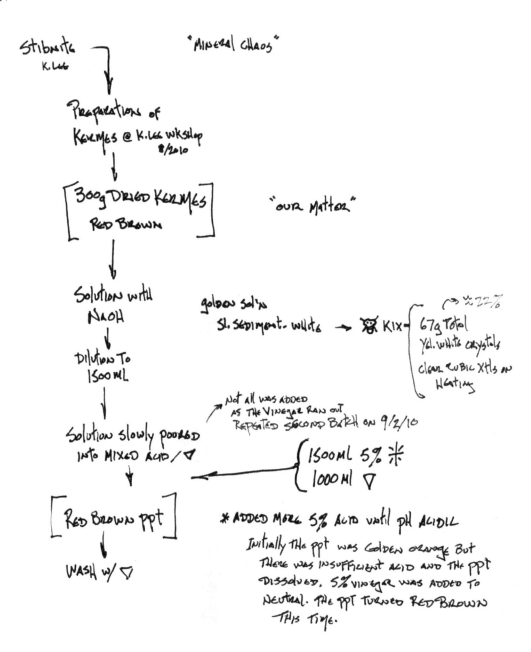

KIx   8/21/10

— Kermes —
Solve et Coagula

Stibnite
K.Lee   "Mineral Chaos"

Preparation of
Kermes @ K.Lee wkshop
8/2010

[300g Dried Kermes]   "our Matter"
Red Brown

Solution with   golden sol'n
NaOH   Sl. Sediment. white → ☒ KIx ⌐ 67g Total   ~22%
                                                      | Yel. white crystals
Dilution To | clear cubic Xtls on
1500 ML   ⌐ Heating

                          → Not all was added
                            as the Vinegar ran out
                            Repeated Second Batch on 9/2/10
Solution slowly poured
into Mixed Acid / ▽   ←   ⌐ 1500ML 5% ✳
                              ⌐ 1000 ml ▽

[Red Brown ppt]   ✳ Added more 5% Acid until pH Acidic

                         Initially the ppt was Golden orange But
WASH w/ ▽   There was insufficient Acid and the ppt
                         Dissolved. 5% vinegar was added to
                         Neutral. The ppt turned Red Brown
                         This Time.

Best Precipitate:

The Brightest colors come From Dilute ☉ and 🜍 solutions

☉ at least 1:5 From Concentrate

🜍 2½% or less

🜍 Pour the ☉ into the Rapidly stirred 🜍

1:50 ☉ into 1% 🜍 → excellent orange ppt

🜍 All the ppts Regardless of Dilutions used,
seem to dry to a Red-Brown Powder

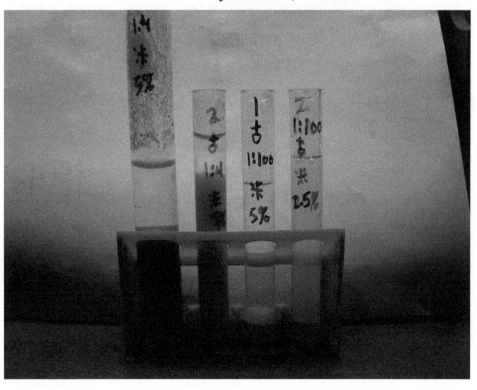

Kermes is also much easier to calcine to a light oxide powder because of its greater purity.

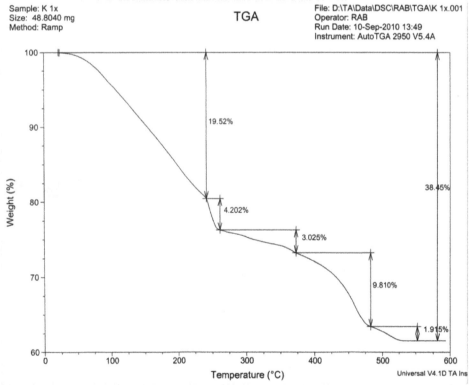

TGA of Kermes redissolved and precipitated a second time. Useful data for distillation or calcination of the Kermes.

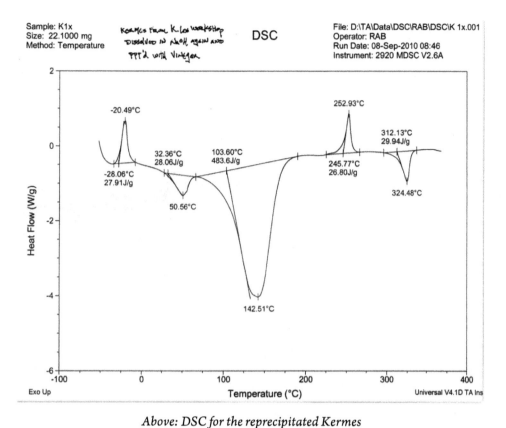

Above: DSC for the reprecipitated Kermes

Below: Overlay of DSC and TGA for reprecipitated Kermes

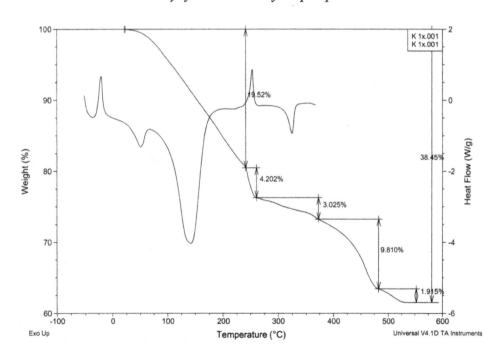

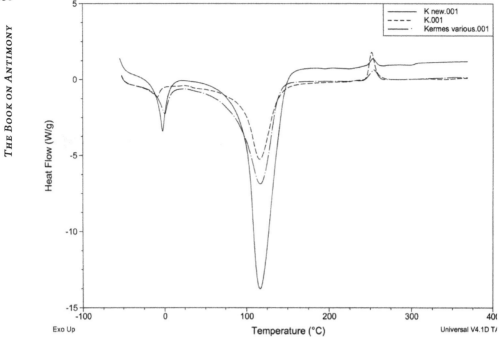

DSC comparison of three different batches of Kermes

Kermes is also a useful starting point for making the metallic Regulus of Antimony:

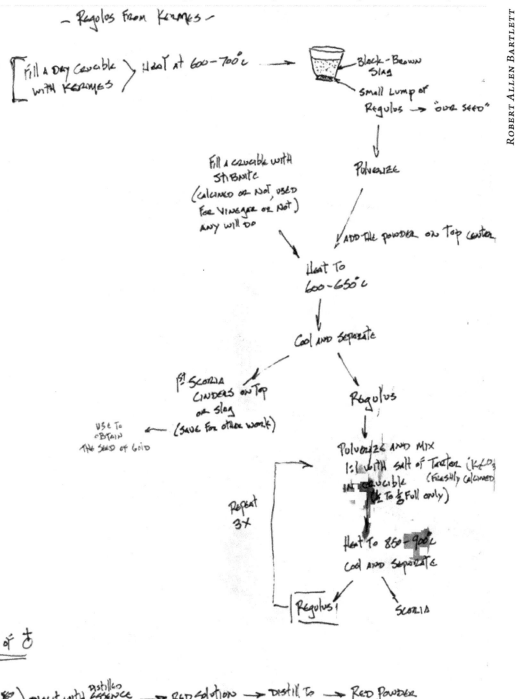

— Regulos from Kermes —

Fill a Dry Crucible with Kermes ⟩ Heat at 600–700°C ⟶ Black–Brown Slag

Small Lump of Regulus ⟶ "our seed"

Pulverize

Fill a crucible with Stibnite (calcined or Not, used for vinegar or Not) any will do

Add the powder on Top center

Heat To 600–650°C

Cool and Separate

1st Scoria Cinders on Top or Slag (save for other work)

Use To obtain the Seed of Gold

Regulus

Pulverize and Mix 1:1 with Salt of Tartar (K₂CO₃) in crucible (Freshly calcined ¼ To ⅓ Full only)

Heat To 850–900°C Cool and Separate

Repeat 3x

Regulus!   Scoria

Balm of ♁

Pulverized Regulus ⟩ Digest with Distilled essence of Turpentine ⟶ Red Solution ⟶ Distill To Dry ⟶ Red Powder

Healing Powers of ♃ | The Balm of Antimony | ⟸ Dissolve in EtOH

ROBERT ALLEN BARTLETT

Above and left: Casting the Regulus and separating the Scoria.
Below: Scoria set to deliquesce

This method was adapted from Indian alchemical works, also known as Rasa Shastra.

ROBERT ALLEN BARTLETT

— Calcination of Kermes By Puta Pakva —

Bisque Fired @ 600°C

Musha Mix plus crucibles ———————— Sealed with clay smeared cloth

Cakes of Kermes ———————

filled

Placed into gaja Puta with ~~Dried Horse Dung~~ For Fuel

ignited 5/22/11

on cooling the crucibles were opened on 5/23/11

The Kermes cakes Had Turned into Transparent glossy crystals
with a gray powdery solid ~~from~~ Towards the Bottom

crystals are shiny clear plates with Hexagonal shape and
Needle shapes Radiating out   of the Gray solids

sampled For analysis By DSC & FTIR

5/25/11 Placed The calcined mass into a Vial and covered with Rain water

A large portion of the crystals seem To Dissolve, solution is clear/pH 5

Decanted clear solution into a Dish & evaporated to crystals

[sampled For analysis as water soluble Salts of Kermes Calcination]

In traditional Indian alchemy, temperatures are controlled by firing materials in pits with specific dimensions and fuels. In this way maximum temperature and duration could be standardized. The table below indicated the various pit sizes and its associated temperature profile. The most common size is the Gaja Puta which is a 22-inch cube and the size used in this experiment.

Table-I Classification of Puṭa Furnaces Using Dried Cowdung Cakes As Fuel

S.N.	Type of Furnace	Size In mm	Number of Cowdung Cakes	Approx. Weight kg
1.	Mahāpuṭa	11250x11250x11250	2000	45
2.	Gajapuṭa	5625x5625x5625	1000	22
3.	Varāhapuṭa	—	800	18
4.	Ardhagajapuṭa	2812x2812x2812	500	11
5.	Kukuṭpuṭa	—	32-40	4
6.	Kapotpuṭa	—	8	1

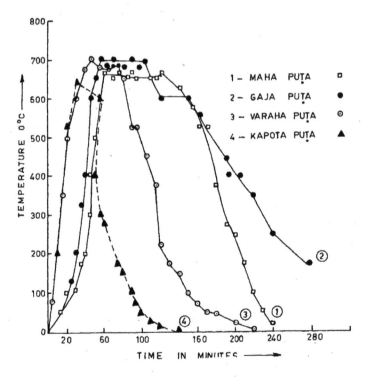

Fig. 18 Time-temperature curves for the heating rate in various puṭa furnaces fired on cowdung cakes

Kermes Calx

↓

Extract w/ RAIN ▽
& Crystallize

[analysed as
  K Calx ▽ Sol]

|

2 crystal Types

↙   ↘

Spiney Like   Plates/Blocks
Sea Urchins   Hexagonal

※✳   ◇○

Not Active   Active

      ↖ Polarized
         Light

↓   ↓

Recrystallized   [For analysis]
                 = Plates"

↓

[For analysis]
"Spines"

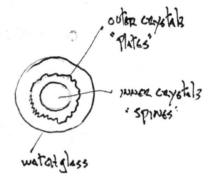

outer crystals
"Plates"

inner crystals
"Spines"

watchglass

* use Differential crystallization
To separate the 2 Types

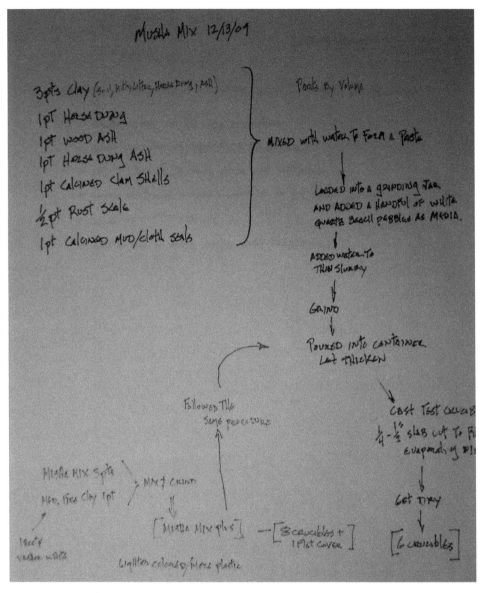

Musha Mix 12/13/09

3 pts Clay (Soil, Kaolin Litter, Horse Dung, Ash)
1 pt Horse Dung
1 pt Wood Ash
1 pt Horse Dung Ash
1 pt Calcined Clam Shells
½ pt Rust Scale
1 pt Calcined Mud/cloth scale

Parts By Volume

Mixed with water to form a paste.

Loaded into a grinding jar and added a handful of white quartz beach pebbles as media.

Added water to thin slurry

Grind

Poured into container Let thicken

Cast test crucible
¼ - 1½" slab cut to fit
evaporating dish

Get dry

[6 crucibles]

Followed the same procedure

Musha Mix 5 pts
Mud, fire clay 1 pt

Mix & grind

[Musha Mix plus]

[3 crucibles + 1 flat cover]

very stable white

Lighter colored, more plastic

In this type of working, it is convenient to make your own crucibles since you can use many in a short time when processing materials. Above is one of the recipes for homemade crucibles I have used successfully many times to make crucibles like those pictured below.

The crucibles are sealed by wrapping them with strips of cotton cloth dipped in a thick slurry of clay to form an "egg," which is then dried before loading into the pit for firing. After firing the seals are carefully broken to open on the crucibles and the contents removed. The calcined solids were extracted with water and on crystallization revealed the presence of two crystalline solids; one was plate-like and the other like sharp spines.

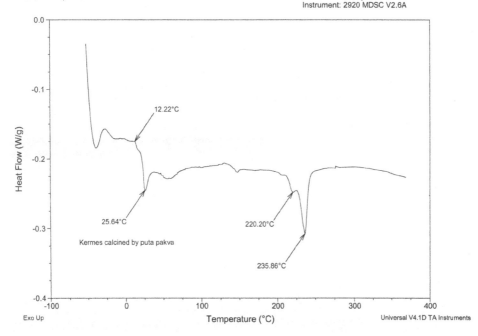

Sample: K Calx
Size: 9.8000 mg
Method: Temperature

DSC

File: D:\TA\Data\DSC\RAB\DSC\K Calx.001
Operator: RAB
Run Date: 24-May-2011 08:17
Instrument: 2920 MDSC V2.6A

12.22°C

25.64°C

220.20°C

235.86°C

Kermes calcined by puta pakva

Heat Flow (W/g)

Temperature (°C)

Exo Up

Universal V4.1D TA Instruments

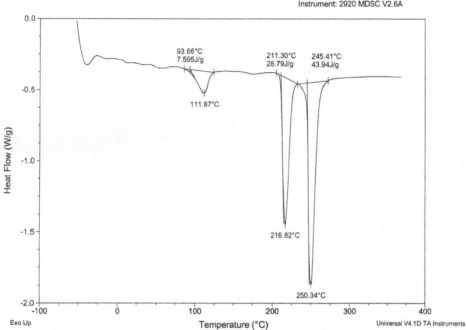

Sample: K calx plates
Size: 24.0000 mg
Method: Temperature

DSC

File: D:\TA\Data\DSC\RAB\DSC\K calx plates.001
Operator: RAB
Run Date: 31-May-2011 09:48
Instrument: 2920 MDSC V2.6A

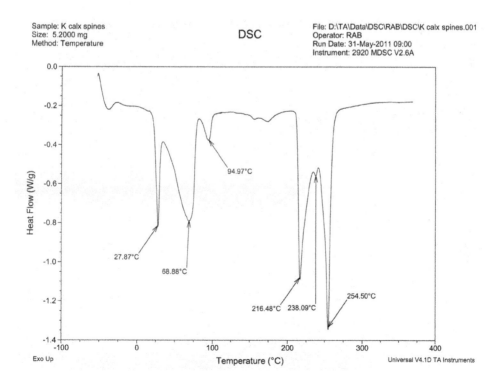

Sample: K calx spines
Size: 5.2000 mg
Method: Temperature

DSC

File: D:\TA\Data\DSC\RAB\DSC\K calx spines.001
Operator: RAB
Run Date: 31-May-2011 09:00
Instrument: 2920 MDSC V2.6A

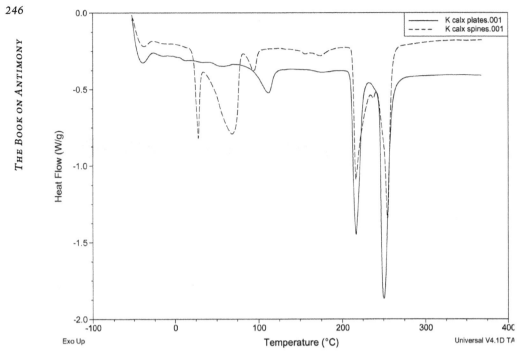

Exo Up

Universal V4.1D TA

DSC comparison of the two crystal types

Incorporating Iron with antimony

There was some interest in trying to incorporate iron into the antimony. The idea was that antimony has crude mineral Sulfur and lacks a true metallic Sulfur, whereas iron has a abundance of metallic Sulfur which it can donate to the antimony as in preparation of the Martial Regulus.

ROBERT ALLEN BARTLETT

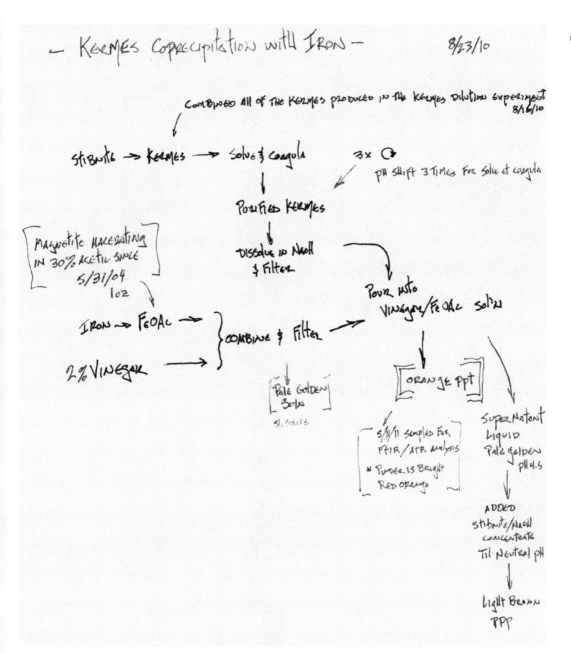

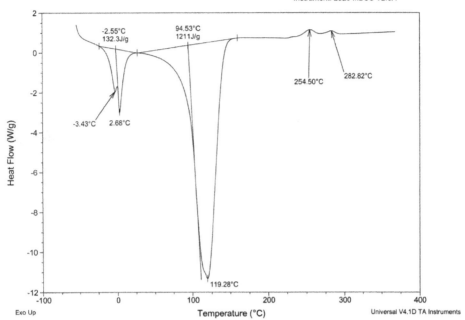

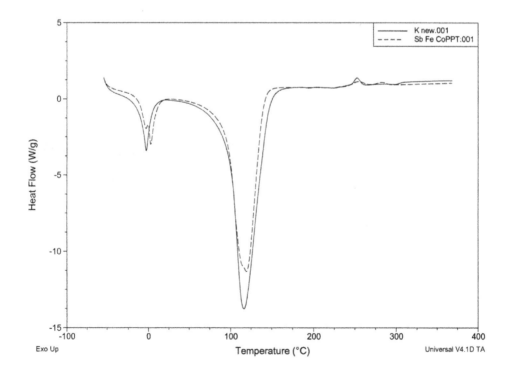

Above: DSC scan of the Kermes coprecipitated with iron

Below: DSC overlay of Kermes and Kermes/Iron coprecipitate

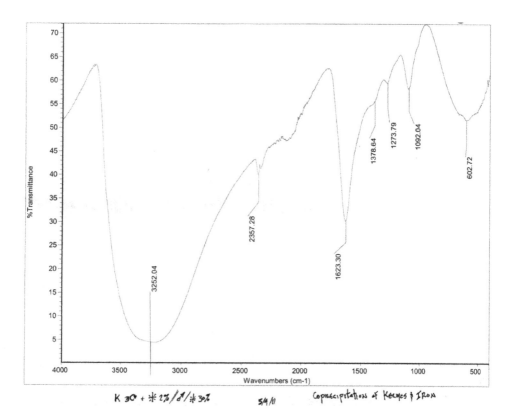

K 30 + ✳ 2% / 8 / ✳ 30%   5/4/11   Coprecipitation of Kermes & Iron

FTIR scan of the Kermes/Iron coprecipitate

ANTIMONY VERMILION.

ANTIMONY VERMILION is a red pigment which will bear comparison in fineness of shade with mercury vermilion, over which it has the advantage of cheapness. In composition it is antimony trisulphide, Sb_2S_3. This compound is obtained by precipitating a solution of antimony trichloride with sulphuretted hydrogen. However, the precipitate, which is a very fine red whilst wet, loses its colour in drying, and the product is almost worthless as a pigment.

In another way it can be obtained in such a condition that it loses nothing of its beauty in drying, but retains its brilliance. Böttger gives the following process: a solution of antimony trichloride is mixed with a solution of sodium hyposulphite (thiosulphate) and the liquid heated so long as a precipitate forms, which is then washed on a filter with water containing acetic acid. If pure water were used for washing, the antimony chloride still present would be decomposed, forming the white oxychloride, which would detract from the shade of the antimony vermilion. In this process particular regard is to be paid to the use of exact quantities of materials. The finest product is obtained when 2 parts of a solution of antimony trichloride, which has exactly the specific gravity 1·35, are mixed with a solution of 3 parts of sodium hyposulphite in 6 parts of water.

According to R. Wagner, antimony vermilion is obtained by dissolving 4 parts of tartar emetic and 3 parts of tartaric acid in 18 parts of water, heating to 60° C., mixing with a solution of sodium hyposulphite (thiosulphate) and heating to 90° C. The precipitate is then carefully washed and dried.

Pure antimony vermilion closely approaches, as we have said, ordinary vermilion in shade, and for a sulphur compound shows a remarkable resistance towards chemical reagents. By dilute acids, ammonia and alkaline carbonates, it is attacked only on long-continued contact, but it is easily decomposed by very dilute hydrochloric acid and by caustic alkalis. A mixture with white lead keeps for a long time, but there can be no question of the permanence of such a mixture, in consequence of the oft-repeated properties of lead pigments. Antimony vermilion is well adapted for oil painting. When ground with oil it exhibits a red of a brilliance in no way inferior to that of genuine vermilion. It may also be used as a water colour, but is not adapted for fresco work, since it is quickly decomposed by lime.

— Antimony Vermilion —

Ref. Wang / Antimony
? 157

ROBERT ALLEN BARTLETT

Antimony Trichloride
(HCl Solutions)

Sodium Thiosulfate $Na_2S_2O_3$

Solution w/ water

* Slowly ADD and allow
Initial ppt to Dissolve

stir constantly
Keep Cool

Clear Solution

* ADD additional Na Thiosulfate To clear
if Necessary

Heat solution in
Water Bath
$50° - 70°C$

Clear solution Turns colored w/ ppt

Pale yellow

orange

[RED] ⟶ Remove From Heat at RED stage

Additional
Heating
Turns ppt

RED-BROWN

BROWN

Black

Let ppt settle

Wash w/ H_2O

[DRY RED POWDER]

DSC sample
12/20/10

This experiment is another form of Kermes formed from the Butter of Antimony and sulfur oxides whose purity we can control in various ways.

PROPERTIES: o No Taste or odor
- o insol. H_2O, Alcohol or essential oils
- o very sl. sol in weak acids
- o sol in conc HCl giving H_2S & $SbCl_3$
- o sol in strong Caustic solutions
- o Blackens at High Temp
- o unaltered By air or Light
- o "a well prepared Vermilion of antimony, ground in oil, gives possibly the purest red color."

Preparation of Sodium Hyposulfite:

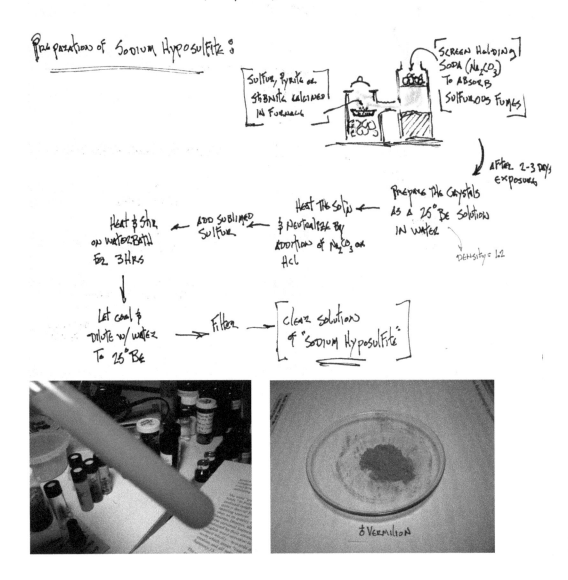

[Sulfur, Pyrite or Stibnite calcined in Furnace]

[Screen Holding Soda (Na_2CO_3) To Absorb Sulfurous Fumes]

After 2-3 days exposure

Prepare the Crystals as a 25° Bé Solution in water

Density = 1.2

Heat the Soln & Neutralize By addition of Na_2CO_3 or HCl

Add sublimed Sulfur

Heat & Stir on water Bath for 3 Hrs

Let cool & Dilute w/ water To 25° Bé → Filter [clear solution of "Sodium Hyposulfite"]

ō Vermilion

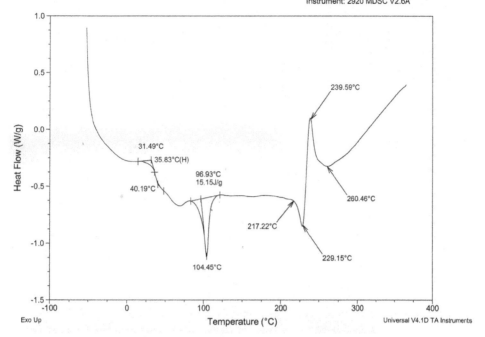

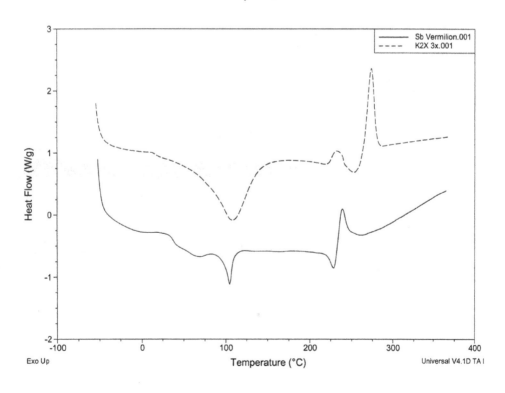

Above: DSC scan of Antimony Vermillion;

Below: DSC overlay comparing three times reprecipitated Kermes with Antimony Vermillion

Sublimation of Stibnite

This experiment relies on the sublimation of Sal Ammoniac to carry some of the Antimony with it which is later washed out, leaving the sublimated antimony.

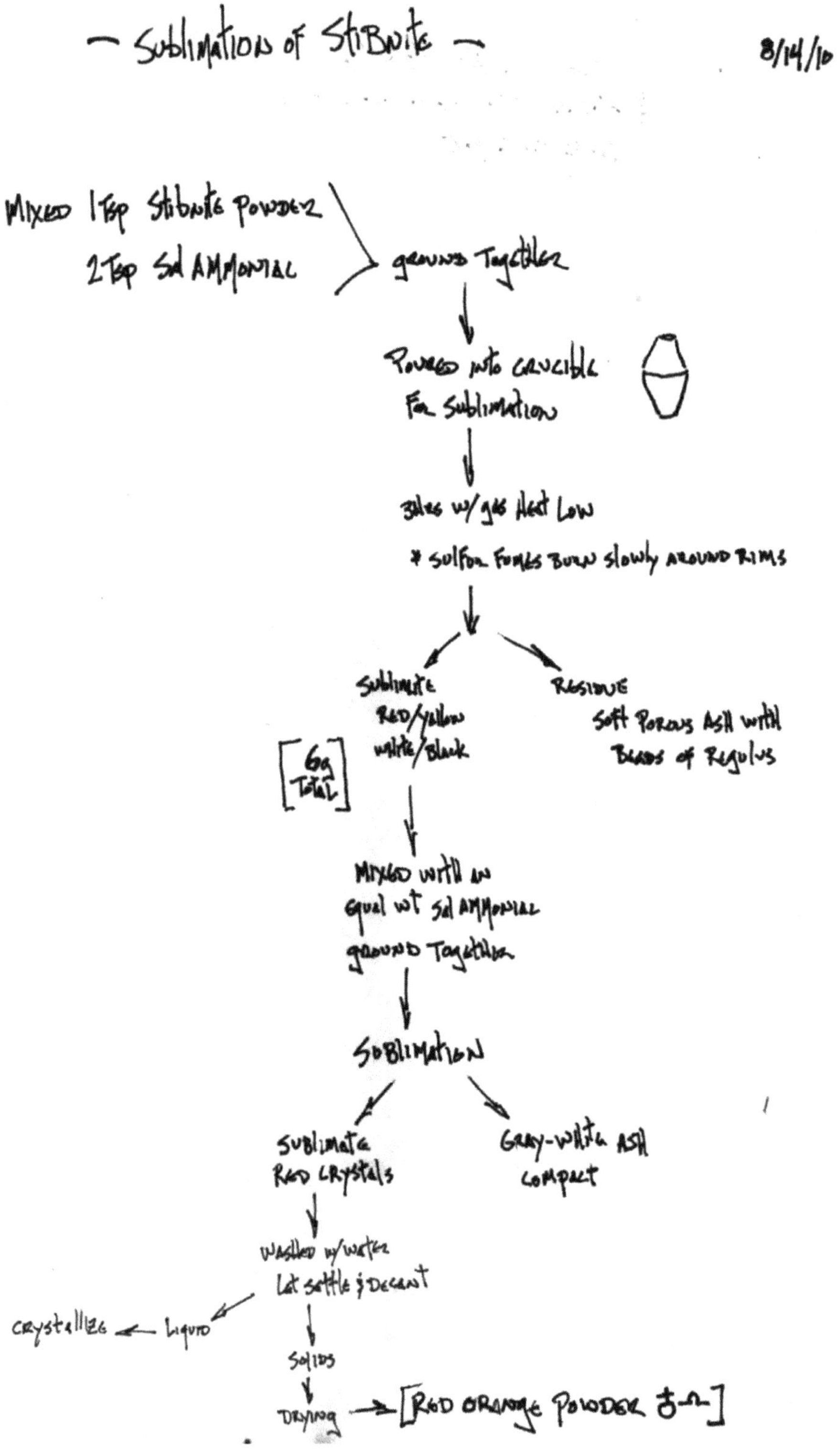

~ Sublimation of Stibnite ~   8/14/10

MIXED 1 tsp Stibnite Powder
2 tsp Sal AMMoniac   } ground Together

↓

Poured into crucible
for Sublimation   ⬡

↓

3hrs w/gas Heat Low

* Sulfor Fumes burn slowly around rims

↓

Sublimate   Residue
Red/yellow   Soft Porous Ash with
white/black   beads of Regulus

[6g
Total]

↓

Mixed with an
equal wt Sal AMMoniac
ground Together

↓

Sublimation

↓   ↓

Sublimate   Gray-white Ash
Red Crystals   compact

↓

Washed w/water
Let settle ; Decant

crystallize ← Liquid

↓

Solids

↓

Drying → [Red orange powder ♁]

Stibnite mixed with Sal Ammoniac and ready for sublimation

Sublimation on a hot plate and the resulting sublimate above

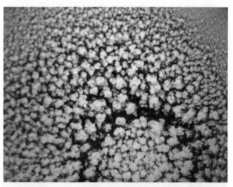

Right: Close-up of the sublimate
Below: Rinsed out with water and dried sublimate freed from sal ammoniac

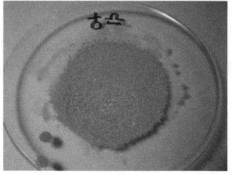

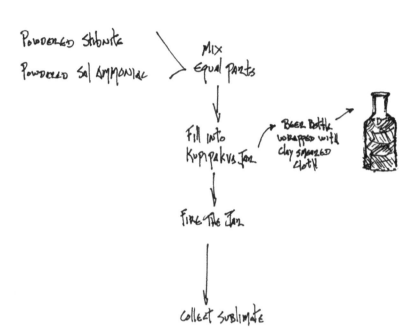

– KUPI PAKVA of STIBNITE –

9/10/10

POWDERED Stibnite
POWDERED Sal AMMONIAC
} MIX
EQUAL PARTS

Fill into
KUPIPAKVA Jar

→ BEER BOTTLE
WRAPPED with
CLAY SMEARED
CLOTH

FIRE THE Jar

Collect SUBLIMATE

Bottle Firing of Stibnite

This method, also adapted from Indian alchemical processes, provides an inexpensive way to sublimate materials in a disposable vessel. This method can be adapted to many of the mineral works, especially those which are very toxic, like mercury or arsenic. It can be set up in some remote place and left to heat up and cool down unattended for the most part. After the sublimation and collection of product, the vessel is simply disposed of.

After the sublimation, the clay smeared cloth wrapping is removed from the bottle. It comes off easily with a knife and quick wipe with a wet towel. Next, a piece of cord is wrapped around the lower section of the bottle and soaked with lighter fluid then ignited. Slowly turn the bottle to heat the area wrapped with cord. When the flame goes out, quickly grasp the heated area with a wet towel. The bottle will pop and come apart cleanly in two pieces from which the sublimate can easily be collected.

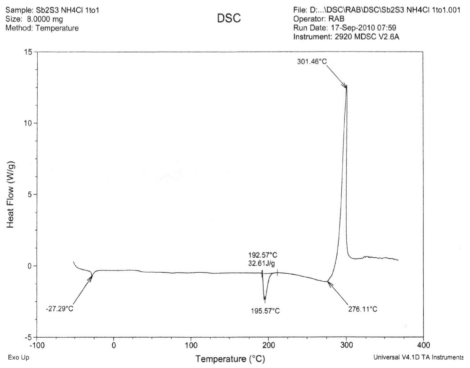

Stibnite 1pt ⎫
NH₄Cl 1pt ⎭ grind
        ↓
    SUBLIMATION
    ↙   ↘
CAPUT   SUBLIMATE
              |
        MIX 1:1 w/ ✳
        & SUBLIMATION
    ↙   ↓
CAPUT   RED-ORANGE
           SUBLIMATE

Sample: Sb2S3 NH4Cl 1to1
Size: 8.0000 mg
Method: Temperature

DSC

File: D:...\DSC\RAB\DSC\Sb2S3 NH4Cl 1to1.001
Operator: RAB
Run Date: 17-Sep-2010 07:59
Instrument: 2920 MDSC V2.6A

DSC of Stibnite and Sal Ammoniac mixture prior to sublimation.
The reaction becomes exothermic starting about 276°C

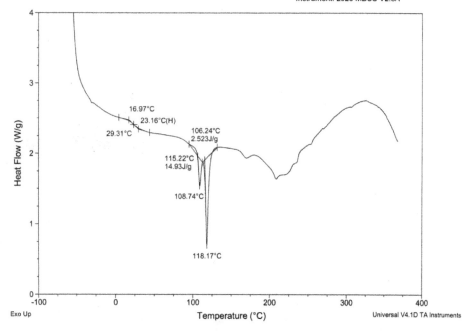

Above: DSC of the final sublimate from Stibnite; Below: TGA of sublimate from Stibnite

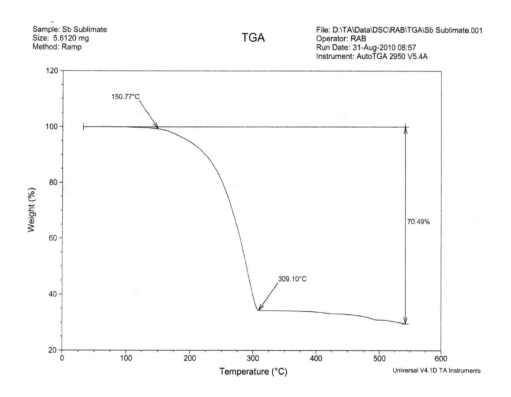

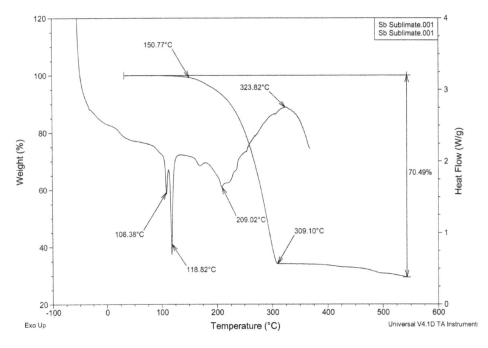

Overlay of DSC and TGA scans of the Stibnite sublimate

Glass of Antimony

One of the amazing properties of antimony is that it can be formed into glass of various colors. Ancient glass and ceramic artifacts bear witness to this knowledge far back in time.

Preparation of the glass begins with the calcination of stibnite or kermes into the oxide. This conversion to the oxide need not be too rigorous, as a small proportion of the sulfide is needed to help form the glass.

– Glass of Antimony –

Ref. Triumphal Chariot
P 62

＊ Kerckring suggests further info
from Beguinis, Crollius, &
Hartman

– Calcination of Antimony –

[stibnite]

↓

GRIND TO PWDR

↓

CALCINE GENTLY IN
THIN LAYER until
FUMING STOPS.   (IF GLOBULES FORM
                 STOP & REGRIND)

↓ (STIR CONTINUOUSLY)

GREY/WHITE POWDER
LIKE ASHES

["CALCINED ANTIMONY"] ➚

– Glass of Antimony –

[CALCINED ANTIMONY]

↓

FUSION TO
MATURITY   TEST W/
                IRON RED

↓

CAST THIN INTO A
HOT COPPER DISH

↓

[CLEAR YELLOW]
Glass
"PURE Glass OF ANTIMONY"

THIS IS THE BEST way without any ADDITIONS

"ENDOWED WITH THE GREATEST VIRTUE & POWER
WHICH MANIFESTS AFTER FURTHER PREPARATION"

OTHER GLASSES WITH ADDITION

CRUDE ♁ 1pt
                    ⟩ RUBY RED GLASS
Venetian BORAX 2pts

CRUDE ♁ 1pt
                ⟩ yellow → MATURES TO WHITE
BORAX 4pts   w/ LONGER Heat

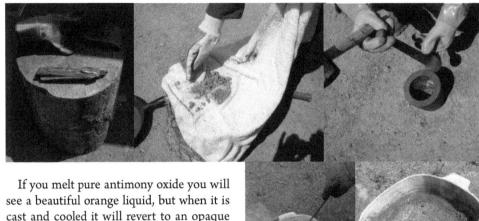

If you melt pure antimony oxide you will see a beautiful orange liquid, but when it is cast and cooled it will revert to an opaque yellowish-white crystalline mass. The presence of antimony sulfide mixed into the antimony oxide will promote the formation of transparent glasses of intense red, yellow, and orange shades.

The finely ground antimony oxide/sulfide is fused in a strong porcelain crucible at a temperature of about 700 to 1000º C, sometimes even up to 1300º C. It helps to add a small amount of the raw stibnite powder in doing this to obtain a deep ruby red glass.

Some use borax as a flux, but this often leads to problems in washing it out it later with water; in fact some claim that borax as well as aluminum lead to alchemical death of the subject and avoid their use at all costs.

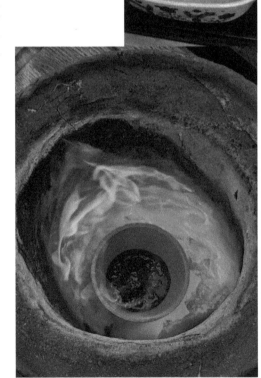

Basil Valentine mentions the use of borax to form the glass, but this is a trap for the unsuspecting beginner because he never mentions washing the borax out afterwards. He also states clearly that glass made without any additions is the best for all uses. However in some cases, the glass refuses to clarify and the use of borax as a flux will work as a last resort.

When the crucible is ¾ full, and entirely molten, stick a thin iron rod into it and pull it out. Look at the glass adhering to the rod—if it is transparent, then it is ready; if it is cloudy, continue heating until it clarifies; however, don't overdo the fusion for too long as the material will be volatilizing throughout the process.

When the melt is ready, use tongs and quickly pour the liquid out into a wide flat dish of copper or a cast iron skillet, then cover it with a lid because it often shatters and flies out of the dish on cooling.

Once cool, you will have the glass of antimony; it should be transparent and generally of a yellow to deep red tint, although by altering proportions and heating it is possible to obtain glasses of other colors, even green and blue.

The glass is held by many to be the preferred starting material for extracting the Sulfur of antimony.

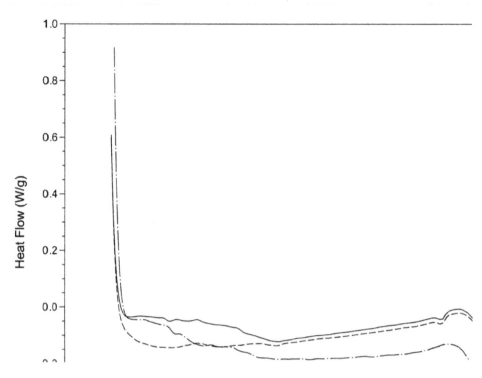

Above: DSC scan of several different Glass pours; Below: TGA of the Glass of Antimony

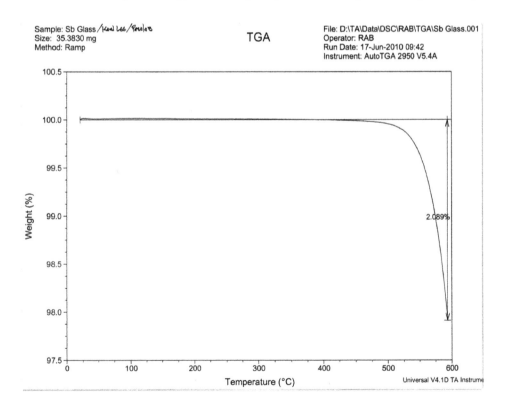

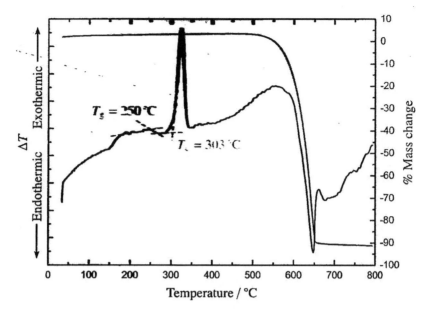

Figure 4-5 TGA/DSC data for the Sb_2O_3 glass under nitrogen, at a heating rate of $10\,°C\,min^{-1}$ in a platinum crucible. An empty alumina crucible was used as the reference. The amount of noise in the data is probably a result of the limited sample mass available for the measurement.

Glass Mixtures

Depending on staring materials, it may be necessary to perform a few trials to make consistently good glass. Below are some of the recipes that have worked out well and may serve as a guide.

C. GLASSER:
1677

STIBNITE ⟶ Gentle calcination til fuming stops.
↓
Fuse to glass

⊛ Glass 3/21/11

Sb_2O_3 300g ⎫
Sb_2S_3 100g ⎬ DARK RED/AMBER
Borax   40g ⎭ SOME opacity

TRY Sb_2O_3 300g
Sb_2S_3 75g
Borax   50g

L. PRINCIPE:

100g Sb_2O_3 ⎫
0.5g CROCUS ♂ ⎬ good AMBER-RED Glass
2g SiO_2 ⎮
4g Sb_2S_3 ⟵ ⎡ K. Lee Stibnite – some opacity but good Glass
⎣ Weatherby Stibnite – good Glass / RED

100g Sb_2O_3 ⎫
4g Colored K. Lee Kernels ⎬ good AMBER Glass
2g SiO_2 ⎭

PARACHEMY NOTE: DROP IN A PIECE OF CHARCOAL TO THE MELT IN ORDER
TO get A TRANSPARENT RED GLASS
TRIED THIS SEVERAL TIMES ON 6/3/12 – SEEMS TO REDUCE THE METAL
FROM THE GLASS

| Crude Antimony | 1 part | |
| Venetian Borax | 2 parts | Ruby Red Glass |

| Crude Antimony | 1 part | |
| Borax | 4 parts | White Glass |

—B. Valentine

| Sb2O3 | 300g | Dark red/amber |
| Sb2S3 | 20g | |

Sb2O3	100g
Crocus Martis	0.5g
Silica	2g
Sb2S3	3g

—L. Principe

In a series of trial glass pours, time duration of fusion versus clarity was explored. A commercial antimony oxide (analysis shown below) was the major component along with small additions of stibnite and silica. Portions of the same glass mixture were fused in a crucible and as soon as the surface of the melt became quiet, timing began.

UNITED STATES ANTIMONY CORPORATION
PO Box 643   1250 Prospect Creek
Thompson Falls, Montana 59873-0643
406-827-3523   FAX: 406-827-3543   E-Mail tfl3543@blackfoot.net

Date MAY 10 2012

Certificate of Analysis Lot# 5.12.MP
Customer: Robert Bartlett USAC : 12.414

Description	Method	Analysis
Antimony Oxide (Sb_2O_3)	ICP-3120, C.D.L.	99.7%
Arsenic (As)	ICP-3120, C.D.L.	0.02%
Iron (Fe)	ICP-3120, C.D.L.	ND
Lead (Pb)	ICP-3120, C.D.L.	0.05 %
Selenium (Se)	ICP-3120, C.D.L.	ND
Average Particle Size	ASTM B-330	0.95 microns
Color		White

John C. Lawrence
Chief Chemist

Notes: C.D.L.- Contract Detection Level
N.D. NO Detection

ROBERT ALLEN BARTLETT

— Antimony Glass —

6/3/2012
$\overline{b}$ Workshop

TIME VERSUS GLASS MATURITY

* Furnace Temp 900°C

* Principle Mix : 100g Sb_2O_3
  0.5g crocus martis
  2g SiO_2
  6g Sb_2S_3 (k.lee)

Fusion until surface becomes calm → start Timer

5 min   Glass is dark/opaque

10 min   Red amber glass with streaks of opacity

15 min   Good glass little opacity

$\left.\begin{array}{c}12\\ \\17\end{array}\right\}$ optimum glass maturity

20 min   Glass getting dark again / lots of opacity

30 min   Glass very dark & opaque

Notes: 1. It helps to gently swirl the crucible contents in the furnace hot zone for a minute or two prior to pouring

2. Cast <u>thin</u> and quickly. Pooling tends to promote opacity & crystals

3. Casting into cold water gives a golden sand of good glass

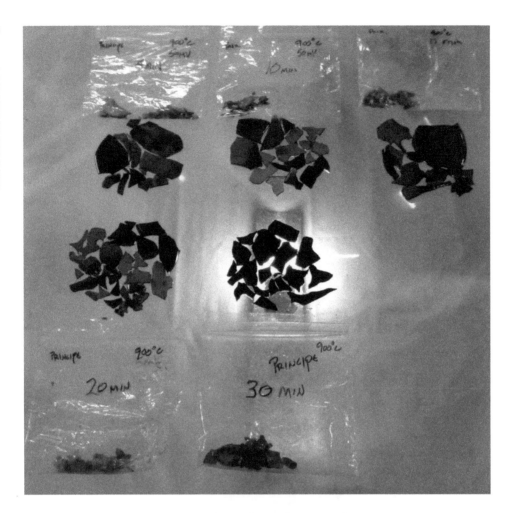

weights

	A	B	C	D	E Compton I	F
Sb_2O_3 (U.S. antimony)	100	200g	100g	100	110	100
KERMES: K. Lee						
Hermada						
Calcined						4 K. Lee
SiO_2 cryst.	2	4		2	1.5	2
Amorph.						
Crocus Martis (se pottery)	0.5	1				
Stibnite: K Lee	6					
Hermada			4g	3g	2.5	
Weatherby		7				
	original Principle Mix Red-Amber Glas	good clear Red glass	Bad - cryst/ Reguline Dark	Good Amber Glass	Very good Golden Glass	excellent golden Glas. clear

More test pours of glass altering ingredients until a good glass resulted and was reproducible.

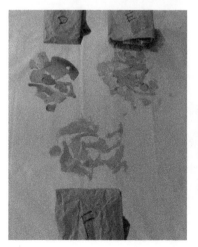

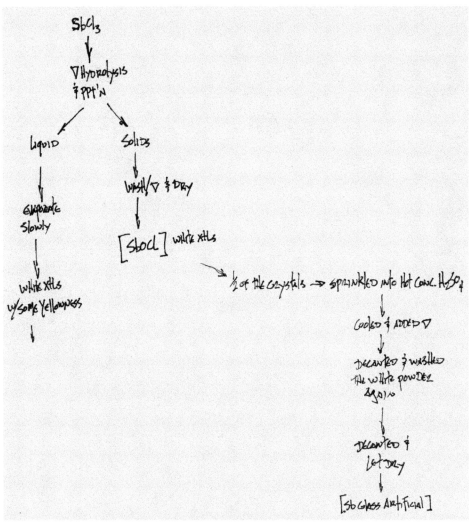

A method for producing antimony glass without a furnace

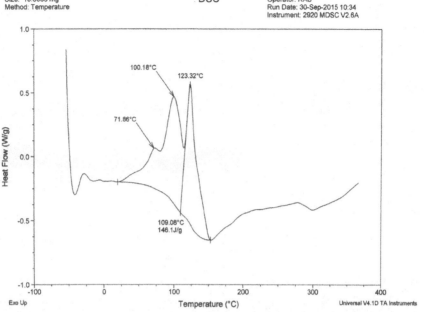

Sample: Sb glass artificial
Size: 18.6000 mg
Method: Temperature

DSC

File: D:...\RAB\DSC\Sb glass artificial.001
Operator: RAB
Run Date: 30-Sep-2015 10:34
Instrument: 2920 MDSC V2.6A

DSC of the Artificial Glass of Antimony

The Principe Formula Experiment

This next experiment began during the workshop on antimony we presented in the summer of 2012 here in the Pacific Northwest. I called it the Principe Formula because it was based on directions mentioned in one of the RAMS manuscripts (Potpourri 2) quoting an earlier *Ambix Journal* article by Dr. Lawrence Principe. Dr. Principe and his associate, William Newman, have published a number of excellent works on alchemy including some practical laboratory works that have stimulated interest in the academic world.

The ultimate aim of the process is the preparation of the "Pure Sweet Oil of Antimony."

The directions are those of Basil Valentine with some interesting suggestions by Dr. Principe regarding the formation of the glass of antimony.

The first suggestion is a small addition of silica. This is added to ensure the formation of a glass. Since silica is a glass former, it will favor the formation of a glassy phase. Most stibnite samples contain enough silica on their own that this usually is not a problem. The molten mass can also pull silica from the crucible walls, however just to be on the safe side especially when dealing with high grade stibnite samples, a small addition of ground silica sand or quartz can provide added insurance that a good glass will form.

The second additive suggested was a small amount of Crocus Martis, which is a very fine iron oxide. Most stibnite samples contain at least a small amount of iron as an impurity, so its addition is questionable, although some would argue that the Sulfur of iron is necessary for gaining access to the Sulfur of antimony, as mentioned earlier in regards to incorporating it with Kermes. Its addition poses some problems later in the final tincture since it will contain iron in solution and, although not toxic, its presence will mask the true Sulfur of antimony. Most of the iron falls out as a sediment after the Tincture ages and matures.

So, in the task at hand our first operation will be to form the Glass of Antimony which is our starting material.

These are Basil Valentine's basic directions for making the glass of antimony. He points out that glass made straight from Stibnite and without any additions is the best way.

Suggested processes for producing the glass of antimony as derived from various texts were indicated above.

Preparing good transparent glass is often a hit or miss affair. This is dependent on the starting materials and their subsequent treatment in the fire.

Here are the materials portioned out and mixed, ready for fusion.

The raw materials for the gas furnace assembled for construction and preliminary alignment of the pieces.

All of the parts were covered and assembled with 2 to 3 inch wide strips of a cotton bed sheet coated with a thick slurry of clay. Note that the torch (a weed burner from the hardware store) enters the furnace at a tangent to one side so that the flame will circle around the crucible and heat from all sides.

The charged crucible is placed directly into the hot furnace to melt. The crucible can be filled to the top with glass mixture as the volume will decrease to about a third on melting. Allow the surface of the melt to become "quiet" and not actively bubbling then allow 5 to 10 minutes before testing with an iron rod. When the glass is matured, it is quickly poured into a cast iron dish in a thin layer.

Fully matured Glass of Antimony ready for extraction

Antimony Glass   6/3/2012

Principe formula   K. Lee Stibnite

ROBERT ALLEN BARTLETT

Sample	Dry Wt.	Wet Wt.	Density
1	8.3879	6.7119	4.993
2	7.9019	6.3279	5.008
3	7.9019	6.3279	5.008
Average			5.003
Std Dev			0.009

Weatherby Stibnite IN PRINCIPLE FORMULA

Sample	Dry Wt.	Wet Wt.	Density
1	1.8722	1.4968	4.975
2	3.6675	2.9393	5.024
3	2.6628	2.1361	5.043
Average			5.014
Std Dev			0.035

Density of Antimony Glass

Table 2-2   Densities reported for Sb_2O_3 glass by various authors [22, 27, 29, 31, 32]. Also shown are densities for the crystalline Sb_2O_3 polymorphs, senarmontite and valentinite, calculated from crystal structure data [3, 4].

Material	Reference	Density ($g\,cm^{-3}$)	Notes
Amorphous Sb_2O_3	Kordes [29]	5.179	—
Amorphous Sb_2O_3	Hasegawa *et al.* [22]	5.07	Made with 5 mol% B_2O_3.
Amorphous Sb_2O_3	Kutsenko *et al.* [31]	5.06	Probably contained SiO_2.
Amorphous Sb_2O_3	Bednarik and Neely [32]	5.105	Contained 1.8 wt.% SiO_2.
Amorphous Sb_2O_3	Johnson *et al.* [27]	5.05	Contained 6(2) at.% chlorine [19].
Senarmontite	Svensson [3]	5.5843	Calculated from the crystal structure.
Valentinite	Svensson [4]	5.8447	Calculated from the crystal structure.

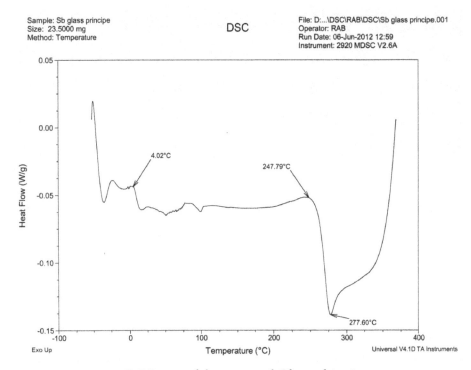

DSC scan of the prepared Glass of Antimony

This is a sample of antimony glass that was poured directly into rainwater. It shattered into an easily grindable mass. Under a microscope the material looks like transparent glass powder. The rainwater was later used to make vinegar of antimony.

Turning Glass into Kermes

Antimony Glass can also be converted into Kermes which allows additional purification and ingress to the material for extraction.

ROBERT ALLEN BARTLETT

— ♁ glass ⟶ KERMES —   1/15/12

Sol'n Turns Black

POWDERED
Sb glass 8/21/11   12g
40% NaOH Sol'N   100 mL } Mix & Heat 2 Hrs

glass Dissolves with some Residue. Black lighter solids Float to Surface

Filter

Pale Golden Solutions
(yellow solids ppt and collect on walls of flask overnight)

Sample#	Dry wts	Solids
GF1	1g	Black / Grey
GF2	2g	yellow

Decant clear solution & Dilute to 1 Liter

Add 5% Distilled White Vinegar To pH 7

No H_2S Evolved

golden orange KERMES

Decant clear Liquid & Discard

Wash ppt w/ Rain ▽

Filter washed ppt

Let Dry

Large Mass of wet ppt (4-5 in³) Bright orange

2 solids

Clear/White Fibrous Exuded Crystals
0.5g
GK3

Solid/easily crumbled Amorphous solid Red orange like Cinnabar
GK4

Placed a wet sample into a vial & covered with strong [symbol]

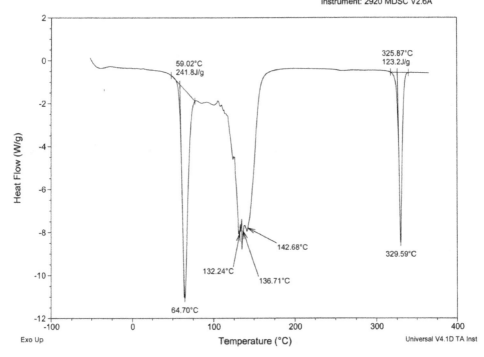

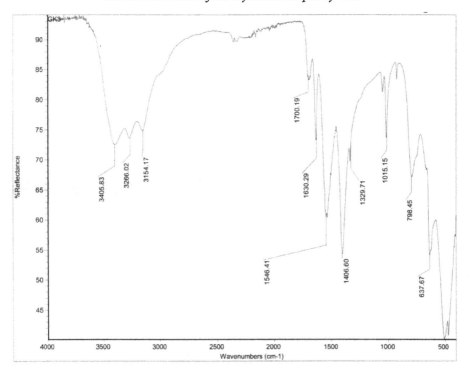

Above: DSC scan of the fibrous crystals that separated from the Kermes;
Below: FTIR scan of the crystalline impurity GK3

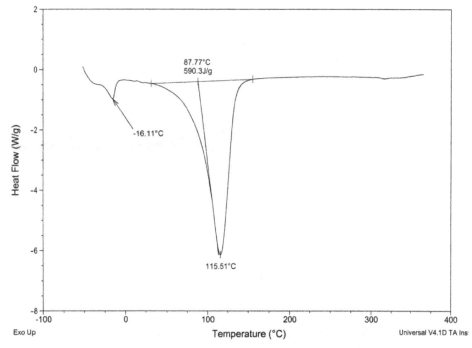

Sample: GK4
Size: 8.8000 mg
Method: Temperature

DSC

File: D:\TA\Data\DSC\RAB\DSC\GK4.001
Operator: RAB
Run Date: 30-Jan-2012 12:11
Instrument: 2920 MDSC V2.6A

ROBERT ALLEN BARTLETT

Above: DSC scan of the Kermes derived from antimony Glass;
Below: FTIR scan of Kermes derived from Antimony Glass

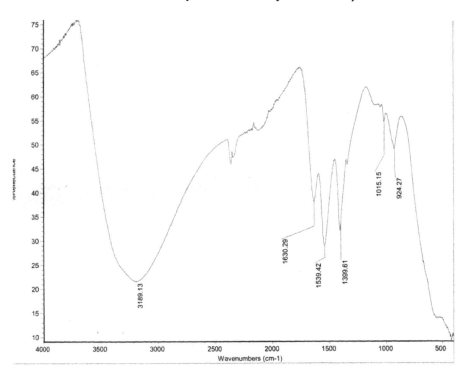

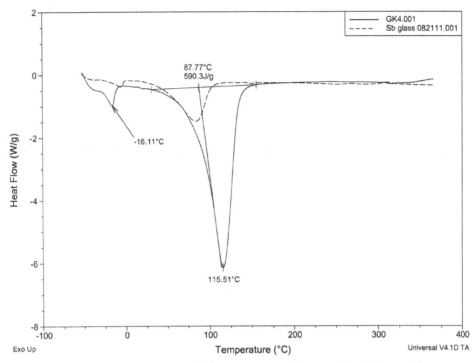

DSC scan of Kermes derived from Antimony Glass and the Glass itself

ROBERT ALLEN BARTLETT

ground & washed
Glass of Antimony

— Glass of Antimony Extractions —

9/25/10

300g GROUND AND WASHED
Glass of Antimony (K. Lee workshop 8/2010)

350 ml DISTILLED white VINEGAR
CONCENTRATED BY FREEZE/THAW 2 TIMES

50 ml GLACIAL ACETIC ACID

COMBINED IN NALGENE
JAR WITH Al₂O₃ GRINDING
MEDIA

SEALED & AGITATED

DIGESTED at 40°C with occasional SHAKING

2/5/11 FILTERED OFF THE PALE ORANGE extract

Glass

VINEGAR extract

ADDED FRESH
VINEGAR (5%) AND
Set To DIGEST

EVAPORATION IN A
DISH at RM. TEMP.

[DSC sample]

RED. ORANGE RESINOUS SOLID
"Glass Acetate"

Grinding of the glass in a ball mill.

Glass pieces, ½ inch alumina cylinder grinding media, and 50% glacial acetic acid containing 1% ammonium carbonate/ ammonium chloride blend were sealed into a Nalgene jar then placed into a rotating frame. This allowed it to grind for hours unattended and extraction of the tincture occurred simultaneously.

After grinding for several hours the solution becomes tinted a red gold color (left).

This was filtered off and the grinding/extraction repeated two more times.

A simple coffee filter was used to separate the tinctured liquid from the glass (facing page). The liquid was allowed to stand and then decanted into a clean flask.

After three extractions, the glass was largely exhausted of its tincture. The extracts are combined and gently distilled to recover the bulk of the vinegar, which can be used for future extractions. The concentrated acid extract is now poured into an evaporating dish to gently dry. On the next page is another flowchart for the process.

Note the addition of a volatile Ammonia salt with the vinegar to "sharpen" it for mineral extractions.

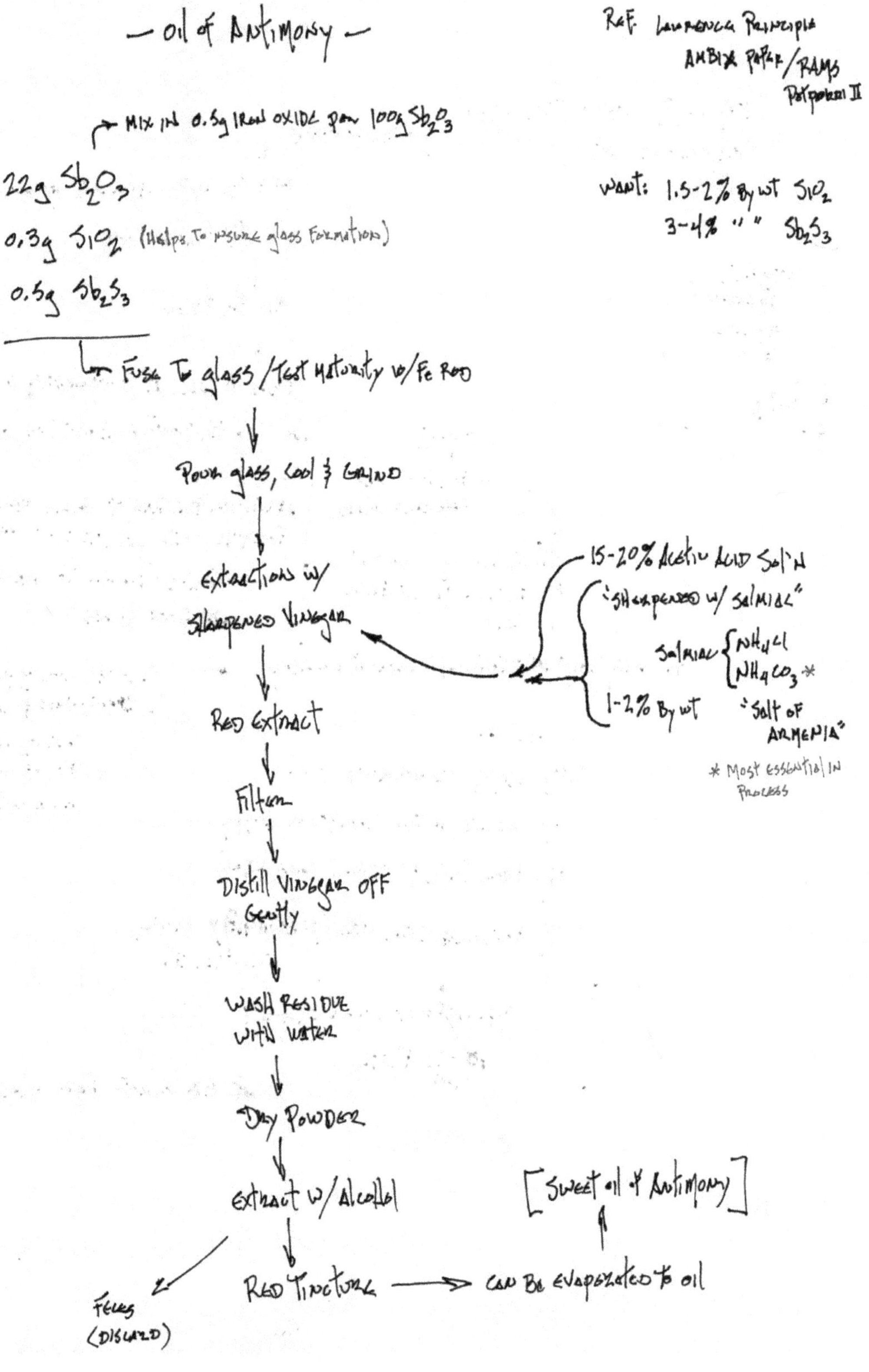

— OIL OF ANTIMONY —

REF: LAWRENCE PRINCIPE
AMBIX PAPER / RAMS
POTPOURRI II

↱ MIX IN 0.5g IRON OXIDE per 100g Sb_2O_3

22g Sb_2O_3

0.3g SiO_2 (Helps to insure glass formation)

0.5g Sb_2S_3

WANT: 1.5-2% BY WT SiO_2
3-4% " " Sb_2S_3

↳ FUSE TO glass / TEST MATURITY W/ Fe ROD

↓

POUR glass, COOL & GRIND

↓

EXTRACTION IN
SHARPENED VINEGAR

15-20% ACETIC ACID SOL'N

"SHARPENED W/ SALMIAC"

SALMIAC { NH_4Cl
           NH_4CO_3 *

1-2% BY WT "SALT OF ARMENIA"

* MOST ESSENTIAL IN PROCESS

↓

RED EXTRACT

↓

FILTER

↓

DISTILL VINEGAR OFF
GENTLY

↓

WASH RESIDUE
WITH WATER

↓

DRY POWDER

↓

EXTRACT W/ ALCOHOL

[SWEET OIL OF ANTIMONY]
↑

↓

FECES
(DISCARD)

RED TINCTURE ⟶ CAN BE EVAPORATED TO OIL

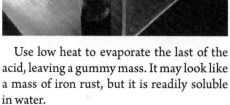

Use low heat to evaporate the last of the acid, leaving a gummy mass. It may look like a mass of iron rust, but it is readily soluble in water.

The solid is dissolved in water and some trapped glass powder falls to the bottom. Decant the clear solution and evaporate again to a gummy mass. I call this Antimony Glassetate so I know its origin right away.

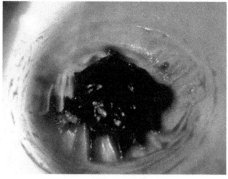

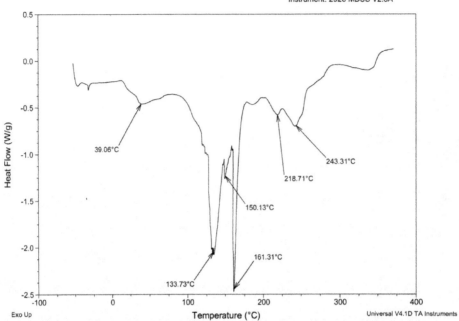

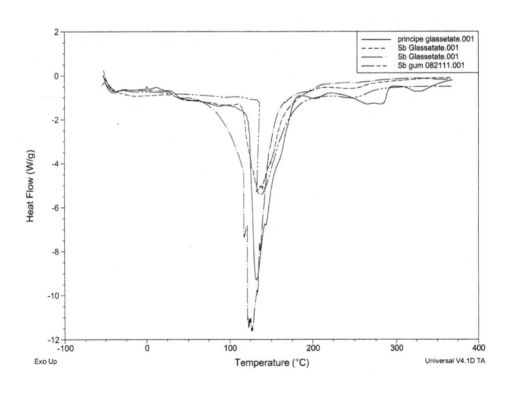

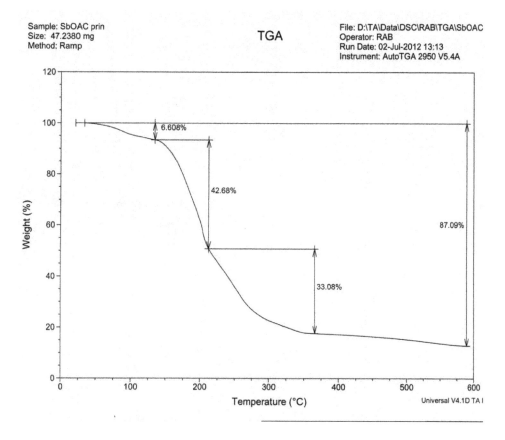

Above: TGA of Antimony Glassetate
Facing page, above: DSC scan of the Acetate Gum from Antimony Glass (Glassetate);
Facing page, below: Comparative DSC of several different Antimony Glassetate extractions

— SWEET OIL OF ANTIMONY / PRINCIPE —

PREPARATION OF THE GUM OF ANTIMONY ~

Sb glass FROM 6/3/12

"VINEGAR" { GLACIAL ACETIC / WATER } 20% ACID → 600 mL
+ 6g NH_4CO_3
+ 1g IX== NH_4Cl

→ PLACED INTO Ball MILL JAR WITH Al_2O_3 MEDIA

↓

GRINDING 20 Hrs

DECANT LIQUID + GROUND GLASS → Filter → GOLDEN-RED EXTRACT

UNGROUND GLASS

ground glass → DRIED → [DRY & Glass POWDER]

ADD 600 ml MORE "VINEGAR"

↓

GRINDING 20 Hrs

DRIED ← ground glass ← Filter ← DECANT LIQUID + glass

[UNGROUND glass]

Lighter golden-RED extract →

COMBINE IN Retort

↓

Gentle Distillation

→ [1 Liter clear Distillate] → BEGAN NEW EXTRACTION 7/1/12

[Small Amount Yellowish Solid]

Final 200 mL Deep Red clear Liquid

↓

Slow evaporation IN DISH / low Heat → THICKENED RED FLUID ≈ 30 mL opaque → WASHED INTO A VIAL WITH WATER

(DSC - PRINCIPE Colloselate)

Let STAND ↓ 2-3 Days

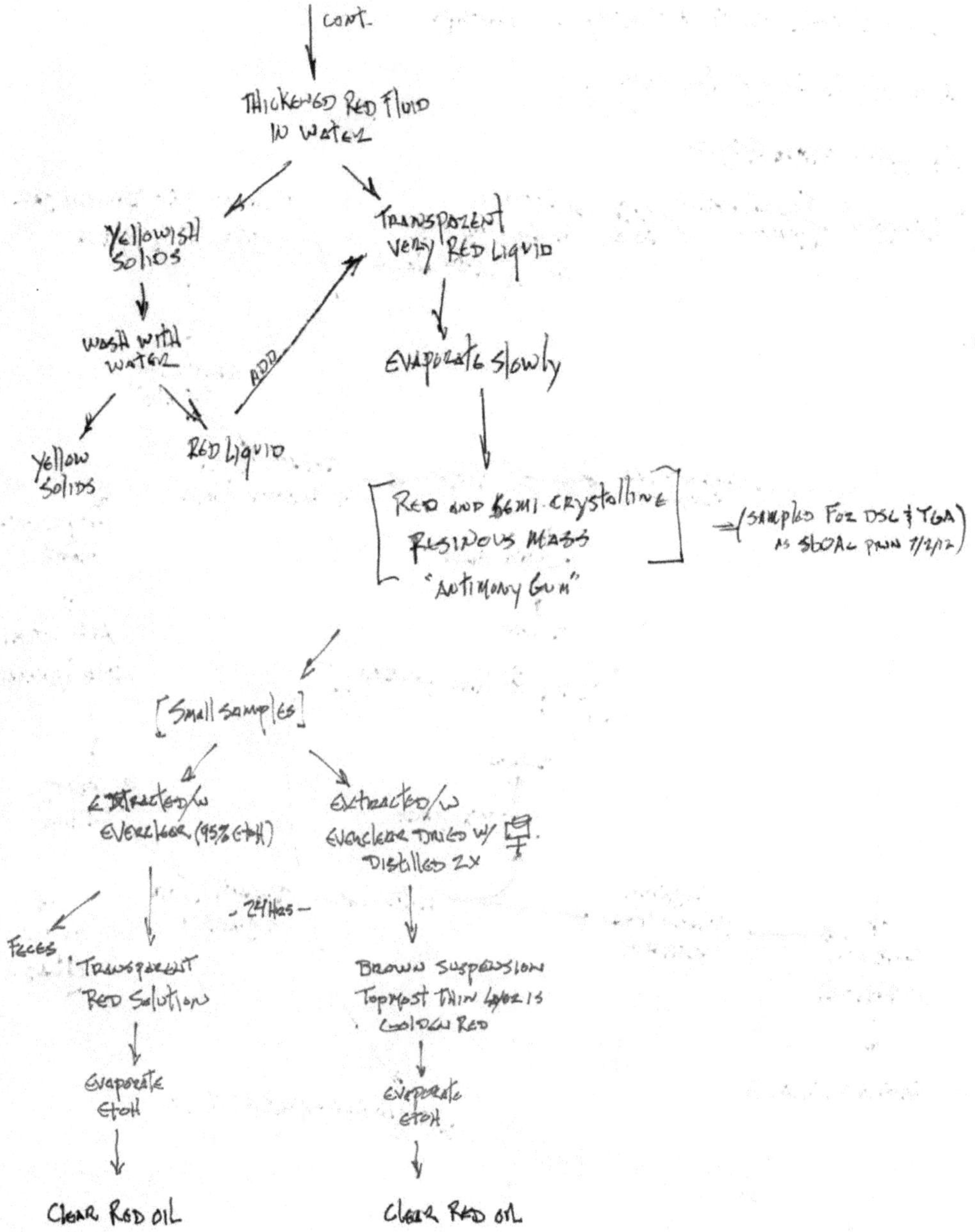

ROBERT ALLEN BARTLETT

| cont.

THICKENED RED FLUID
IN WATER

→ YELLOWISH
SOLIDS

→ TRANSPARENT
VERY RED LIQUID

WASH WITH
WATER

ADD

EVAPORATE SLOWLY

YELLOW
SOLIDS

RED LIQUID

[RED AND SEMI-CRYSTALLINE
RESINOUS MASS]

"ANTIMONY GUM"

→ (SAMPLES FOR DSC & TGA)
AS SbOAc PNW 7/2/12)

[SMALL SAMPLES]

EXTRACTED/W
EVERCLEAR (95% EtOH)

EXTRACTED/W
EVERCLEAR DRIED W/
DISTILLED 2X

— 24 HRS —

FECES

TRANSPARENT
RED SOLUTION

BROWN SUSPENSION
TOPMOST THIN LAYER IS
GOLDEN RED

EVAPORATE
EtOH

EVAPORATE
EtOH

CLEAR RED OIL

CLEAR RED OIL

Now that we have the acetate from the glass isolated and clean, we can move to the extraction of its Fixed Oil.

The acetate is redissolved into dried alcohol and allowed to stand. Let any sediments fall, then, decant the clarified solution into a clean evaporating dish. Allow the alcohol to evaporate and collect the oil that remains.

Dissolve the residue again into dried alcohol and let it stand to settle. Once the solution is clarified, carefully decant or draw it off with a syringe into a watchglass. As the alcohol evaporates, the oil collects at the bottom of the watchglass. Collect the oil into a clean vial and preserve for use in preparing a tincture.

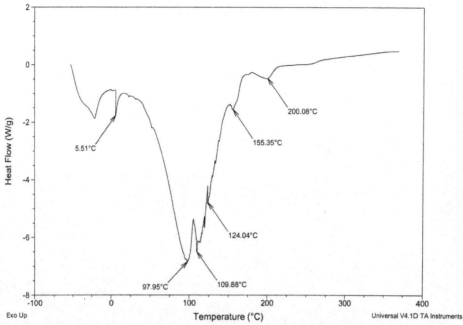

Above: DSC of the Fixed Oil from Antimony Glass
Below: TGA of the Fixed Oil from Antimony Glass

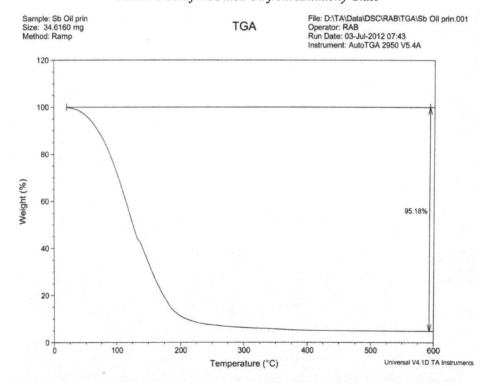

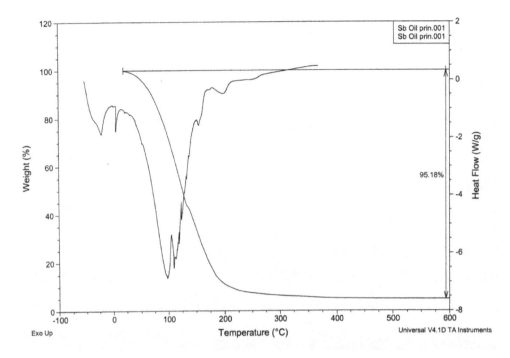

Above: Overlay of DSC an TGA for the Fixed Oil from Antimony Glass

Below: FTIR scan of the Fixed Oil from Antimony Glass

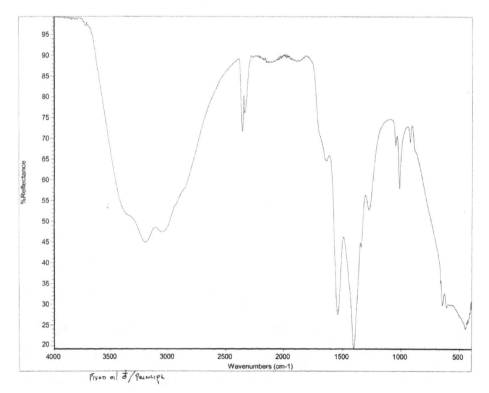

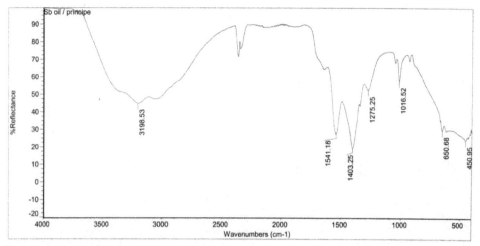

Fri Jun 15 13:07:10 2012 (GMT-07:00)
FIND PEAKS:
    Spectrum: Sb oil / principe
    Region: 4000.00   400.00
    Absolute threshold: 59.331
    Sensitivity: 50
    Peak list:

Position:	450.95	Intensity:	24.010
Position:	650.68	Intensity:	29.637
Position:	1016.52	Intensity:	57.807
Position:	1275.25	Intensity:	52.723
Position:	1403.25	Intensity:	19.359
Position:	1541.18	Intensity:	27.356
Position:	3198.53	Intensity:	44.846

Above: Details of FTIR scan of the Fixed Oil

Below: DSC and TGA overlay of the Acetate extracted from the Antimony Glass

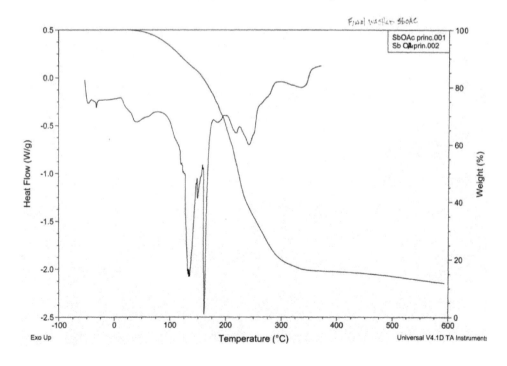

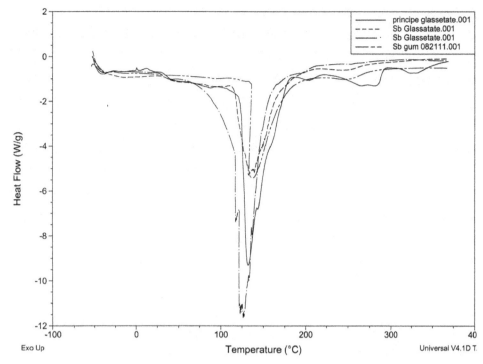

Above: DSC overlay of several different batches of the Antimony Glass Acetate

Below: DSC comparison of the Glass Acetate and resulting Oil

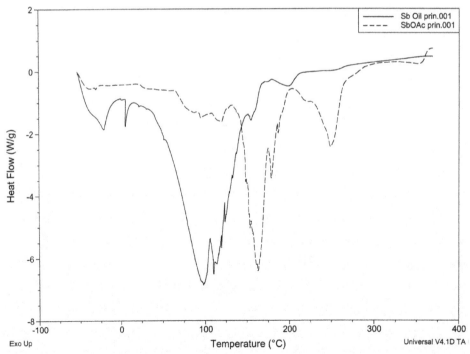

A laser shining through the tincture reveals its colloidal nature, and ultraviolet light, its fluorescence.

Sample: principe Tr Sb
Size: 6.0000 mg
Method: Temperature

DSC

File: D:...\DSC\RAB\DSC\principe Tr Sb.001
Operator: RAB
Run Date: 12-Jun-2012 14:05
Instrument: 2920 MDSC V2.6A

3.27°C

132.98°C   206.79°C

39.80°C

71.86°C

Heat Flow (W/g)

Temperature (°C)

Exo Up

Universal V4.1D TA Instru

DSC scan of the final Fixed Tincture from the antimony Glass

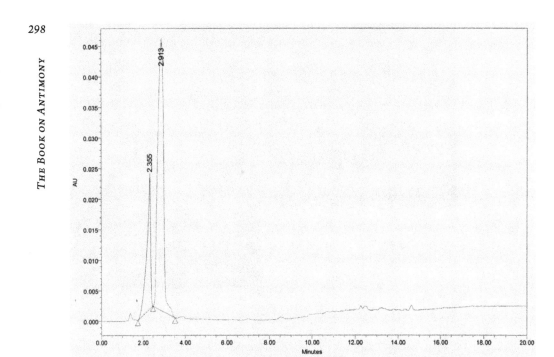

Sample Name: prin Sb Tr Date Acquired: 6/12/2012 12:25:14 PM Vial: 4 Injection: 1

HPLC scan of the Fixed Tincture of Antimony from the Glass

Distillation of the Glass/Acetate resin

The gummy resin obtained by extracting the glass with acetic acid and concentration can also be distilled by degree in order to obtain the oil volatilized and free from any of the body that may be present in the gum.

The following trial distillation uses simple test tubes and bent glass tubing:

4/30/11 Placed 4cc of the Red orange Fluid Resin into a long Test Tube

Began Distillation By Degrees

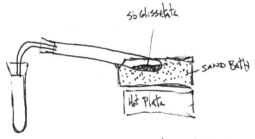

Sb Glassetate

SAND BATH

Hot Plate

1st a clear phlegm came over (≈ 1½ cc)

collected separately

Analysis By HPLC 5/3/11

FtIR 5/5/11

2nd an Greenish distillate came over (≈ 1 cc)

RINSED VESSEL & RESIDUE WITH ACETONE, Let evaporate to oil.

soln in EtH

3rd Replaced receiver with a Ball of Glass wool placed into the Tube. Heated slowly up to Foll Red Heat. Let cool

Rinsed Glass wool and Tube w/ Acetone → very little oil Recovery

Removed Black caput Mortuum From Tube — This is Fairly Magnetic

The trial distillation worked well, so a larger amount of the gum was distilled from a small distillation train with an electric crucible as heat:

☿ Gum Distillation —

7/4/12

3.3g SbOAc/PMN placed into ♯ $\frac{14}{38}$ Glass Still with electric crucible heat.

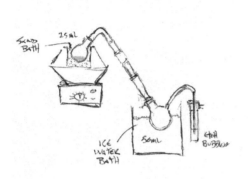

SAND BATH
25 mL
ICE WATER BATH
50 mL
EtOH BUBBLER

GRADUALLY INCREASED Heat To 500°C MAX

* Small amount of clear distillate

* Bubbles up to Neck like a Resin

* Very little remains at flask bottom

Let Cool

Using the alcohol from bubbler Backwashed all glassware into the distillation flask

Poured into a Vial and Let Stand

Settles into 3 Layers

* Collected the layers separately

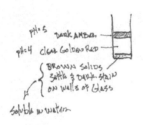

pH 5 DARK AMBER
pH 4 CLEAR GOLDEN RED
BROWN SOLIDS SETTLE & DARK STAIN ON WALLS OF GLASS
Soluble in water

☿ glass ♀

FTIR scan of the Gum prior to distillation

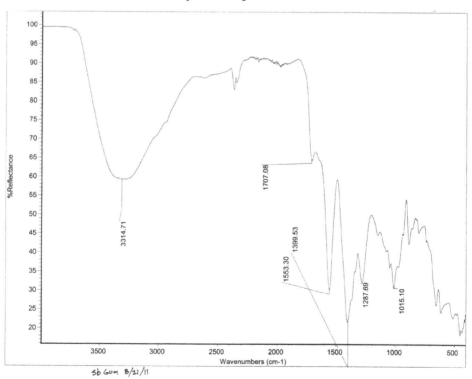

Distillation in progress

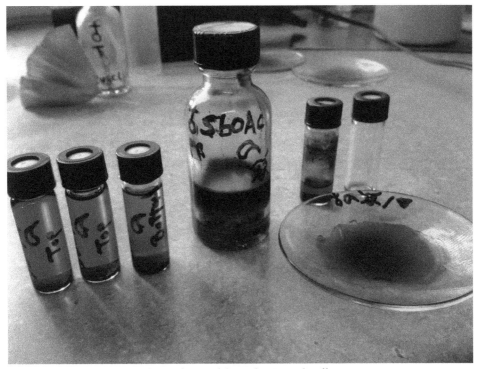

Products obtained from the Gum distillation

Residue from the distillation washed out with water and set to dry in a dish.

Gentle evaporation of the distillate to obtain the Oil (left) and Caput Mortuum (right).

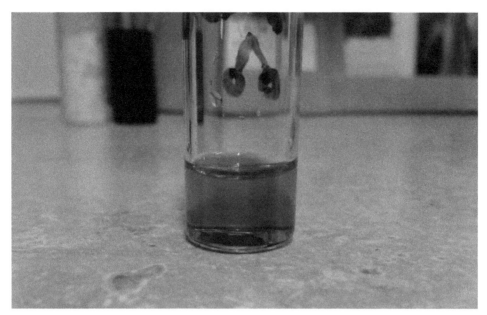

Oil of Antimony from the Gum distillation

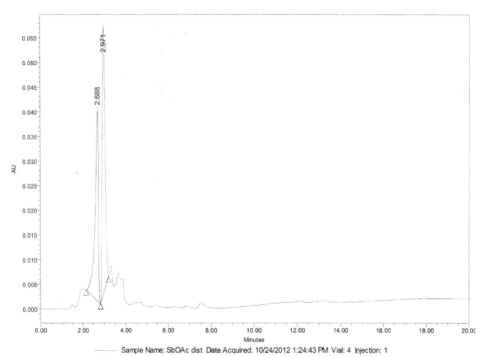

Sample Name: SbOAc dist Date Acquired: 10/24/2012 1:24:43 PM Vial: 4 Injection: 1

HPLC of oil distilled from the Gum

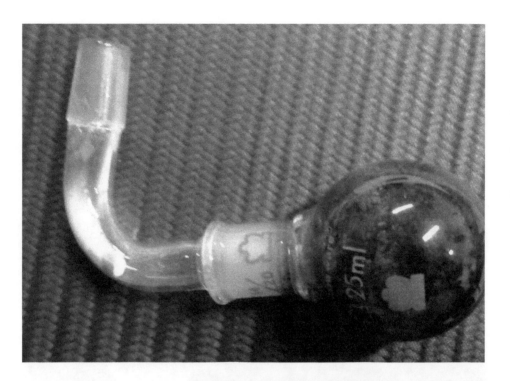

The distillation flask (above) was rinsed out with distilled water and placed into a dish to dry.

Crystallized salts from the "Caput Mortuum" or "Dead Head" remaining in the distillation still pot. This is also called the "Black Dragon." The salts were recrystallized from distilled water.

The Salt of Antimony recrystallized and ready to imbibe with its oil.

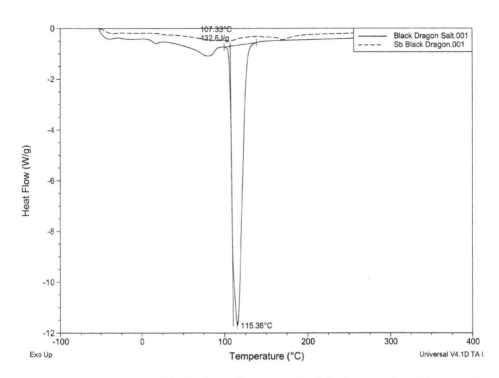

Above: DSC comparison of the black distillation residue (Black Dragon) and the crystal-line salts obtained from it by water extraction; Below: FTIR scan of the Black Dragon.

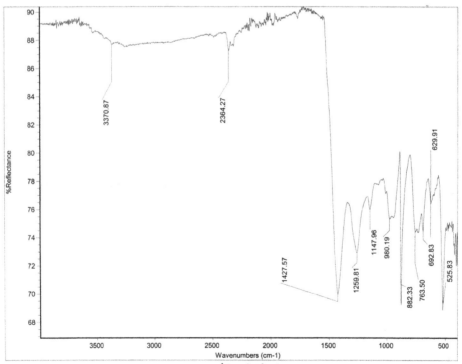

Black Dragon (Residue from Sb Glassetate Distillation)

The recrystallized Salt saturated with the distilled oil.

Reaching maturity after a long period of digestion.

Regulus

The term Regulus means, "the little king," and the Regulus of Antimony has always been used to refer to metallic antimony reduced from its ore. When it is well prepared and purified, you will see a starry pattern on the surface of the metal. The metal itself is quite brittle and reduces to a powder fairly easily. Hidden in the Regulus is the spirit of antimony.

Regulus is also the name of the important fixed star at the heart of the zodiacal sign of Leo, home of the Sun. The close connection between gold and antimony is central to many alchemical works.

Gold and Antimony

There is a very ancient method of refining gold which you will often come across in alchemical texts and involves the use of stibnite.

One of the interesting properties of stibnite is that it dissolves gold quite rapidly. This property was used for purifying gold from other metals used in its alloys.

The impure metal containing gold was melted with antimony sulfide (stibnite). The impurities such as copper and silver formed sulfides which could be skimmed off as a slag, but the gold went into solution with the antimony as it reduced to metallic form.

The antimony-gold alloy was then heated in a stream of air, causing antimony to volatilize as the trioxide, leaving behind the purified gold much like the cupellation with lead in the fire assay.

The process, often illustrated as a "gray wolf devouring the king," was repeated several times to completely purge the gold of foreign metals as well as to imbibe some of the life force of the antimony into the gold. Due to this property, antimony was sometimes referred to as "Aries of the Philosophers," because the Sun is exalted in the sign of Aries.

If you would operate by means of our bodies, take a fierce gray wolf, which, though on account of its name it be subject to the sway of warlike Mars, is by birth the offspring of ancient Saturn, and is found in the valleys and mountains of the world, where he roams about savage with hunger. Cast to him the body of the King, and when he has devoured it, burn him entirely to ashes in a great fire. By this process the King will be liberated; and when it has been performed thrice the Lion has overcome the wolf, and will find nothing more to devour in him. Thus our Body has been rendered fit for the first stage of our work.

Know that this is the only right and legitimate way of purifying our substance: for the Lion purifies himself with the blood of the wolf, and the tincture of its blood agrees most wonderfully with the tincture of the Lion, seeing that the two liquids are closely akin to each other. When the Lion's hunger is appeased, his spirit becomes more powerful than before, and his eyes glitter like the Sun. His internal essence is now of inestimable value for the removing of all defects, and the healing of all diseases. He is pursued by the ten lepers, who desire to drink his blood; and all that are tormented with any kind of sickness are refreshed with this blood.

For whoever drinks of this golden fountain, experiences a renovation of his whole nature, a vanishing of all unhealthy matter, a fresh supply of blood, a strengthening of the heart and of all the vitals, and a permanent bracing of every limb. For it opens all the pores, and through them bears away all that prevents the perfect health of the body, but allows all that is beneficial to remain therein unmolested.

The Twelve Keys of Basil Valentine, Key 1

The most common way of producing the regulus begins with Stibnite or the Kermes mineral. Although these minerals can be directly smelted into the metallic regulus, they are generally mixed with a variety of fluxing and reducing agents which promote a greater yield and higher purity. The fundamental principle involved in this method is that, when iron is added, the sulfur of the stibnite ore has more affinity for the iron, and consequently iron sulfide is formed, even at a comparatively low temperature, the antimony being separated out in the metallic state. Owing to the high specific gravity of the iron sulfide, it is difficult to completely separate it from the metallic antimony: and for this reason, sodium sulfate and carbon are added in order to produce sodium sulfide, which, combining with the iron sulfide forms a fusible slag of low specific gravity. Sodium sulfate or Glauber's salt (named after the German alchemist Rudolf Glauber) is one of a number of salts used as fluxing agents in the formation of Regulus.

Following below are a few recipes used successfully in preparing the Regulus of Antimony:

SHARKEY'S NOTES

SULFUR IS THE PRINCIPLE RESPONSIBLE FOR CONGEALING ☿ MERCURY OR "HARDENING" IT IN ORDER TO MAKE A METAL.

EXCESS SULFUR CAN LEAD TO GREAT HARDNESS

- IRON, BEING VERY HARD, HAS THIS EXCESS OF SULFUR

- ANTIMONY HAS AN EXTERNAL, IMPURE SULFUR AND UTTERLY LACKING IN THE METALLINE SULFUR NECESSARY TO FORM A METAL.

THIS METALLINE SULFUR, THE ANTIMONY MUST GET FROM IRON

THIS SULFUR, PHILALETHES CALLS "FIERY DRAGON"

♈ ARIES/HOUSE OF ♂   THE SUNS EXALTATIONS

STAR REGULUS ALSO CALLED "SALT OF NATURE"

♄   ♂   ☿♂

THE MARRIAGE OF SATURNIA AND MARS PRODUCES

"CHILD OF SATURN"
"DAUGHTER OF ♄"

"OUR CHAOS" = STIBNITE OR ♁REGULUS (BORN OF A FERROUS FIERY SOUL AND A MERCURIAL SUBSTANCE DRAWN FROM SATURNIA)

— Martial Regulus of Antimony —

Ref. Mark House / Newton / Flamel on
Star Regulus

ROBERT ALLEN BARTLETT

A.

30g Iron Nails (Red Hot)

90g Purified Stibnite

10g Iron Powder

30g Niter

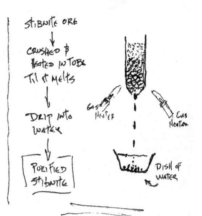

STIBNITE ORE

↓

CRUSHED &
HEATED IN TUBE
Til it Melts

↓

DRIP INTO
WATER

↓

PURIFIED
STIBNITE

GAS Heater   GAS Heater

DISH OF
WATER

B.

120g Purified Stibnite

90g Potassium Sodium Tartrate

60g Niter

50g Iron Powder

C.

90g Purified Stibnite

80g Potassium Sodium Tartrate

40g Niter

40g Iron Powder

D.

90g Purified Stibnite

50g Raw Red Tartar

40g Niter

30g Iron Nails

10g Iron Powder

✱ THIS MIX IS EXPLOSIVE

✱ SAID TO CONTAIN MORE SEED OF GOLD

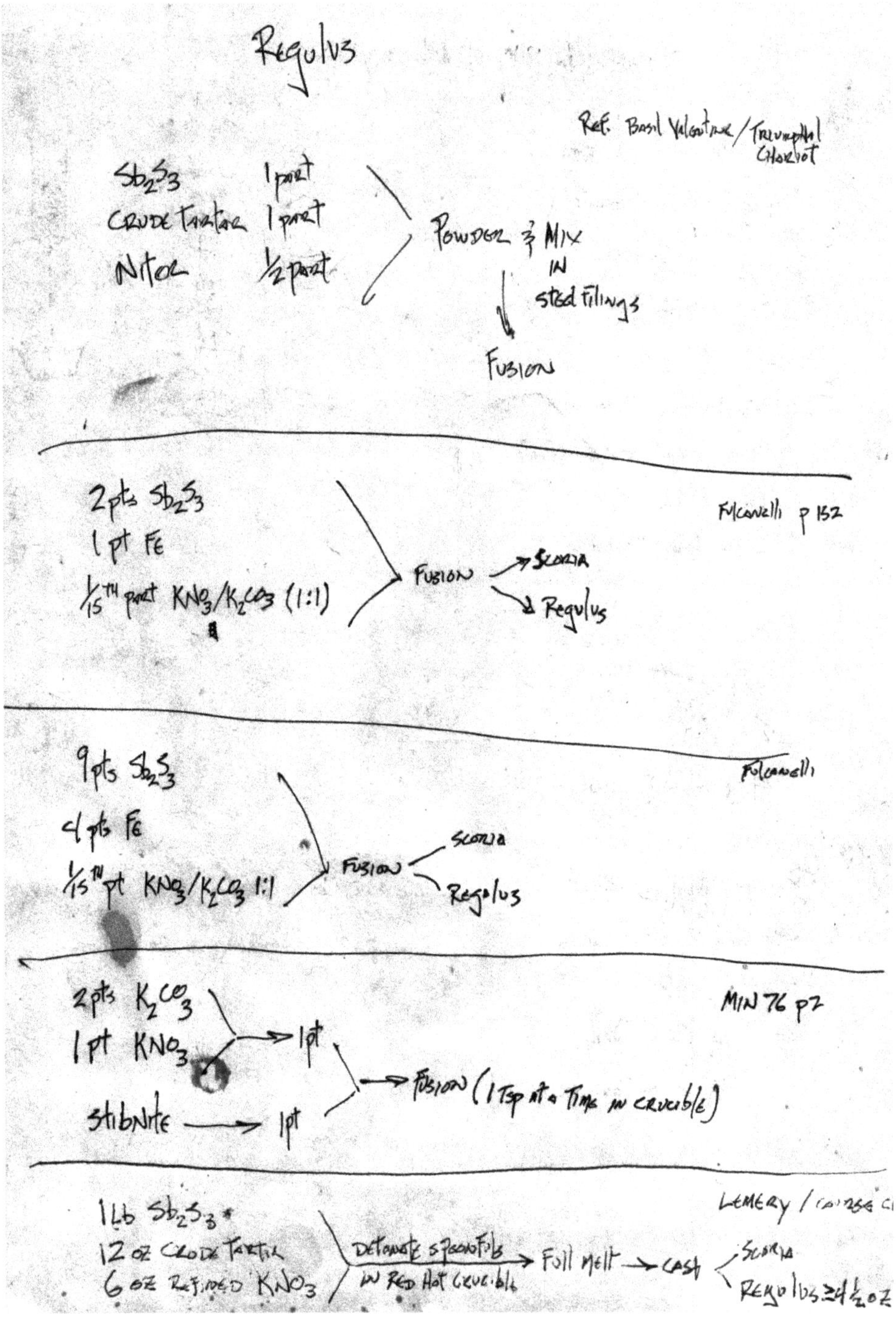

Regulus

Ref. Basil Valentine / Triumphal Chariot

Sb_2S_3 — 1 part
CRUDE Tartar — 1 part
Niter — $\frac{1}{2}$ part

⟩ POWDER & MIX
IN
steel Filings

↓
FUSION

---

2 pts Sb_2S_3
1 pt Fe
$\frac{1}{15}$TH part KNO_3 / K_2CO_3 (1:1)

⟩ FUSION →→ SCORIA
→ Regulus

Fulcanelli p 152

---

9 pts Sb_2S_3
4 pts Fe
$\frac{1}{15}$TH pt KNO_3 / K_2CO_3 1:1

FUSION — SCORIA
— Regulus

Fulcanelli

---

2 pts K_2CO_3
1 pt KNO_3 →→ 1pt
Stibnite →→ 1pt

→ FUSION (1 Tsp at a Time in crucible)

MIN 76 p7

---

1 Lb Sb_2S_3
12 oz CRUDE Tartar
6 oz REFINED KNO_3

⟩ Detonate spoonfuls → Full melt → CAST
in Red Hot crucible

— SCORIA
⟨
REGULUS 3.4$\frac{1}{2}$ oz

LEMERY / course C.

Martial Regulus

ROBERT ALLEN BARTLETT

MATERIAL	WEIGHT (IN GRAMS)				
STIBNITE	160	120	100	100	80
CRUDE RED TARTAR	110	80			55
Potassium Sodium Tartrate				50	30
Potassium Nitrate	55	80	40	40	40
IRON	30	60	30	30	25
TARTARIC ACID			50		

$900 - 1000°C$ Fusion Temp

* ADD SPOONFULS AT A TIME TO HOT CRUCIBLE THEN COVER

POUR INTO IRON CONE WHEN TEMP° REACHES MAX $950 - 1000°C$

PURIFICATION: * MELT REGULUS @ $630°C$

* ADD SPOONFULS OF NITER (ONE AT A TIME)

* HEAT TO $850 - 900°C$ THEN POUR WHEN ALL IS LIQUIFIED

Isaac Newton recommended 2 parts stibnite, 1 part of iron filings, and 4 parts of burnt tartar. The mixture is fused in a crucible and allowed to cool slowly.

From the 1919 monograph *Antimony* by Chung Yu Wang, we read:

The proportion of iron used must not be in any way too high, as, if sulfides of lead and arsenic are present in the ores, they will then be reduced by the excess iron, and enter into the antimony as impurities. In most cases the theoretical proportion of iron required to desulfurize the antimony sulfide is not sufficient, because, when sodium sulfate and carbon are used,

part of the iron is used in decomposing the sodium sulfate. According to Karsten, it has been found by experiment that with 10% of Glauber salt and 2 to 3% coal, 44% iron is required; whereas Liebig states that 42% is sufficient, while Hering uses only 40%.

The following proportions are given by Berthier:- Antimony Sulfide, 100; Forge Scale, 60; Soda 45 to 50; Coal Dust 10."

A slag or scoria forms at the surface and easily comes off the metal with a hammer blow when cooled. Save this scoria from the first reduction of the ore to metal; it is said to contain the "Seed of Gold."

— Martial Regulus From Stibnite —

Sb_2S_3 (K. Lee // Ground By P. Bartsch) — 200g

Cream of Tartar (spanish / storwest Botanycals) — 100g

Niter — 80g

Iron — 60g { 10g Fe Powder / 50g Fe Shot 1/16"

440g

400g used for Fusion 8/21/11

Added By Teaspoonfuls To Hot Crucible

↓

Totally Liquifies
Tap & Pour into
Cast Iron Ladle

↓

Black/Dense Scoria
↳ contains small globules of Regulus
* Yellows & Reddens on air exposure

Clean & Very Shiny
Regulus — 56g Recovered [minus that in scoria]

The metal or regulus at the bottom of the crucible may show some signs of starring, but generally requires additional purification by grinding and fusion with niter to bring out the stars (three images above).

The use of iron in the reduction produces iron sulfide by taking the sulfur from the stibnite, leaving the antimony free as metal which sinks to the bottom.

Other methods of obtaining the regulus include the use of niter in the mixture. For example, 12 parts stibnite, 5 parts iron filings, 6 parts niter, and 9 parts raw tartar. Even small iron nails can be used for the reduction in place of iron filings.

The inclusion of raw tartar is said to increase the yield of the "seed of gold" in the scoria during the first fusion.

The exact proportions will depend on the quality of the stibnite you begin with.

A word of caution: the mixtures with niter are essentially a form of gunpowder, which you will be placing into a very hot crucible. Add material slowly or you will soon find out why the ancients called this process "detonation."

The regulus, once obtained, is ground and mixed with twice its weight of niter, then fused again in a crucible to purify it. This purification may be repeated several times in order for the starry qualities to develop in the metal. This "Star Regulus of Antimony" is also called the "Martial Regulus" because of the iron used in its production.

Niter is a powerful oxidizer and the purification of the regulus with its aid must be done quickly or you will lose a significant portion of the metal as scoria. Some operators just sprinkle a thin layer of niter on the molten regulus for the purification step in order to reduce the amount of oxidation. Others suggest varying proportions of niter and salt of tartar. Melting under a layer of charcoal will reduce oxidation losses.

Basil Valentine recommends the following procedure:

Take of the best Hungarian Antimony, and crude Tartar equal parts, and of Salnitre half a part; grind them well together, and afterwards flux them in a Wind-furnace; pour out the flowing Matter into a Cone, and there let it cool; then you will find the Regulus, which thrice or oftner purge by Fire, with Tartar and Nitre, and it will be bright and white, shining like Cupellate Silver, which hath fulminated and overcome all its Lead.

Triumphal Chariot

The final proportions of niter and salt of tartar, as well as the number of times the fusion must be repeated will depend on the quality of the stibnite used in the beginning. A little trial and error upon smaller quantities can save precious regulus from turning into scoria. Also, pouring the molten regulus into a hot iron mold and allowing it to slowly cool will enhance the crystallization into the Star formation.

Again, in the monograph *Antimony* by Chung Yu Wang, there is described a smelting industry "secret" for enhancing the star formation in regulus by preparing a special flux:

The custom of the trade is to sell antimony as "starred" or crystallized on the upper surface, and therefore it is necessary to obtain this star on the surface. This is achieved by melting the metal with a peculiar flux known as the "antimony flux," a substance not easily prepared, and one which is often difficult to obtain at first; but once obtained; its subsequent production is easy. The process of making this flux is a rule-of-thumb one, and is carried out thus:- Three parts of ordinary American potash are melted in a crucible, and two parts of ground liquated sulfide of antimony are mixed in. when the mixture is complete and the fusion has become quiet, the mass is poured out and tried on a small scale in order to find out whether it yields a good "star"; if it does, the ingot of metal obtained is broken and the metal is then examined, in order to judge whether it is free from sulfur. But if not, the flux is remelted and more of one ingredient or the other is added, as experience dictates.

A bit later, he adds, "It has been observed that a small quantity of the oxide mixed with the sulfide improves the appearance of the metal."

In a process developed by Herrenschmidt, the star effect can be achieved in a single operation by melting, in a crucible, balls of the following composition:

Antimony Oxide
Powdered Anthracite
Carbonate of Soda
Water (to form a paste)

The exact proportions are not given as it is a patented process but we see iron is not required for removing the sulfur from antimony because the oxide is used in a simple reduction with carbon.

The loss of antimony occasioned during the process is due to volatilization and slagging: 64% is the yield, as given by Karsten, when crucibles are used; but Berthier gives 65 to 67%; whereas, theoretically, the yield should be 71.5%.

Remember that many of these mixtures present an explosion hazard. The descriptive names for these processes used by the old adepts were pyrotechnics and detonation, so work slowly and with caution. Be sure to have adequate personal protection, including safety goggles or full-face shield and heavy gloves. Don't forget that you are dealing with a dragon.

Preparing the regulus of antimony is always an exciting undertaking which seems to create its own sacred space.

The illustration below is from *The Book of Lambsprinck*, written by a German adept around 1600. In it we see the "Scaly Dragon" (stibnite) being subdued by Mars (iron).

Scoria

There are alchemical texts which suggest saving the scoria from the Regulus preparation as still having value, but details beyond that are vague. Below are a few suggested experiments on the Scoria

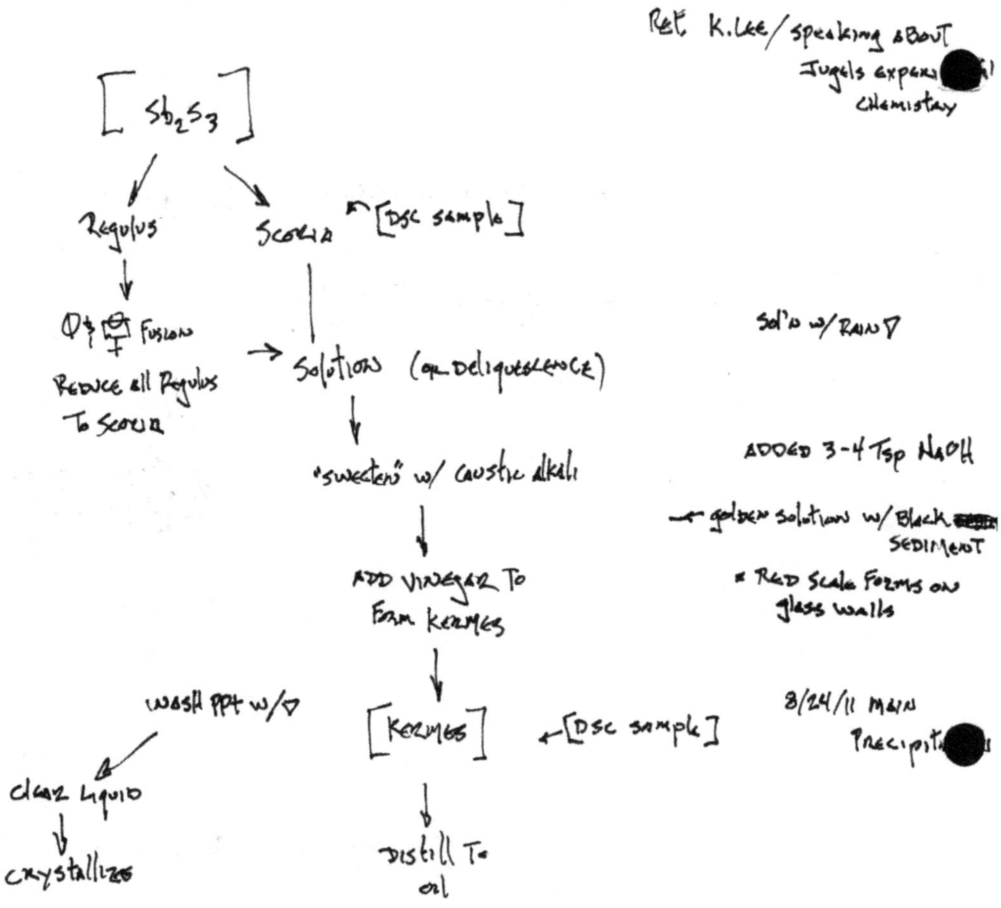

Ref K.Lee / speaking about
Jugels experiment
chemistry

$[Sb_2S_3]$

↓ Regulus   ↘ Scoria ⌐[Dsc sample]

O & ♂ Fusion   → Solution (or Deliquescence)   Sol'n w/ RAIN ▽

Reduce all Regulus
To Scoria

              "sweeten" w/ caustic alkali   ADDED 3-4 Tsp NaOH

                                                 ← golden solution w/ Black
                                                   SEDIMENT

              ADD VINEGAR To   * RED Scale Forms on
              Form KERMES   glass walls

wash ppt w/▽   [KERMES] ←[Dsc sample]   8/24/11 MAIN
                                                 Precipitate

clear liquid   ↓
  ↓   DISTILL To
crystallize   oil

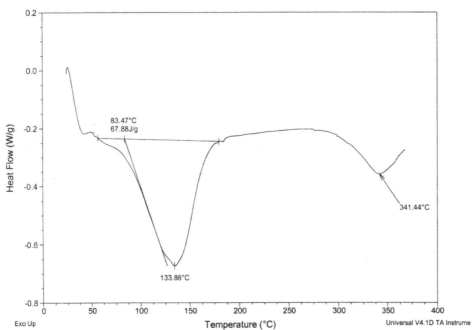

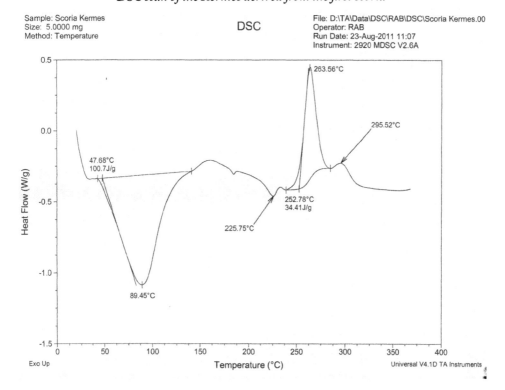

DSC scan of the First Scoria from antimony regulus
DSC scan of the Kermes derived from the first scoria

Sample: 1st Scoria Kermes
Size: 35.0490 mg
Method: Ramp

TGA

File: D:...\DSC\RAB\TGA\1st Scoria Kermes.001
Operator: RAB
Run Date: 01-Sep-2011 09:43
Instrument: AutoTGA 2950 V5.4A

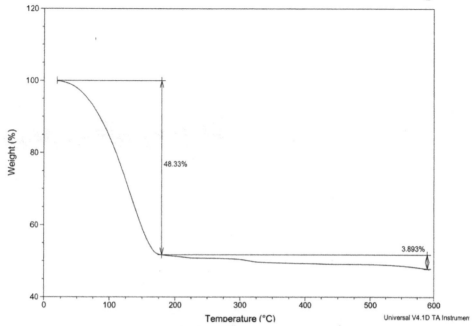

48.33%

3.893%

Universal V4.1D TA Instrumen

TGA of the first scoria Kermes
DSC scan of the Deliquescent Salt obtained from the first scoria

Sample: Scoria deliq
Size: 36.0000 mg
Method: Temperature

DSC

File: D:\TA\Data\DSC\RAB\DSC\Scoria deliq.001
Operator: RAB
Run Date: 03-Nov-2010 10:38
Instrument: 2920 MDSC V2.6A

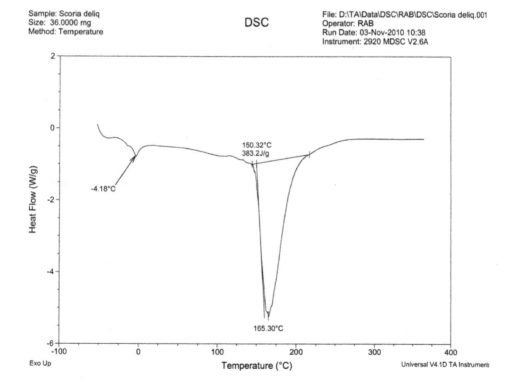

150.32°C
383.2J/g

-4.18°C

165.30°C

Exo Up

Universal V4.1D TA Instrument

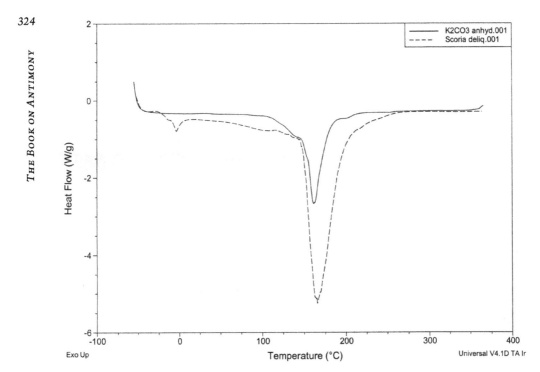

DSC comparison of Scoria deliquesced salt and the Salt of Tartar (K$_{2CO3}$)

This experiment was based on a phone conversation between Karl Lee and Myself regarding the work of the Danish alchemist known as Merelle. This was proposed as an alternate method of producing the crystalline material she writes about.

K. Lee / pHone

ROBERT ALLEN BARTLETT

SCORIA

↓

Dehyddse

↓

PPt KeRMes
w/ HOAc

↓

Dry & extract
w/ AlcaHest
    └→ From Pb OAc Distillation

↓

evaporate
to crystals

↓

[Merelle crystals]   "seed of gold"

Butter of Antimony

SbCl₃, Antimony Trichloride also known as Antimonous Chloride

SbH_3 is highly toxic, be aware of this fact and do all Sb + acid reactions with adequate ventilation.

Properties:
Colorless, fuming, crystalline, caustic, soft masses. (hence formerly called Butter of Antimony), which melt at 73° and boil at 223° and which absorbs water from the air and is deliquescent. Antimony Trichloride is soluble in hydrochloric acid; if this solution or solid Antimony Trichloride is treated with considerable water, a white crystalline precipitate of Antimony Oyxchloride, SbOCl, is obtained. This was formerly called Algarot powder. It contains various amounts of Antimony Trioxide according to the method of preparation: 2SbCl3 + 3H20 => Sb2O3 + 6HCl or SbCl3 + H20 => SbOCl +2HCl.

The Sulfide was commonly used as the crude form was obtained directly from the ore, the oxides are much more common today. The Hydrochloric acid needs to be pretty strong. A more modern preparation has you concentrate the solution, add concentrated(35%) Hydrochloric acid, and distill that. The HCl removes remaining water as the 20% azeotrope, the excess HCl keeps the SbCl3 from hydrolyzing.

$SbCl_3$ can also be made from the metal and Chlorine gas.

Preparation
By dissolving Antimony Sulphide or Antimony Trioxide in Hydrochloric acid:
Sb2S3+6HCl => 2SbCl3 + 3H2S
Sb2O3 + 6HCl => 2SbCl3 + 3H2O
This is then distilled, when first H2S, if the Sulfide is used, then the excess of Hydrochloric acid, and finally the Antimony Trichloride pass over.
In our case there is no need to distill if using HCl, see below.

Soluble Antimony compound can be made by dissolving Antimony metal in HCl + Hydrogen Peroxide in a reflux apparatus. A weighed amount of powdered Antimony metal together with concentrated HCl was placed into the reflux apparatus and with 10ml portions of 30% w/v Hydrogen Peroxide added until all the Sb was dissolved. It would be better to slowly drop in the HP over a period of a few hours. When all the Antimony is dissolved the liquid is evaporated until a yellow syrupy liquid is obtained. This liquid is weighed and the % Antimony ascertained. The liquid is suitable for the Sb source of DTO coat. The liquid is a mixed valency inorganic polymer of Sb Chloride, I am reliably informed.

Practical

- **From the Oxide + HCl**
  The molecular weight of Sb2O3 is 291.5.
  The molecular weight of HCl is 36.5.
  36.4 grams (0.125 mole) of ceramic grade Antimony Trioxide was placed into a beaker and 114 grams 32% Hydrochloric acid was added.
  Use higher concentration acid if you have it.

Making antimony oxychlorides[1]

- $4\,SbCl_3 + 5\,H_2O \xrightarrow{35°C} Sb_4O_5Cl_2 + 10\,HCl$

- $(or\ SbCl_3 + H_2O \xrightarrow{35°C} SbOCl + 2\,HCl)$

- Wash with diethyl ether and suction filter.

- Dry in an oven at 80°C.

- $(5\,SbOCl \xrightarrow{220°C} Sb_4O_5Cl_2 + 4\,SbCl_3)$

- $11\,Sb_4O_5Cl_2 \xrightarrow[\text{Under Argon}]{440°C} 5\,Sb_8O_{11}Cl_2 + 4\,SbCl_3$

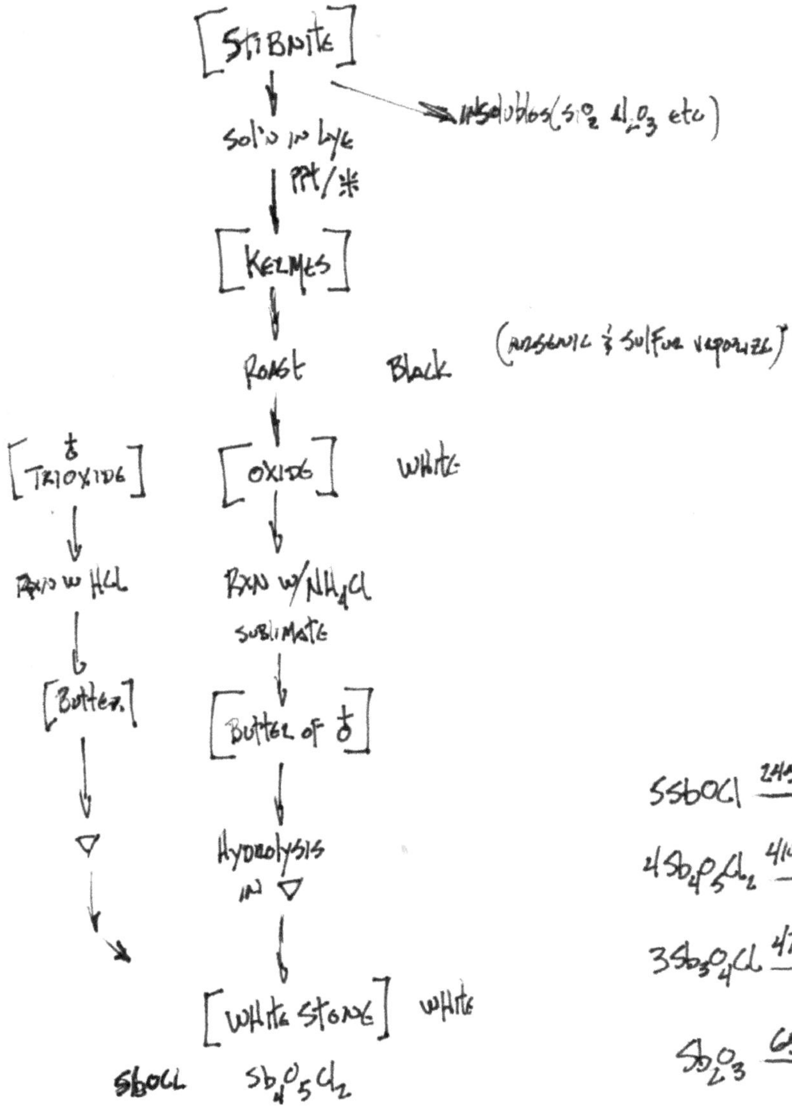

[STIBNITE]

→ INSOLUBLES (SiO_2 Al_2O_3 etc)

Sol'n in LYE

PPT/❄

[KERMES]

ROAST   Black   (ARSENIC & SULFUR VAPORIZE)

[TRIOXIDE]   [OXIDE]   WHITE

RXN w/ HCl   RXN w/ NH_4Cl

                    SUBLIMATE

[Butter]   [BUTTER of ☿]

▽   HYDROLYSIS
                IN ▽

                [WHITE STONE]   WHITE

SbOCl $Sb_4O_5Cl_2$

$$5SbOCl \xrightarrow{245-280°C} Sb_4O_5Cl_2 + SbCl_3$$

$$4Sb_4O_5Cl_2 \xrightarrow{410-475°C} 5Sb_3O_4Cl + SbCl_3$$

$$3Sb_3O_4Cl \xrightarrow{475-565°C} 4Sb_2O_3 + SbCl_3$$

$$Sb_2O_3 \xrightarrow{658°C} Sb_2O_3 (L)$$

glass

The Butter of Antimony is poured directly into distilled water as a concentrated acid
solution, and it is immediately hydrolyzed
into a cloud of heavy white precipitate that
settles to the bottom.

The clarified liquid is decanted away from
the solids which are to be washed with distilled water several times by decantation.
The precipitate is then carefully dried and
stored in a glass vessel.

Some have recognized this as the Universal Magnesia or White Stone of the ancients.

ROBERT ALLEN BARTLETT

When the dried oxychloride was mixed with an equal amount of very pure granular copper and fused (which occurred rapidly within a simple glass test tube) it resulted in a lump of silver colored alloy that was malleable.

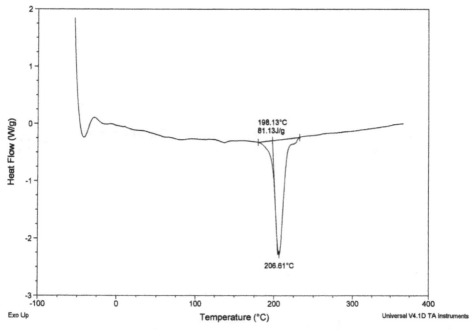

Above: DSC scan of the Antimony Oxychloride; Below: TGA of Antimony Oxychloride

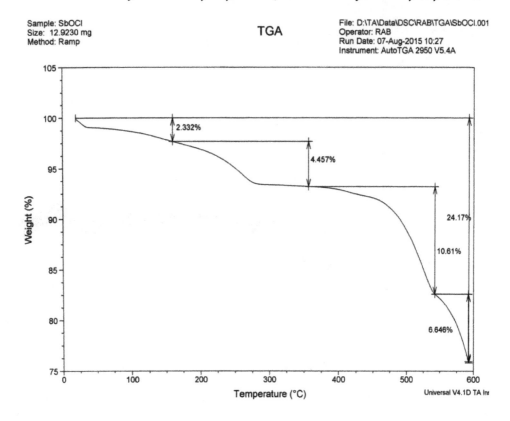

Ref. H. Boerhaave
Practice p 317
Process 196

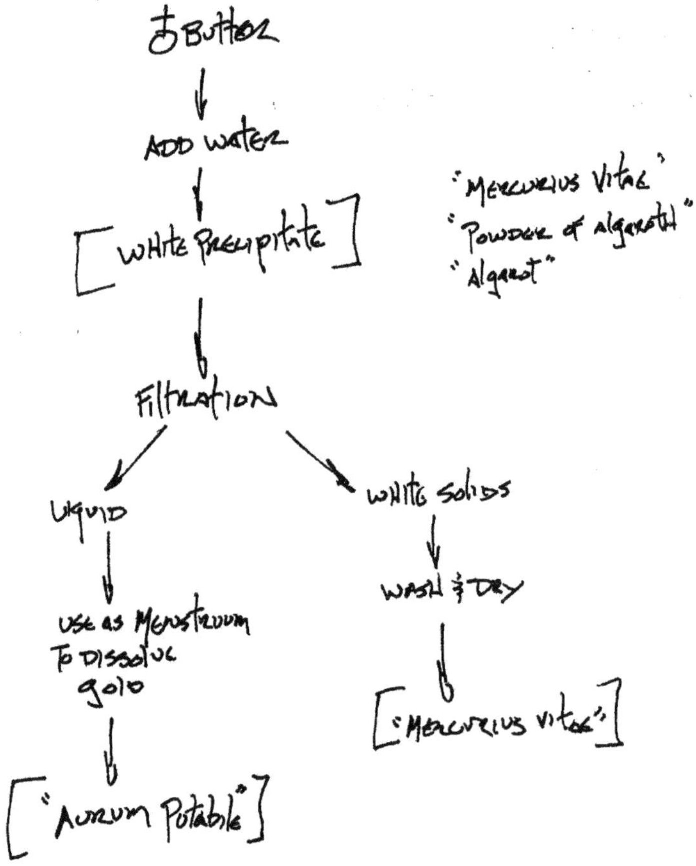

♄ Butter

↓

ADD WATER

↓

[WHITE PRECIPITATE]

↓

"MERCURIUS VITAE"
"POWDER OF ALGAROTH"
"Algarot"

FILTRATION

↙　　　　↘

LIQUID　　　　　WHITE SOLIDS

↓　　　　　　　↓

USE as MENSTRUUM　　WASH & DRY
TO DISSOLVE
GOLD　　　　　　↓

↓　　　　["MERCURIUS VITAE"]

["AURUM POTABILE"]

THIS FIRST FILTERED LIQUID IS
AN EXCELLENT MENSTRUUM OR
"SPIRIT OF SEA SALT", IMPROPERLY
CALLED "PHILOSOPHIC SPIRIT OF VITRIOL",
AND CAPABLE OF DISSOLVING GOLD ♁
INTO AURUM POTABILE FOR IT CONTAINS
THE STRONG ACID SPIRIT OF THE SEA SALT

"SCARCE ANY KNOWN MENSTRUUM CAN, FOR POWER, BE COMPARED THEREWITH;
AS PERFORMING THOSE STRANGE THINGS WHICH THE ILLUSTRIOUS BOYLE RELATES
IN HIS MENSTRUUM PERACUTUM; ESPECIALLY WHEN EVAPORATED TO ABOUT ¼
OF ITS ORIGINAL QUANTITY;

This following experiment is from Rudolf Glauber's collected works. He calls the Butter of Antimony, Proserpina and compares it to the "Fires of Hell." This is another case where Iron and Antimony are united and in this process, become a powerful extraction medium for minerals and metals.

ROBERT ALLEN BARTLETT

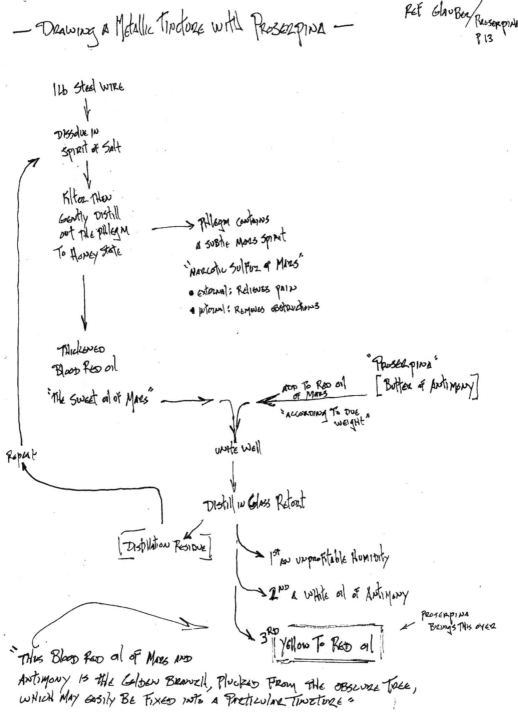

— DRAWING A Metallic Tincture with PROSERPINA —

REF GlauBer/PROSERPINA P 13

1lb Steel WIRE

Dissolve in Spirit of Salt

Filter THen Gently Distill out the phlegm To Honey State

→ Phlegm contains a subtle Mars Spirit "NARCOTIC Sulfur of Mars"

• external: Relieves pain
• internal: Removes obstructions

THICKENED Blood Red oil "The Sweet oil of Mars" →

ADD To Red oil of Mars ← "Proserpina" [Butter of Antimony]

"ACCORDING To DUE weight"

Repeat

UNite Well

Distill in Glass Retort

[Distillation Residue]

→ 1ST An unprofitable Humidity

→ 2ND a White oil of Antimony

→ 3RD [Yellow To Red oil]

PROSERPINA Brings THis over

"THis Blood Red oil of Mars and Antimony is the Golden Branch, Plucked From the obscure Tree, which may easily be Fixed into a Particular Tincture."

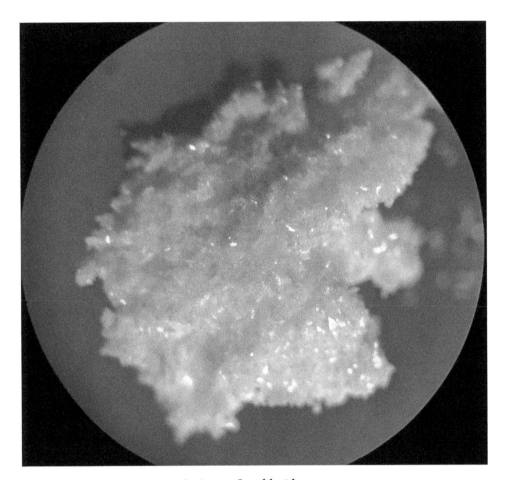

Antimony Oxychloride

In the very excellent book, *Cracking the Philosophers Stone,* by modern day alchemical researcher Erik LaPort, the author describes the preparation and use of antimony oxychloride by alchemists of all times as the philosopher's "White Stone." A classic description is that of the Greek alchemist Synesius around 370 CE.

∼ CHrysopoeia ∼

Synesius of Cyrene - student of Hypatia
5570 AD

∼ Template For Synesius's White Stone of Hermes ∼

White Serpent + Eagle of Hermes = White Stone of Hermes

White Stone + Gold Calx = Tincture

1. EXALTATION: Calcine Stibnite To Flowers of Antimony, and then Distill the
Flowers with Sal Ammoniac (NH_4Cl) To achieve Butter of Antimony ($SbCl_3$)

2. WHITENING: Hydrolysis of Butter of Antimony To create the Dual-Soul, the one,
The Serpent, the White Stone, Mercurius Vitae ($Sb_4O_5Cl_2$)

3. REDDENING: A Reaction Between the White Stone (Dual-Soul $Sb_4O_5Cl_2$) and
The Sun (Body, Gold) Referred To alchemically as Fermenting,
or Joining the Dual-Soul with Body To create the Tincture of the Philosophers

$$Sb_2S_3 \xrightarrow{\text{Calcine}} Sb_2O_3$$

$$Sb_2O_3 + NH_4Cl \xrightarrow{\text{Distill}} SbCl_3$$

$$SbCl_3 + H_2O \longrightarrow \underset{\text{White Stone}}{Sb_4O_5Cl_2}$$

$$Sb_4O_5Cl_2 + Au \longrightarrow Au \cdot SbOCl$$
$$\text{Red Stone}$$

The two substances, sal ammoniac and flowers of antimony represent energetic rather than material aspects. Together they comprise a unified feminine or lunar dual-soul that can later be conjoined with the perfect male or solar body of gold.

Soul (Sb_2O_3) + spirit (NH_4Cl) = Dual soul (doubled living mercury)

Dual soul + Body (gold calx) = Perfect triune being (body, soul, spirit united)

Synesius explains that only one stone – the white stone – consists of the whole magistery, is comprised of only two formal elements and is the end of the end of the magistery.

Its dual nature is soul-spirit representing pure energy devoid of bodily incarnation and it was for this reason that it was valued over the red tincture by Alexandrian philosophers.

The white stone is antimony oxychloride ($Sb_4O_5Cl_2$)

[Ba - Ka]

```
          Flowers              Eagle
Fiery earth = $Sb_2O_3$   Airy-water = deliquesced $NH_4OH$
```

Flowers + eagle = sophic Hermes (Tetrasomia)

Sophic Hermes ($SbCl_3$) ⟶ Hydrolysis == Antimony oxychloride = The white stone

White Magnesia
Foliated Earth
The One
Serpent
Mercurius Duplicatus
Mercurius Vitae
Universal Stone
Stone of the Philosophers
Algaroth Powder

- Synesius   Tetrasomia + Gold = Quintessence
- Stephanos   White Magnesia + Gold = Coral Gold
- Paracelsus   Stone of the Philosophers + Gold = Tincture of philos.
- Khunrath   Universal Stone + Gold = Specific Stone

Along a similar line of experiments with Butter of Antimony are those employing the equally dangerous mercury chloride or "Corrosive Sublimate." The following example was another attempt to unite iron and antimony using mercury chloride as the medium.

ROBERT ALLEN BARTLETT

SEE: MIN 42 p4
APHORISMS
URBIGERUS

Sb_2S_3 GREEN DRAGON

$HgCl_2$ SERPENT

ALSO SEE; WALBER/PROSERPINA

1pt   ☉ Sb_2S_3 ⎫

1pt   ☿ $HgCl_2$ ⎬ Deliquesce → Putrefy → Distill /Sublimate

Attraction of UNIVERSAL ♀

UNIVERSAL Menstruum

"CINNABAR of ☿"
↳ makes RED OIL

---

*   1pt Sb_2S_3 ⎫
      $FeCl_3$ ⎬

1pt $HgCl_2$

want
4-5% Fe per wt. Sb
IN MARTIAL Regulus

**   1pt $SbCl_3$ ⎫
      $FeCl_3$ ⎬

1pt $HgCl_2$

NEEDS TO BE ANIMATED WITH SCORIA PRIMAE

---

* $1g\, Sb_2S_3 → .72g\, Sb ⇒ @ 5\% Fe → .04g\, Fe ∴ .1g\, FeCl_3$

** $1g\, SbCl_3 → .53g\, Sb ⇒ @ 5\% Fe → .03g\, Fe ∴ 0.08g\, FeCl_3$

$FeCl_3$ 34.43% Fe
M.P. 300 /volatilizes

$SbCl_3$ 53.37 % Sb
M.P 73°C

Sb_2S_3 71.68% Sb
M.P. 550°C

4/5/06   1g Sb_2S_3 (HERMADA MINE) ⟩ PLACED INTO 40 mL VIAL AND EXPOSED TO MOONLIGHT & NIGHT AIR
         0.1g $FeCl_3$

         1g $SbCl_3$
         0.1g $FeCl_3$ ⟩ IN 40 mL VIAL AS ABOVE
                DELIQUESCES INTO A RED FLUID, CLEAR

4/23/06 ADDED AN EQUAL AMOUNT OF $HgCl_2$ TO EACH OF THE 3 VIALS & SEALED

6/18/06 Sb_2S_3/$HgCl_2$ - APPEARS UNCHANGED

         Sb_2S_3/$FeCl_3$/$HgCl_2$ - VESSEL IS FILLED TO NEAR TOP WITH WHITE CRYSTALS. THE MATTER AT BOTTOM OF VIAL
                IS GOLDEN YELLOW WITH A FEW DARK AREAS. INSIDE VIAL IS FROSTED WITH WHITE SMOKE

         $SbCl_3$/$FeCl_3$/$HgCl_2$ - DEEP GOLDEN RED LIQUID AND CRYSTALS

2/10/2010 Sb_2S_3/$HgCl_2$ APPEARS UNCHANGED AS A BLACK POWDER
                SOME SMALL AMOUNT OF WHITE SUBLIMATED CRYSTALS ON GLASS

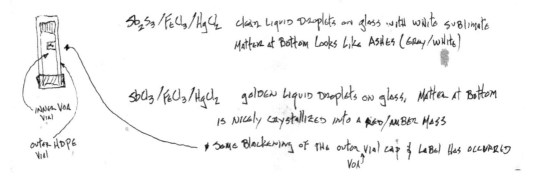

INNER VOA VIAL

outer HDPE VIAL

         Sb_2S_3/$FeCl_3$/$HgCl_2$ CLEAR LIQUID DROPLETS ON GLASS WITH WHITE SUBLIMATE
                MATTER AT BOTTOM LOOKS LIKE ASHES (GRAY/WHITE)

         $SbCl_3$/$FeCl_3$/$HgCl_2$ GOLDEN LIQUID DROPLETS ON GLASS, MATTER AT BOTTOM
                IS NICELY CRYSTALLIZED INTO A RED/AMBER MASS
                * SOME BLACKENING OF THE OUTER VIAL CAP & LABEL HAS OCCURRED
                   VOA

After a long digestion, the first formula turned into a homogenous mass of ruby crystals.

Throughout this work, no attempt is being made to turn alchemy into simple chemistry; they are two separate paradigms that I have tried to keep separate over the years. The analytical data is presented more in the sense of Aleister Crowley's *The Method of Science, The Aim of Religion*. The materials we work with may be imbued with some "imponderable force" we can't measure at the present time; but the materials themselves as vehicles of such forces can be examined from many different angles. And each angle shines a new bit of light as patterns, connections and correspondences emerge. Matter is stamped with an energetic signature and the instrumental scans are like fingerprints. What happens within the flasks initiates us into the inner workings of Nature, the processes and changes we see are mirrored around us and within us. The more we understand about Nature's operations, the more we can assist the perfection of our materials and ourselves. Antimony is filled with wonders and has much to teach us.

Antimony is hermaphroditic, male and female, of both natures, Sulphur and, Mercury, fixed and volatile, the first-born of the metallic nature, middle substance between Mercury and metal, the only natural solvent and natural fire with which all things can be mixed, the Dragon and the devouring Lion, the solvent and the coagulant.

Joseph Du Chesne, *Treatise on Metallic Medicine*, 1641

In the modern periodic table of elements, antimony is listed under the group 5A elements along with nitrogen, phosphorus, arsenic, and bismuth. They all share similar properties in their chemical action. Alchemically speaking, these elements are held to be the activators or animators of matter.

Just as nitrogen and phosphorus are widely used in agriculture as fertilizers to induce heavy growth, antimony is often considered

as the fertilizer of the mineral world. Antimony is held to bring in the necessary fire to accelerate metallic evolution.

In addition, as each of the metals is held to be under the rulership of a particular planet, antimony is said to ruled by the planet Earth. When the metal "dies," its spirit has nowhere to go but here again. Because of this, antimony is said to be immortal; its spirit is fixed to the sphere of the Earth and can be transferred to other metals in order to reanimate them and awaken their generative power.

Vinegar of Antimony

One of the very important preparations from antimony is the Vinegar of Antimony, which is its pure fixed Mercury. It is called vinegar because it is prepared by a fermentation process and it tastes sour, like vinegar.

The fermentation itself takes some time, several months at the least, but the preparation is well worth the effort. The resulting "vinegar" is a menstruum which can extract a tincture from any of the minerals or metals and lend its life force to reanimate them. It also possesses remarkable healing virtues internally and externally. Some believe it is a specific against many forms of cancer.

Basil Valentine gives a very clear description of its preparation in his *Triumphal Chariot of Antimony* as follows.

Melt the Minera of Antimony, and purify it, grind it to a Subtile Powder, this Matter put into a Round Glass, which is called a Phial, having a long Neck, pour upon it distilled Water, that the Vessel may be half full. Then having well closed the Vessel, set it to putrefy in Horse-dung, until the Mineral begins to wax hot, and cast out a Froth to the Superficies: then 'tis time to take it out; for that is a Sign the Body is opened. This digested Matter put into Cucurbit, which well close, and extract the Water, which will have an acid

Taste. When all the Water is come off, intend the Fire, and a Sublimate will ascend; this again grind with the Feces, and again pour on the same Water, and a second time abstract it, then it will be more Sharp. This Operation must be repeated, until the Water be made as Acid, as any other Sharp distilled Vinegar of Wine. But the Sublimate, the oftner the Operation is repeated, the more it is diminished. When you have obtained this Acid Vinegar, take fresh Minera as before and pour this Vinegar on it, so as it may stand above it three Fingers; put it into a Pelican, and digest it two days in Heat, then the Vinegar becomes red, and much more sharp then before. Cant this clean off, and distil it without addition in B.M. The Vinegar comes off white, and the Redness remains in the bottom, which extracted with Spirit of Wine is an excellent Medicine. Again rectify the Vinegar in B.M. that it may be freed from its Phlegm; lastly dissolve in its proper Salt, viz: in four ounces of it, to one ounce of the Salt, and force it strongly by Ashes; then the Vinegar becomes more sharp, and acquires greater Strength, and virtue.

may be covered with Water, which either must be put into the Recipient, or pass out by distilling into the same; otherwise the Spirit's of the Antimony will be lost, and more then half part of the same perish, or the Work require much more time for its perfection. When the whole Water hath passed over by Alembeck, the Fire is to be increased, and three Days, and as many Nights continued without intermission. Then let all cool, and the Sublimate, as he teaches, must again be mixed with the Antimony; this Labour for three Days and Nights must be re-assumed, and afterwards repeated to the third time. Then your Water will be acid, as common Vinegar. If you tinge this Vinegar with new Minera of Antimony, you will have a Tincture, which Basilius names his Balsome of Life, so often described, but never sufficiently commended. O, did Mortals know what Mysteries lie absconded in this Tincture, I question whether they would be desirous to set about any other Preparation of Antimony. All things are in this One. I have spoken, O Lover of Chymistry, do thou act.

You will notice that the process begins with the melting and purification of stibnite, which is the liquation process described above. Remember to use the catch basin water from this process where Basil directs you to add distilled water.

Theodor Kerkring, in his commentary to Valentine's *Triumphal Chariot*, adds some additional tips for success in the preparation:

For six pounds of Antimony are required sixteen pounds of Distilled Water, and when (after Digestion) we would distil it, a certain manual Operation must be observed, on which depends the Success of the whole Work almost. For the Alembeck must be so placed, as his Pipe or Beak

It is important to calcine out any free sulfur prior to the digestion in order to prevent the formation of sulfuric acid. This should be a long, gentle calcination, slowly up to about 200 °C maximum.

– VINEGAR of ANTIMONY –

Stibnite
↓
CRUSH TO FINE
POWDER
↓
Calcination
70 – 80°C 20 – 30 Hrs
90 – 100°C 10 Hrs
↓
Fermentation
→ MIX 3 pts Stibnite
7 pts Distilled Rain Water   } By wt

Seal Flask and Digest @ 40 – 50°C
- Shake often -
↓
Distillation
Start at 60°C and slowly Raise To 350° – 400°C
over about 3 days
↓
Let cool
(Look for Red & yellow sublimate)
↓
Pour Distillate Back on   - - - → { SAVE STIBNITE RESIDUE
Residue   For other work }

at 3x

→ Final Distillate → ADD water From Bubbler → To Final Distillation →

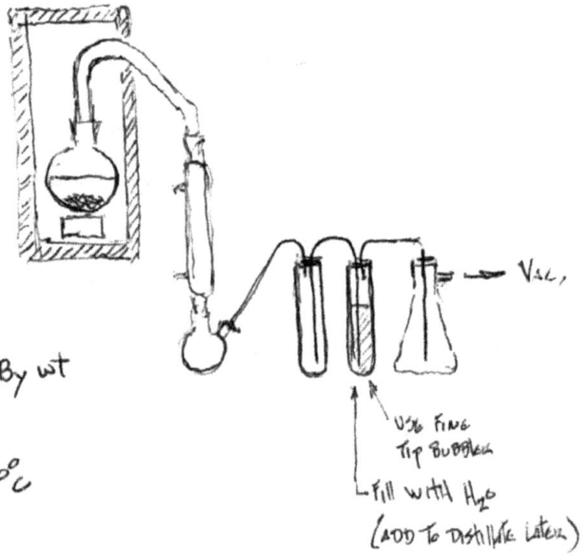

Use Fine
Tip Bubbler

Fill with H_2O
(ADD To Distillate Later)

Vac,

VINEGAR OF ☿ (CONT)

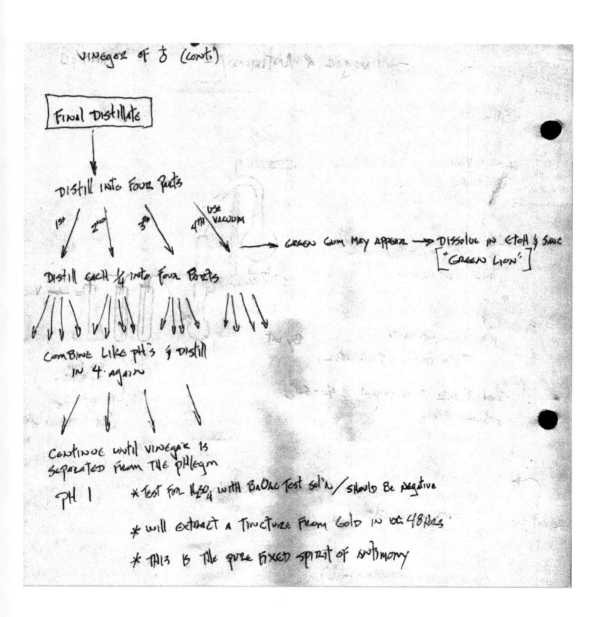

Final Distillate

↓

DISTILL INTO FOUR PARTS

1ˢᵗ 2ⁿᵈ 3ʳᵈ 4ᵗʰ USE VACUUM → GREEN GUM MAY APPEAR → DISSOLVE IN EtOH & SAVE ["GREEN LION"]

DISTILL EACH ¼ INTO FOUR PARTS

COMBINE LIKE pH's & DISTILL IN 4 AGAIN

CONTINUE UNTIL VINEGAR IS SEPARATED FROM THE PHLEGM

pH 1   * TEST FOR H_2SO_4 WITH BaOAc TEST SOL'N / SHOULD BE NEGATIVE

          * WILL EXTRACT A TINCTURE FROM GOLD IN ≈ 48 HRS

          * THIS IS THE PURE FIXED SPIRIT OF ANTIMONY

344

An alternate method for producing Vinegar of Antimony is provided by "The Golden Chain of Homer."

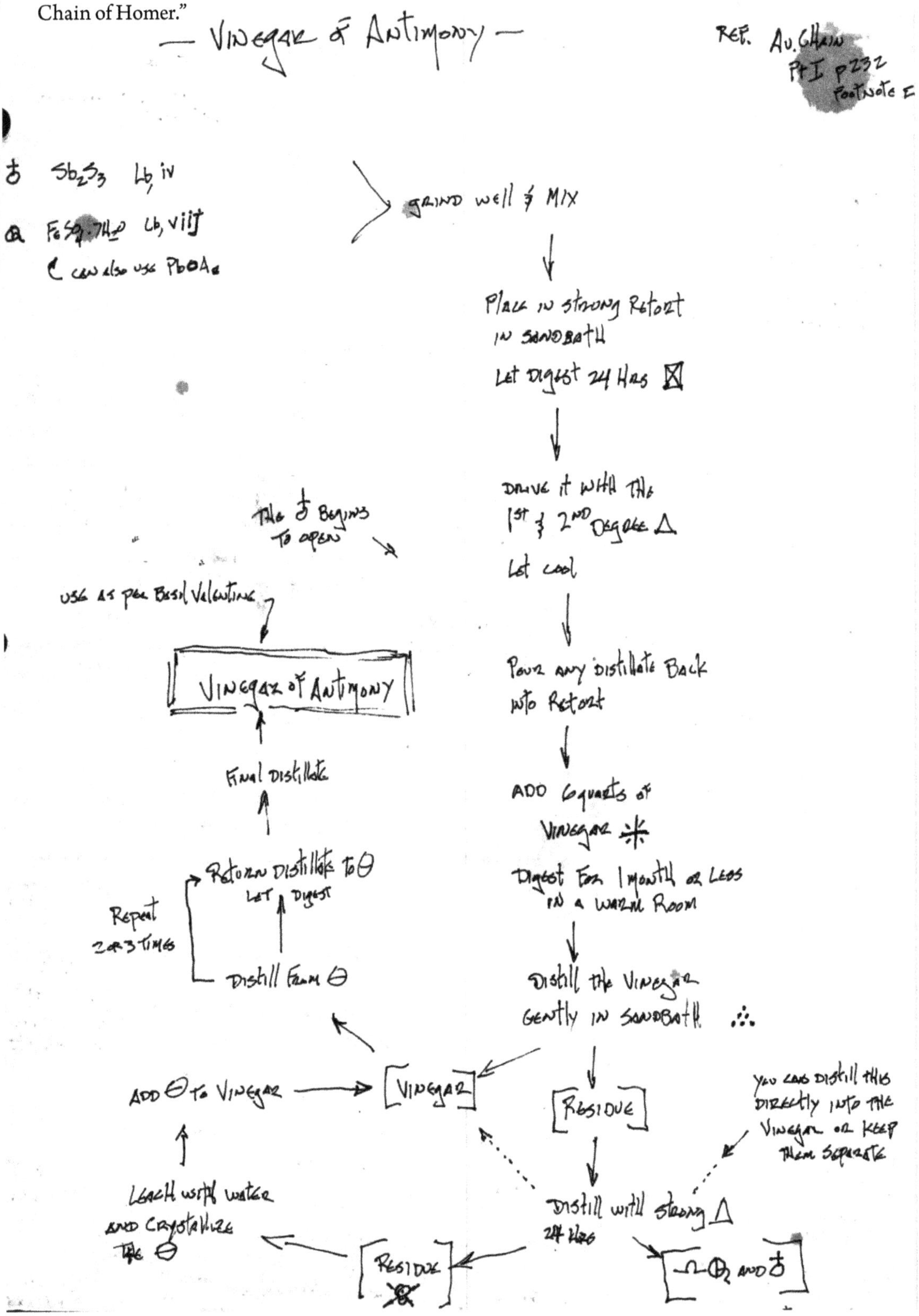

— VINEGAR OF ANTIMONY —

REF. AU. CHAIN
Pt I p232
FootNote E

☿ Sb_2S_3 ℔ iv

♁ $FeSO_4 \cdot 7H_2O$ ℔ viij

☾ can also use $PbOAc$

GRIND WELL & MIX

↓

Place in strong Retort in sandbath

Let Digest 24 Hrs ☒

↓

Drive it with the 1st & 2nd Degree △

Let cool

↓

Pour any Distillate Back into Retort

↓

ADD 6 quarts of Vinegar ✳

Digest for 1 month or less in a warm Room

↓

Distill the Vinegar Gently in sandbath ∴

The ☿ Begins to open

Use as per Basil Valentine

[VINEGAR OF ANTIMONY]

↑ Final Distillate

Return Distillate to θ
Let Digest

Repeat 2 or 3 times

Distill from θ

ADD θ to Vinegar → [VINEGAR] ←

Leach with water and crystallize the θ

↓

[RESIDUE ✗]

[RESIDUE]

Distill with strong △ 24 Hrs

[△ θ₂ AND ☿]

you can Distill this Directly into the Vinegar or Keep them Separate

ROBERT ALLEN BARTLETT

✳ IF S_g = 1lb   7/25/08

MEDIA
SBNITE → 20g
VITRIOL → 37½g   } GROUND SEPARATELY THEN MIXED IN FLASK   Dark gray sparkling Granules

FRESHLY RECRYSTALLIZED
FROM RAIN ♀ + ½ ml H_2SO_4
$FeSO_4 \cdot 7H_2O$
From Seattle Pottery Supply

DIGESTION @ 40°C   Matter Sweats & Circulates

BEGAN SLOW DISTILLATION IN SANDBATH   12:15 pm 8/2/08

Some Sublimate on glass
PH 5

Poured clear Distillate Back on to RESIDUE
Let Digest @ 40°C

OFF at 8pm
T_{max} = 460°F

Black & White Solid
Top | Bottom

SOLIDS HAVE ABSORBED THE LIQUID AND IS A THICK PASTE DARK GRAY

Clear Liquid
PH 2-3

┌─────────────┐
│ VINEGAR OF ☿ │
└─────────────┘

Clear Distillate
Residue   Acetic odor with SULFUROUS UNDERTONE

ADDED 60 mL ✳   → Distilled White Vinegar CONCENTRATED BY FREEZING 3X
8/4/08
DIGESTION @ 40°C

VINEGAR 6 qts = 12 lbs = 60g

Distillation 7/2/10

10/19/08 DISTILLATION BY DEGREES FOR 12 Hrs
FINAL TEMP = 1550°F
(8442)

RED & yellow Sublimate
• Cloudy Distillate
• SO_3 odor/used Bubbler

COHOBATE DISTILLATE WITH RESIDUE

10/26/08 SEPARATED THE DISTILLATE TO ANOTHER FLASK
* ADDED WATER TO RESIDUE

//STRONG SO_2
PH = 1

USED BUBBLER H_2O To Collect

REPEAT
Distillation 11/22/08
DIGESTION 11/8/08

Filtration 10/31/08

Black VERY MAGNETIC
RESIDUE

BLACK DISTILLATION RESIDUE
A Black Crystalline POWDER / Metallic Luster
VERY MAGNETIC

COMBINED DISTILLATE & ☿s

CLEAR LIQUID

GRIND, EXTRACT w/ BUBBLER ⧖

CRYSTALLINE SALT ← EVAPORATE

CRYSTALLINE SALT ← EVAPORATE ← CLEAR LIQUID ← FILTER ← BLACK RESIDUE ✳

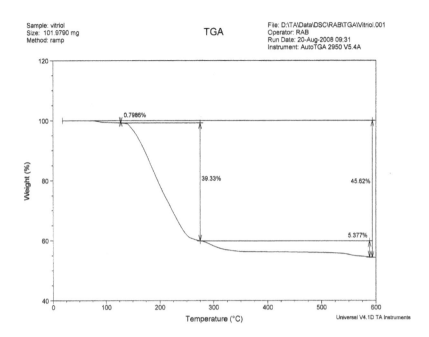

TGA of Iron Vitriol (Ferrous Sulfate Heptahydrate)

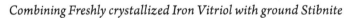

Combining Freshly crystallized Iron Vitriol with ground Stibnite

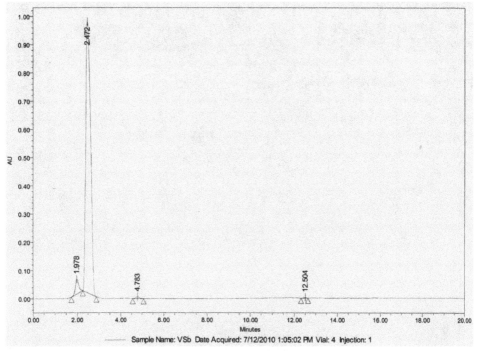

HPLC of the distilled Vinegar of Antimony

Distillation of the Vinegar of Antimony per the Golden Chain method

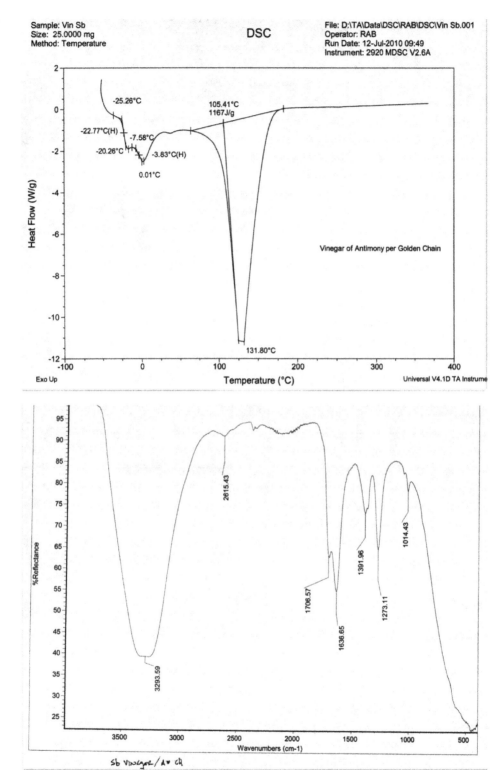

FTIR scan of the Vinegar of Antimony per Golden Chain

Oil of Antimony

Also many Oils may be prepared of Antimony, some per se and without Addition, and many others by Addition. Yet they are not endued with the same Virtues, but each enjoys its own, according to the Diversity of its Preparation. So Antimony, when prepared by the Addition of Water, assumes another nature and Complexion for operating, than when prepared by Fire only. And although every Preparation of it ought to be made by Fire, without which the Virtue of it cannot be manifested: yet consider, that the Addition of Earth gives it wholly another Nature, than the Addition of Water. So also when Antimony is sublimed in Fire through the Air, and further prepared, another Virtue, other Powers.
—Triumphal Chariot

Fixed Red Oil

There are many ways to obtain an oil from antimony as we have already seen above, and the properties of these oils vary with their method of preparation. One of the most important and valuable of these is the "Fixed Red Oil." This experiment was a revision of the Principe Experiment detailed earlier.

— FIXED OIL OF ANTIMONY —   12/24/12

Sb-27 – 12/24/12

Glass of ☿ : Sb_2O_3 200g (U.S. Antimony Corp.)

         Crocus Martis 1g (Sea. Pottery Supply)

         Silica   4g   (Aerosil)

         Stibnite   7g   ⟶ FUSED INTO RED GLASS
       ⌐ WEATHERBY   AT ANTIMONY
       └ MINE/RAB   WORKSHOP 2012

12/24/12

   149g RED GLASS
   300mL 50% ACETIC
   1g SAL AMMONIAC   ⟶ PLACED INTO GRINDING JAR w/ Al_2O_3 MEDIA
   1g AMMONIUM CARBONATE
                                        ↓
                                  GRINDING   10 Hrs 12/24
                                             10 Hrs 12/25

                                        ↓
                              Digestion @ RM Temp
                              Shake occasionally

                                  Filtered 2/3/13

                         Solids ↙   ↘ LIQUID
                                              (ORANGE)
                            ↓
                     Repeated extraction
                     with 300mL Fresh
                     Solvent
148.7g Total Recovered (99.8%)   ↓
132.9g wt collected ground glass   2/9/13 Filtration
15.8g wt unground Glass
     ↑   ↙   ↘ LIQUID
     └ DRIED ← Solids ←   COMBINED
                                           EXTRACTS INTO A
                                           RETORT FOR
                                           DISTILLATION
                                              ↓

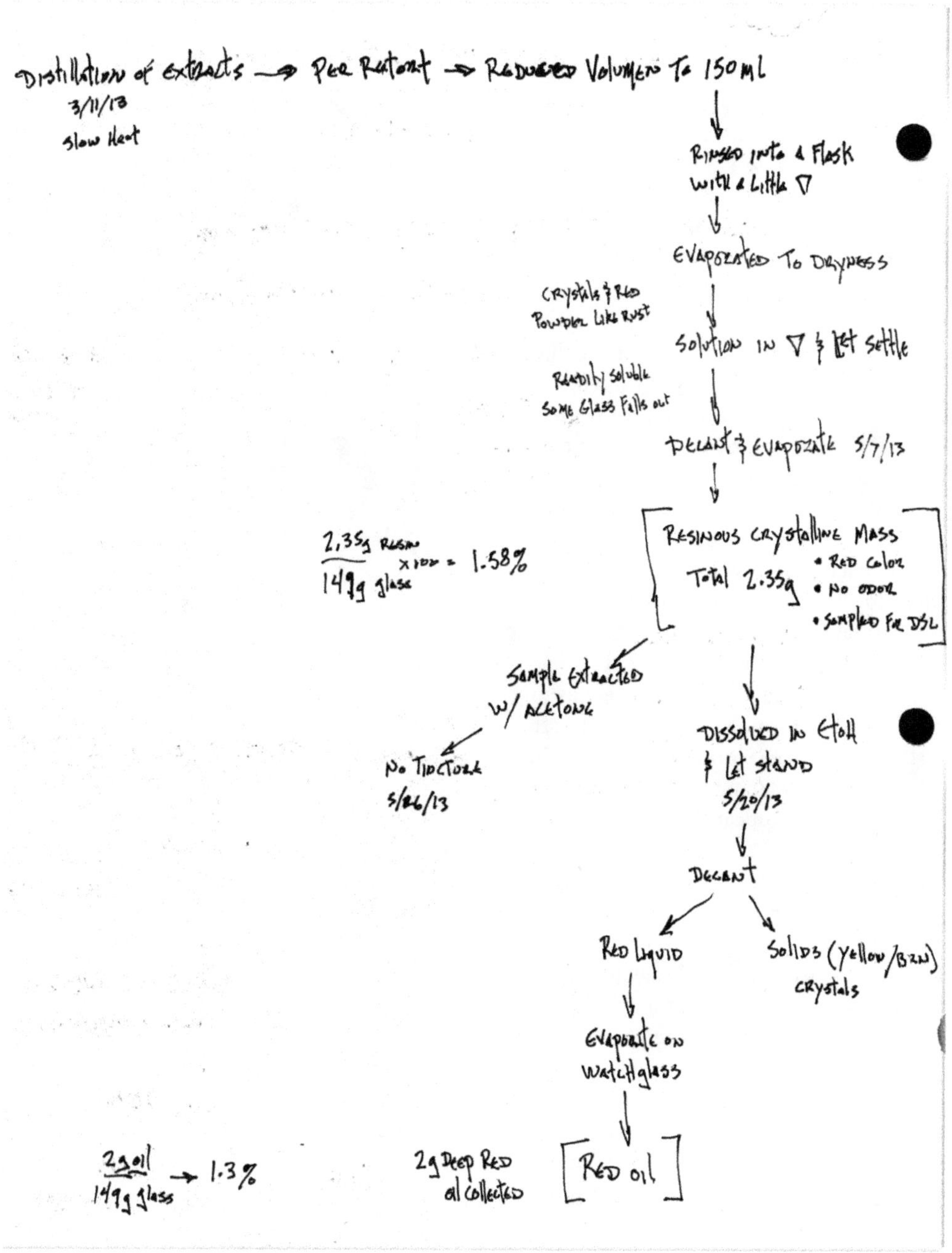

Distillation of extracts ⟶ Per Retort ⟶ Reduced Volumes To 150 mL
3/11/13
Slow Heat

Rinsed into a Flask
with a Little ▽

Evaporated To Dryness

Crystals & Red
Powder Like Rust

Solution in ▽ & Let Settle

Readily Soluble
Some Glass Falls out

Decant & Evaporate 5/7/13

$$\frac{2.35g \ Resin}{149g \ glass} \times 100 = 1.58\%$$

RESINOUS CRYSTALLINE MASS
Total 2.35g
• Red Color
• No Odor
• Sampled for DSL

Sample Extracted
w/ Acetone

Dissolved in EtOH
& Let Stand
5/20/13

No Tincture
5/26/13

Decant

Red Liquid

Solids (Yellow/Brn)
Crystals

Evaporate on
Watchglass

$$\frac{2g \ oil}{149g \ glass} \longrightarrow 1.3\%$$

2g Deep Red
oil Collected

[Red oil]

The preparation begins with the calcination of purified stibnite or kermes into the oxide form. The oxide is ground very fine and made into glass of antimony. This glass is powdered and then extracted with a strong solution of vinegar sharpened by the addition of sublimated Sal Ammoniac and Ammonium Carbonate (also known as *Hirschhornsalz*, or Hart's Horn salt). Let the extraction continue for several weeks at about 40 °C and agitate it once in awhile, especially in the first few days, or it will coalesce into a thick mass. After this time the solution will take on a golden to deep red color. Filter off the extract, and repeat with fresh vinegar.

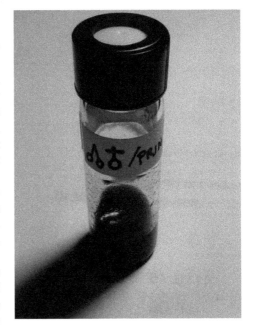

Combine all of the extract and filter it into a distillation vessel. Gently distill the liquid until it becomes thickened, then add some water to dissolve the residue and continue the distillation.

Repeat this washing with water to remove as much of the acid as possible. This washing can also be performed using alcohol; in this case, ethyl acetate is formed and readily distills out so the washing is faster. The resulting residue will appear as a golden brown, gummy resin.

Place the resin into a suitably sized distillation vessel and proceed to distill as in the acetate work. Drops of red oil will come over, which are carefully collected by dissolving them into absolute alcohol. Rinse any of the oil adhering to the glassware out with alcohol and combine all of the liquid into a container. Seal and allow it to stand for several days, and then decant the clear tinted extract for use. This "Fixed Tincture of Antimony" has powerful healing properties unrecognized by modern medicine.

ROBERT ALLEN BARTLETT

— THE RED OIL OF ANTIMONY —

THIS IS THE SAME RED OIL of Basil Valentine
FOR THE FIRE STONE
It contains THE FIRE OF ANTIMONY AND
THE Vegetable Life FROM ACETIC/ACETATE

```
┌─────────────────────┐
│  RED OIL of ♁        │
└─────────────────────┘
          ↑
  DRY DISTILL Crystals
          ↑
  Digest At 40°C
  1-2 Months
          ↑
┌─────────────────┐
│  ANTIMONY       │
│  ACETATE        │
└─────────────────┘
          ↑  Crystallize
  Gently DISTILL
  To REMOVE All
  ACID
          ↑
MIX WITH          ← ┌──────────────┐      Repeat Til
ABS. Alcohol &      │ Concentrate  │      No ACID
CIRCULATE           │      +       │ ←
                    │ Residual ACID│
                    └──────────────┘
```

Stibnite
    ↓
┌──────────────────┐
│ Oxysulfide   │
│ (By Calcination or│
│ Kermes)   │
└──────────────────┘
    ↓
COMBINE
&
Circulate   ←
    ↓
DISTILL Extract
To REMOVE Bulk of
LIQUID Gently

RED
WINE VINEGAR
    ↓
CONCENTRATE
BY FREEZING
    ↓
DISTILL
    ↓
Strong
Vinegar

Copper Metal
SCRAP
    ↓
HEAT TO
OXIDIZE
    ↓
Copper Oxide

MIX &   ← Copper Oxide
DIGEST
    ↓
FILTER & Crystallize
    ↓
Copper Acetate
    ↓
DRY DISTIL
    ↓
┌──────────────────┐
│ RADICAL VINEGAR │
│ (BLUE TINT)   │
└──────────────────┘
    ↓
MUST HAVE THIS TO go To
THE RED STAGE
It is THE Spirit of Copper

Detailed earlier was the process used at Paralab to create an Unfixed Tincture from the Fume using acetone as the primary solvent. Antimony can also be extracted with a specially prepared volatile solvent in order to produce an "Unfixed Tincture."

The solvent for this is the so-called "Kerkring Menstruum" or "Philosophical Alcohol." This preparation is attributed to Dr. Theodore Kerkring who mentions it in his commentary to Basil Valentine's *Triumphal Chariot of Antimony*.

This is an example of a vegetable spirit being "magnetized" or "determined" to activity in the mineral realm by contact with prepared salts.

In this menstruum, we make use of the salt Ammonium Chloride (NH_4Cl) or Sal Ammoniac to sharpen the alcohol. Preparation of the menstruum begins with the sublimation of Sal Ammoniac.

This is easily done using Corning Ware casseroles over electric or gas heat. After the first sublimation, the sublimed crystals will take on a pale yellow color; collect them and sublime again.

The sublimate will appear more yellow-orange and even reddish in areas; collect and sublime a third time. After this third sublimation, the crystals will appear very yellow orange to red-yellow and are ready for use. Store them in a glass container sealed from moisture.

Next, we need a very strong alcohol, 95% at least and preferably from red wine. The alcohol should be additionally dried by adding one or two ounces freshly dried salt of tartar (potassium carbonate) per liter. Allow this to digest at least for a day, then distil just prior to use.

When we have prepared these two ingredients, they are combined at the New Moon in the proportion of 4 parts Sal Ammoniac to 10 parts Alcohol. Seal them in a glass vessel and let digest at about 40 °C for a month at least.

After digestion, the whole matter is gently distilled to near dryness. Collect the distillate and distill it again two more times. The final distillate will be the "Kerkring Menstruum"; seal it tightly in a glass vessel for use. Collect together all of the residues from the distillations and save them as well; they can be used to "charge" more alcohol several times.

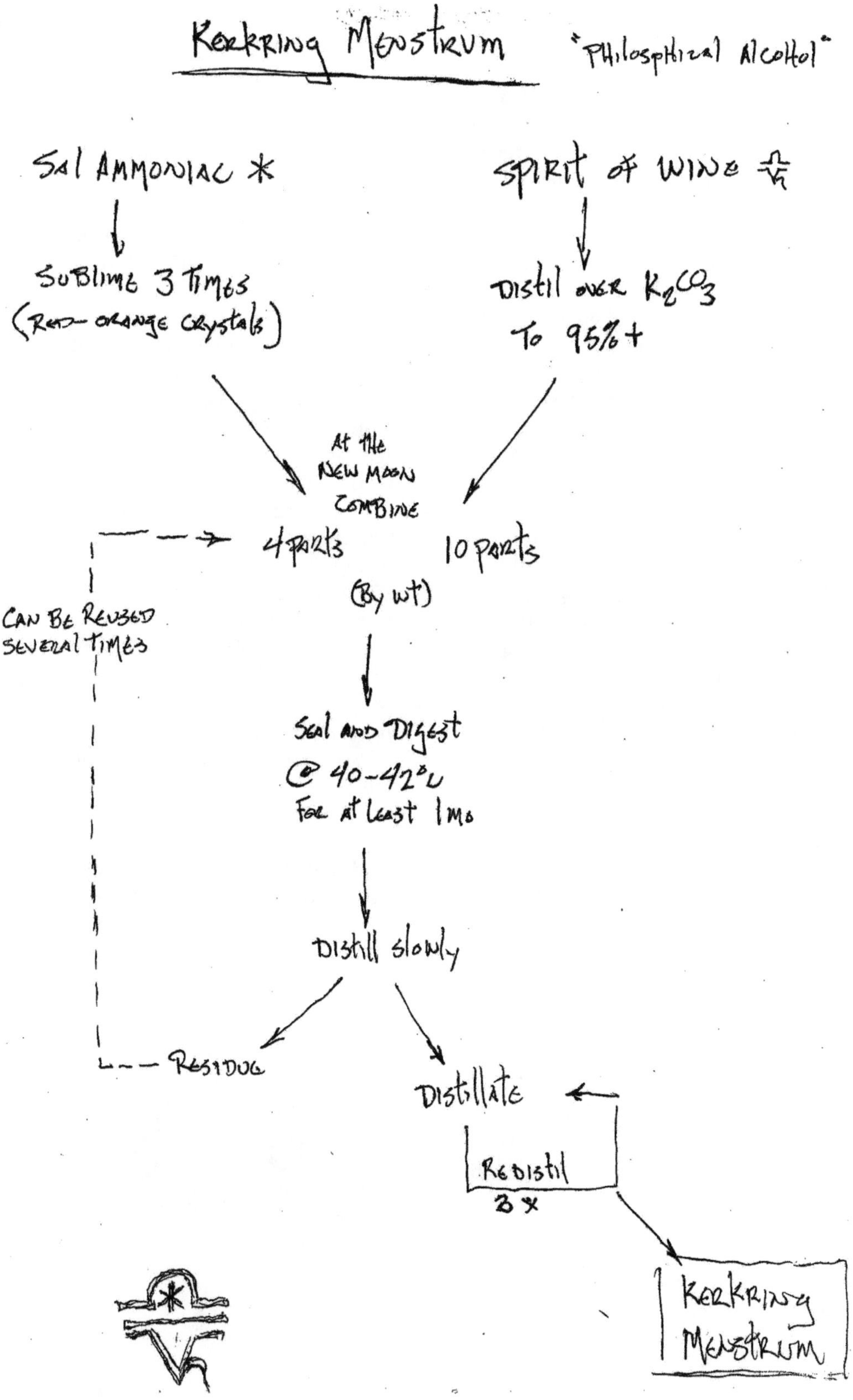

ROBERT ALLEN BARTLETT

Kerkring Menstruum   "Philosphical Alcohol"

Sal Ammoniac *

Sublime 3 Times
(Red-orange Crystals)

Spirit of Wine

Distil over K_2CO_3
To 95%+

At the
New Moon
Combine

4 parts   10 parts

(By wt)

Can Be Reused
Several Times

Seal and Digest
@ 40-42°C
For at least 1mo

Distill slowly

Residue

Distillate

Redistil
3 x

Kerkring
Menstruum

One of the best solvents or menstruums to use for preparing the unfixed tincture of antimony is "The Acetone of the Wise" or "The White Wine Spirit" derived from the distillation of a metallic acetate. After isolating and rectifying the wine spirit, sharpen it with sal ammoniac just as was done with the Kerkring Menstruum.

We can use either of these prepared solvents to extract powdered antimony glass, calcined stibnite or calcined kermes.

This calcination should be done very slowly and carefully; at no time should globules of fused material be allowed to form.

A slow roasting at 90 ºC for a day is wise, then very gradually increase the heat with constant stirring until the matter begins to lighten. When the material is becoming lighter gray, indicating the sulfur is nearly vaporized out, the temperature can be increased. Grind to a fine powder, and then continue the calcination to a light gray or even to whiteness. Always keep in mind that these vapors are very toxic, so have adequate ventilation or work outside.

Place the powder into a flask and cover it with one of the solvents, then seal it tightly. Allow this to digest at 40 ºC for a month or two at least. The menstruum will take on a golden color and slowly deepen to red-amber. Remember to shake it well once in a while.

Filter off the colored extract into a distillation flask and slowly distill the extract to recover our menstruum.

A red oil will remain in the flask. The oil is dissolved into strong alcohol and allowed to stand several days before filtering for use. This is an "Unfixed Tincture from Antimony."

If the extraction was performed with acetone there is an option which provides an additional purification step for our antimony extract. The acetone extract we filter off from the antimony is placed into a large, tall container. Into this, pour an equal volume of a saturated solution of sodium bicarbonate (baking soda) in water. A brown precipitate will form and fall to the bottom. Decant off the liquid and save the precipitate. Wash it with water several times, allowing it to settle and decanting the water off each time. Finally collect the precipitate on a filter and let it dry gently.

The dried powder is extracted with strong alcohol which has been dried over potassium carbonate. The resulting tincture is filtered off for use and represents a more purified form of the Unfixed Tincture from Antimony.

In each case, fixed or unfixed oil, it is important to have little or no water present in the alcohol used for the final tincture extraction. This will prevent solution of any toxic antimony salts that may have carried through the process.

Also, the oil may be "sweetened" by gently distilling the tincture and then returning the distillate to the residue. This should be repeated several times. A small amount of "feces" will drop out with each cycle and the final tincture will mature.

Medicinally, the volatile or unfixed tinctures are warming, energizing, toning in their effects, while the fixed tinctures are cooling, and contracting. Unfixed tinctures are said to be more effective in acute illnesses, while Fixed tinctures are more useful for chronic problems.

Remedies that are unfixed heal unfixed diseases and the radically fixed nonvolatile ones expel fixed diseases which do not move the excrements through evacuation but through sweating and by other means.
—Isaac Newton, *Keynes Ms 64*

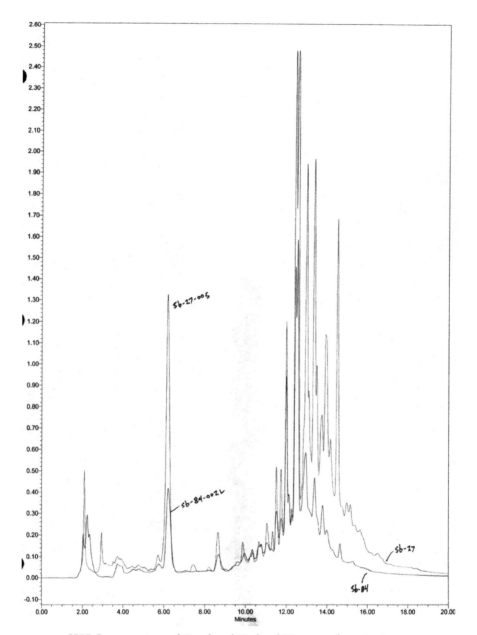

HPLC comparison of Fixed and Unfixed Tinctures from Antimony

Fixing the Unfixed

This experiment was an attempt to convert the Unfixed oil to a Fixed oil:

— Fixing Unfixed Oil of Antimony —   2/10/13

Sb-84 To 27

Unfixed → Fixed

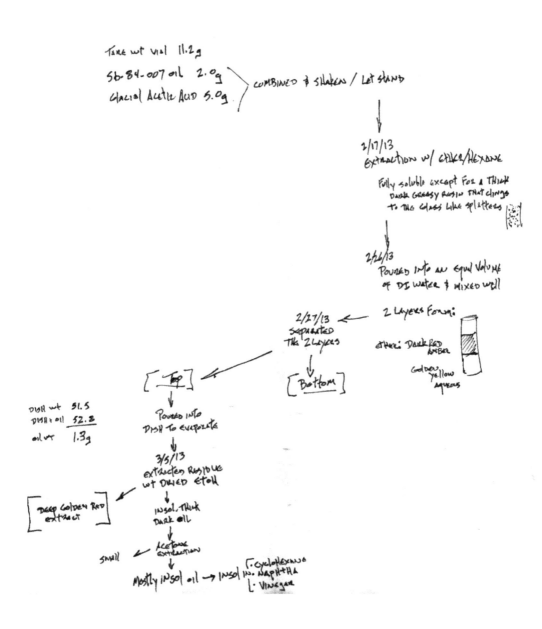

Tare wt vial   11.2g

Sb-84-007 oil   2.0g
Glacial Acetic Acid 5.0g   Combined & Shaken / Let Stand

2/17/13
Extraction w/ CHX2/Hexane

Fully soluble except for a thick
dark greasy resin that clings
to the glass like splatters

2/26/13
Poured into an equal volume
of DI water & mixed well

2 Layers form:

2/27/13
Separated
The 2 Layers   Ether: Dark Red Amber

Golden Yellow Aqueous

[Top]   [Bottom]

Dish wt   51.5
Dish + oil 52.8
oil wt   1.3g

Poured into
Dish to evaporate

3/5/13
Extracted Residue
wt Dried EtOH

Deep Golden Red
Extract

Insol. Thick
Dark Oil

small   Acetone
Extraction

Mostly Insol oil → Insol in. Naphtha   Cyclohexane
Naphtha
Vinegar

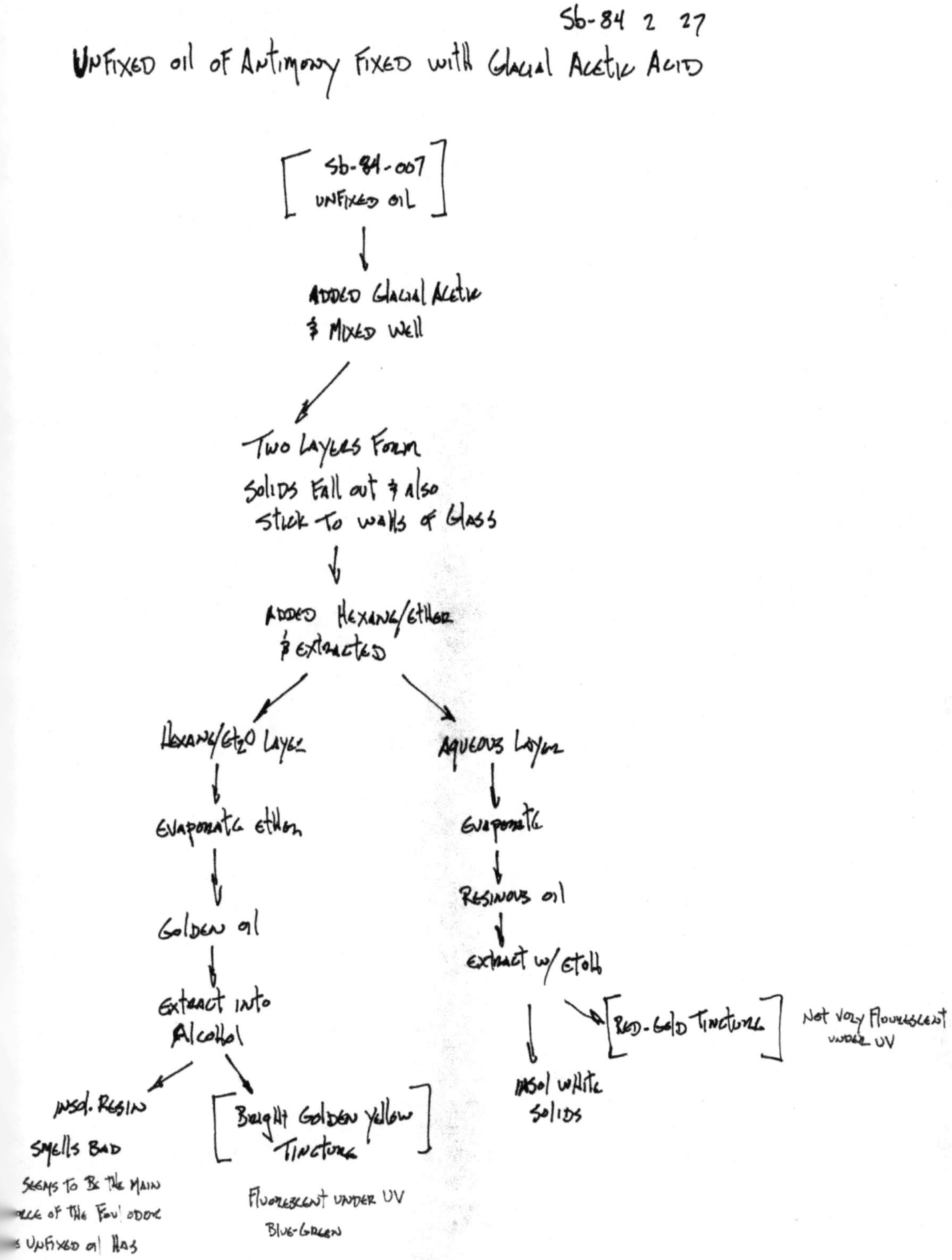

UNFIXED OIL OF ANTIMONY FIXED WITH GLACIAL ACETIC ACID

ROBERT ALLEN BARTLETT

[Sb-84-007
UNFIXED OIL]

↓

ADDED GLACIAL ACETIC
& MIXED WELL

↓

TWO LAYERS FORM
SOLIDS FALL OUT & ALSO
STICK TO WALLS OF GLASS

↓

ADDED HEXANE/ETHER
& EXTRACTED

↓ ↓

HEXANE/Et₂O LAYER   AQUEOUS LAYER

↓ ↓

EVAPORATE ETHER   EVAPORATE

↓ ↓

GOLDEN OIL   RESINOUS OIL

↓ ↓

EXTRACT INTO   EXTRACT W/ EtOH
ALCOHOL

↓   [RED-GOLD TINCTURE]   NOT VERY FLUORESCENT
UNDER UV

INSOL. RESIN   [BRIGHT GOLDEN YELLOW   INSOL WHITE
TINCTURE]   SOLIDS
SMELLS BAD

SEEMS TO BE THE MAIN
SOURCE OF THE FOUL ODOR   FLUORESCENT UNDER UV

THE UNFIXED OIL HAS   BLUE-GREEN

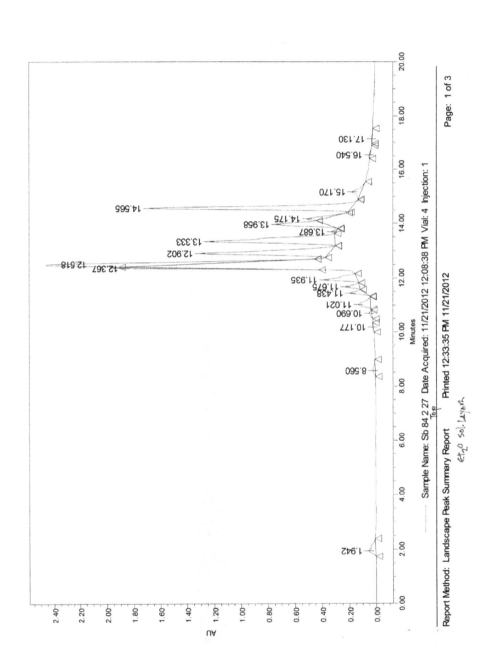

HPLC of the Unfixed oil made Fixed by acetic acid treatment

Unfixed oil + Sb-84-007
+
Acetic Acid
↓
extract w/Et₂O + Hexane
↓
Ether layer
evaporate
→ [oil dissolved in EtOH]

Peak Summary with Statistics

	Sample Name	Inj.	Peak Name	RT (min)	Area (µV*sec)	% Area	Height (µV)	Amount	Units	Vial
1	Sb 84 2 27	1		1.942	947978	1.72	49902			4
2	Sb 84 2 27	1		8.560	300359	0.54	17403			4
3	Sb 84 2 27	1		10.177	75245	0.14	6418			4
4	Sb 84 2 27	1		10.690	185316	0.34	17995			4
5	Sb 84 2 27	1		11.021	1142721	2.07	91097			4
6	Sb 84 2 27	1		11.438	786092	1.42	115893			4
7	Sb 84 2 27	1		11.675	671446	1.22	102722			4
8	Sb 84 2 27	1		11.935	2212251	4.01	245659			4
9	Sb 84 2 27	1		12.367	1984454	3.59	582095			4
10	Sb 84 2 27	1		12.518	8897859	16.11	1035445			4
11	Sb 84 2 27	1		12.902	9716776	17.59	956213			4
12	Sb 84 2 27	1		13.333	10550978	19.11	934813			4
13	Sb 84 2 27	1		13.687	159240	0.29	29552			4
14	Sb 84 2 27	1		13.958	3236955	5.86	372930			4
15	Sb 84 2 27	1		14.175	1009796	1.83	125906			4
16	Sb 84 2 27	1		14.565	12287004	22.25	1505665			4
17	Sb 84 2 27	1		15.170	892031	1.62	64537			4
18	Sb 84 2 27	1		16.540	83819	0.15	7373			4
19	Sb 84 2 27	1		17.130	84741	0.15	5664			4
Mean				12.304	2906582.256		329856.868			
Std. Dev.				3.297	4082030.362		450602.25			
% RSD				26.79	140.44		136.605			

Acquisition Log

Peak summary details for Unfixed oil made Fixed

Sublime one part of Antimony with a fourth part of Sal Armoniack, with subtile Fire. The Salt carries up the Sulphur of Antimony, red as Blood. Grind this Sublimate to a fine Powder, and if you took at first one pound of Antimony, grind with it again five ounces of Sal Armoniack, and Sublime as before. The Sublimate, dissolve in a moist place. Or otherwise, take the Sublimate, and edulcorate it from the Salt added, gently dry it, and you will have Sulphur, which burns like Common Sulphur, which is sold at the Apothecaries. From this Sulphur extract its Tincture with distilled Vinegar, and when you have abstracted the Vinegar by gentle Heat of B.M. and by a subtile Operation again distilled the remaining Powder, you will have (if in this Operation you erre not) a most Excellent Oil, grateful, Sweet, and pleasant in its use, without any Corrosiveness or peril.

The final powder mentioned above, which is distilled "by a subtile operation," is distilled as in the acetate process, by which you will obtain a red oil. For small amounts, this distillation can be performed in glass test tubes connected with glass tubing.

True Sulfur of Antimony

Take crude Hungarian Antimony, put that ground to a subtle Powder, into a Glass Cucurbit with a flat bottom: pour thereon the true Vinegar of Philosophers rendered more acid with its own Salt. Then set the Cucurbit firmly closed in Horse-dung, or B.M. to putrefy the Matter for forty Days, in which time the body resolves itself, and the Vinegar contracts a Colour red as Blood. Pour off the Vinegar, and pour on fresh, and do this so often, as until the Vinegar can no more be tinged. This being done, filter all the Vinegar through Paper, and again set it, put into a clean Glass firmly closed in Horse-dung, or B.M. as before, that it may putrefy for forty

Days; in which time the Body again resolves itself, and the Matter in the Glass becomes as black as Calcanthum, or Shoemakers Ink. When you have this Sign, then true Solution is made, by which the further Separation of Elements is procured. Put this black matter into another Cucurbit, to which apply an Alembick, and distil off the Vinegar with Moderate Fire; then the Vinegar passeth out clear, and in the bottom a sordid matter remains; grind that to a subtle Powder, and edulcorate it with distilled Rain Water, then dry it with gentle heat, and put it in a Circulatory with a long Neck (the Circulatory must have three Cavities or Bellies, as if three Globes were set one above another, yet distinct or apart each from other, as Sublimatories, with their Aludel [or Head] are wont to be made, and it must have a long Neck like a Phial, (or Bolthead) and pour on it Spirit of Wine highly rectified, til it riseth three Fingers above the Matter, and having well closed the Vessel, set it in a moderate Heat for two Months.

Then follows another new Extraction, and the Spirit of Wine becomes transparently red as a Ruby, or as was the first Extraction of the Vinegar, yea more fair. Pour off the Spirit of wine thus tinged, filter it through Paper, and put it into a Cucurbit (the black Matter which remains set aside, and separate from this Work; for it is not profitable therein) to which apply an Head and Receiver, and having firmly closed all Junctures, begin to distil in Ashes with moderate Fire: then the Spirit of wine carries over the Tincture of Antimony with it self, the Elements separate themselves each from other, and the Alembeck and Recipient seem to resemble the form of pure Gold transparent in Aspect. In the end some few Feces remain, and the Golden Colour in the Glass altogether fails. The red Matter, which in distilling passed over into the Receiver, put into a Circulatory for ten Days, and as many Nights. By that Circulation Separation is made; for the Oil thereby acquires Gravity, and separates itself to the bottom from the Spirit of Wine; and the Spirit of Wine is again Clear, as it was at first, and swims upon the Oil. Which admirable Separation is like a Miracle in Nature: Separate this Oil from the Spirit of Wine by a Separatory.

This Oil is of a singular and incredible Sweetness, with which no other thing may be compared, it is grateful in the Use, and all Corrosiveness is separated from it. No man can by Cogitation judge, by Understanding comprehend, what incredible Effects, potent Powers, and profitable Virtues are in this Royal Oil. Therefore this Sulphur of Antimony, I have given no other Name, than my Balsam of Life.
—*Triumphal Chariot*

— ANTIMONY ☉ ♀ ☿ —

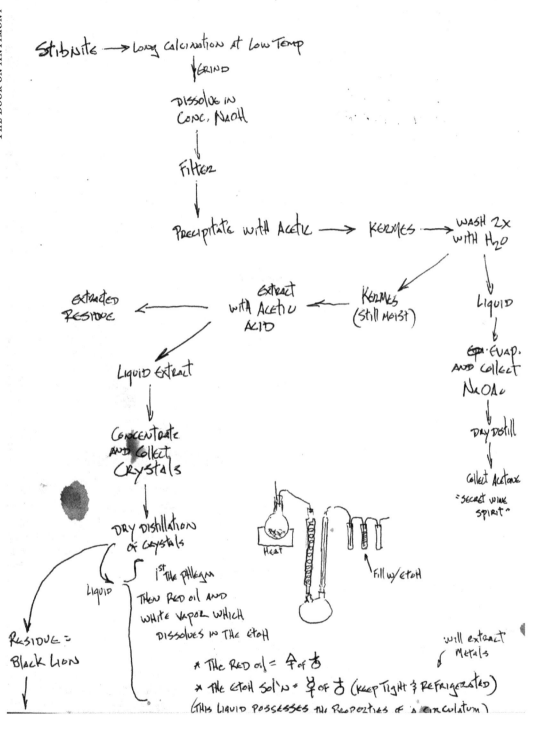

Stibnite → Long Calcination At Low Temp

↓ GRIND

DISSOLVE IN CONC. NaOH

↓

Filter

↓

Precipitate with Acetic → KERMES → WASH 2X WITH H_2O

KERMES (Still Moist) ← LIQUID

Extract WITH ACETIC ACID ←

EXTRACTED RESIDUE ←

Liquid Extract

↓

Concentrate AND Collect Crystals

↓

Dry Distillation of Crystals

Liquid { 1st The Phlegm THEN RED oil AND WHITE VAPOR WHICH DISSOLVES IN THE EtOH

RESIDUE = Black Lion

Heat

Fill w/ EtOH

will extract ₰ Metals

EVAP. AND Collect NaOAc

↓

DRY DISTILL

↓

Collect Acetone "SECRET WINE SPIRIT"

* THE RED oil = ♀ of ♁
* THE EtOH Sol'n = ☿ of ♁ (KEEP TIGHT & REFRIGERATED)
(THIS LIQUID POSSESSES THE PROPERTIES OF A CIRCULATUM)

ROBERT ALLEN BARTLETT

THE BLACK LION → GRIND FINE

↓

PLACE IN A THICK
EARTHENWARE
CRUCIBLE
SET ON A LAYER OF KAOLIN
AND HEAT TO 1000°C

↓

BOIL THE CRUCIBLE IN
DISTILLED WATER TO
LEACH THE MATERIAL OUT

↓

FILTER & EVAPORATE
LIQUID

↓

COLLECT
CRYSTALS   θ or ♄

* KEEP DRY & OUT OF AIR

* THEY ARE THE MAGNETS OF THE PHILOSOPHERS

* THEY HAVE THE PROPERTY OF FIXING THE
  PHILOSOPHICAL MERCURY

— FIRE STONE —

* PLACE THE CRYSTALS IN THE DISTILLATION TRAIN ~~WHERE~~ IN PLACE OF THE EtOH.
  DISTILL A FRESH LOAD OF KERLYS ACETATE THROUGH IT.
  IT WILL FIX THE ☿ OF ♄ IN THE SALT.
  THEN IT ONLY NEEDS THE PURIFIED OIL TO MAKE THE FIRE STONE

Summi Philosophi & Chemici

Joachim Tanckivs

De Oleo Antimonii Tractatus.

ROGERII BACONIS ANGLI

Summi Philosophi & Chemici.

Stibium, as the Philosophers say, is composed from the noble mineral Sulphur, and they have praised it as the black lead of the Wise. The Arabs in their language, have called it Asinat vel Azinat, the alchemists retain the name Antimonium. It will however lead to the consideration of high Secrets, if we seek and recognize the nature in which the Sun is exalted, as the Magi found that this mineral was attributed by God to the Constellation Aries, which is the first heavenly sign in which the Sun takes its exaltation or elevation to itself. Although such things are thrown to the winds by common people, intelligent people ought to know and pay more attention to the fact that exactly at this point the infinitude of secrets may be partly contemplated with great profit and in part also explored. Many, but these are ignorant and unintelligent, are of the opinion that if they only had Stibium, they would get to it by Calcination, others by Sublimation, several by Reverberation and Extraction, and obtain its great Secret, Oil, and Perfectum Medicinam. But I tell you, that here in this place nothing will help, whether Calcination, Sublimation, Reverberation nor Extraction, so that subsequently a perfect Extraction of metallic virtue that translates the inferior into the superior, may profitably come to pass or be accomplished. For such shall be impossible for you. Do not let yourselves be confused by several of the philosophers who have written of such things, *i.e.*, Geber, Albertus Magnus, Rhasis, Rupecilla, Aristoteles and many more of that kind. And this you should note. Yes, many say, that when one prepares Stibium to a glass, then the evil volatile Sulphur will be gone, and the Oil, which may be prepared from the glass, would be a very fixed oil, and would then truly give an ingress and Medicine of imperfect metals to perfection. These words and opinions are perhaps good and right, but that it should be thus in fact and prove itself, this will not be. For I say to you truly, without any hidden speech; if you were to lose some of the above mentioned Sulphur by the preparation and the burning, as a small fire may easily damage it, so that you have lost the right penetrating spirit, which should make our whole Antimonii corpus into a perfect red oil, so that it also can ascend over the helm with a sweet smell and very beautiful colors and the whole body of this mineral with all its members, without loss of any weight, except for the foecum, shall be an oil and go over the helm. And note also this: How would it be possible for the body to go into an oil, or give off its sweet oil, if it is put into the last essence and degree? For glass is in all things the outermost and least essence. For you shall know that all creatures at the end of the world, or on the last and coming judgement of the last day, shall become glass or a lovely amethyst and this according to the families of the twelve Patriarchs, as in the families of jewels which Hermes the Great describes in his book: As we have elaborately reported and taught in our book *De Cabala*.

You shall also know that you shall receive the perfect noble red oil, which serves for the translation of metals in vain, if you pour acetum correctum over the Antimonium and extract the redness. Yes not even by Reverberation, and even if its manifold Beautiful colors show themselves, this will not make any difference and is not the right way. You may indeed obtain and make an oil out of it, but it has no perfect force and virtue for transmutation or translation of the imperfect metals into perfection itself. This you must certainly know.

And now we proceed to the manual labor, and thus the practica follows.

Take in the Name of God and the Holy Trinity, fine and well cleansed Antimonii ore, which looks nice, white, pure and internally full of yellow rivulets or veins. It may also be full of red and blue colors and veins, which will be the best. Pound and grind to a fine powder and dissolve in a water or Aqua Regis, which will be described below, finely so that the water may conquer it. And note that you should take it out quite soon after the solution so that the water may conquer it. And note that you should take it out quite soon after the solution so that the water will have no time to damage it, since it quickly dissolves the Antimonii Tincture. For in its nature our water is like the ostrich, which by its heat digests and consumes all iron; for given time, the water would consume it and burn it to naught, so that it would only remain as an idle yellow earth, and then it would be quite spoilt. Consider by comparison Luna, beautiful clean and pure, dissolved in this our water. And let it remain therein for no more than a single night when the water is still strong and full of Spirit, And I tell you, that your good Luna has then been fundamentally consumed and destroyed and brought to nought in this our water.

And if you want to reduce it to a pure corpus again, then you will not succeed, but it will remain for you as a pale yellow earth, and occasionally it may run together in the shape of a horn or white horseshoe, which may not be brought to a corpus by any art. Therefore you must remember to take the Antimonium out as soon as possible after the Solution, and precipitate it and wash it after the custom of the alchemists, so that the matter with its perfect oil is not corroded and consumed by the water.

THE WATER; WHEREIN WE DISSOLVE THE ANTIMONIUM, IS MADE THUS:

Take Vitriol one and a half (alii 2. lb.) Sal armoniac one pound, Arinat (alii Alun) one half pound / Sal niter one and a half pound, Sal gemmae (alii Sal commune) one pound, Alumen crudum (alii Entali) one half pound. These are the species that belong to and should be taken for the Water to dissolve the Antimonium.

Take these Species and mix them well among each other, and distill from this a water, at first rather slowly. For the Spiritus go with great force,, more than in other strong waters. And beware of its spirits, for they are subtle and harmful in their penetration. When you now have the dissolved Antimony, clean and well sweetened, and its sharp waters washed out, so that you do not notice any sharpness any more, then put into a clean vial and overpour it with a good distilled vinegar. Then put the vial in Fimum Equinum, or Balneum Mariae, to putrefy forty (al.i four) days and nights, and it will dissolve and be extracted red as blood. Then take it out and examine how much remains to be dissolved, and decant the clear and pure, which will have a red colour, very cautiously into a glass flask. Then pour fresh vinegar onto it, and put it into Digestion as before, so that that which may have remained with the faecibus, it should thus have ample time to become dissolved. Then the faeces may be discarded, for they are no longer useful, except for being scattered over the earth and thrown away. Afterwards pour all the solutions together into a glass retort, put into Balneum Mariae, and distill the sharp vinegar rather a fresh one, since the former would be too weak, and the matter will very quickly become dissolved by the vinegar. Distill it off again, so that the matter remains quite dry. Then take common distilled water and wash away all sharpness, which has remained with the matter from the vinegar, and then dry the matter in the sun, or otherwise by a gentle fire, so that it becomes well dried. It will then be fair to behold, and have a bright red color. The Philosophers, when they have thus prepared our Antimonium in secret, have remarked how its outermost nature and power has collapsed into its interior, and its interior thrown out and has now become an oil that lies hidden in its innermost and depth, well prepared and ready. And henceforth it cannot, unto the last judgement, be brought back to its first essence. And this is true, for it has become so subtle and volatile, that as soon as it senses the power of fire, it flies away as a smoke with all its parts because of its volatility. Several poor and common Laborers, when they have prepared the Antimonium thus, have taken one part out, to take care of their expenses, so that they may more easily do the rest of the work and complete it, They then mixed it with one part Salmiac, one part Vitro (alii. Nitro, alii. Titro), one part Rebohat, to cleanse the Corpera, and then proceeded to project this mixture onto a pure Lunam. And if the Luna was one Mark, they found two and a half Loth good gold after separation; sometimes even more. And therewith they had accomplished a work providing for their expenses, so that they might even better expect to attain to the Great Work. And the foolish called this a bringing into the Lunam, but they are mistaken. For such gold is not brought in by the Spiritibus (alii. Speciebus), but any Luna contains two Mark gold to the Loth, some even more. But this gold is united to the Lunar nature to such a degree that it may not be separated from it, neither by Aquafort, nor by common Antimonium, as the goldsmiths know. When however the just mentioned mixture is thrown onto the Lunam in flux, then such a separation takes place that the Luna quite readily gives away her implanted gold either in Aquafort or in Regal, and lets herself separate from it, strikes it to the ground and precipitates it, which would or might otherwise not happen. Therefore it is not a bringing into the Lunam, but a bringing out of the Luna.

But we are coming back to our Proposito and purpose of our work, for we wish to have the Oil, which has only been known and been acquainted with this magistry, and not by the foolish.

When you then have the Antimonium well rubified according to the above given teaching, then you shall take a well rectified Spiritum vini, and pour it over the red powder of Antimony, put it in a gentle Balneum Mariae to dissolve for four days and nights, so that everything becomes well dissolved. If however something should remain behind, you overpour the same with fresh Spiritu vini, and put it into the Balneum Mariae again, as said before, and everything should become well dissolved. And in case there are some more faeces there, but there should be very little, do them away, for they are not useful for anything. The Solutiones put into a glass retort, lute on a helm and connect it to a receiver, also well luted, to receive the Spiritus. Put it into Balneum Mariae. Thereafter you begin, in the Name of God, to distill very leisurely at a gentle heat, until all the Spiritus Vini has come over. You then pour the same Spiritum that you have drawn off, back onto the dry matter, and distill it over again as before. And this pouring on and distilling off again, you continue so often until you see the Spiritum vini ascend and go over the helm in all kinds of colours. Then it is time to follow up with a strong fire, and a noble blood red Oleum will ascend, go through the tube of the helm and drip into the recipient. Truly, this is the most secret way of the Wise to distill the very highly praised oil of Antimonii, and it is a noble, powerful, fragrant oil of great virtue, as you will hear below in the following. But here I wish to teach and instruct you who are poor and without means to expect the Great Work in another manner; not the way the ancients did it by separating the gold from the Luna. Therefore take this oil, one lot, [ancient weight unit used for the weighing of gold and silver coins - about 1/30 pound] eight lot of Saturn calcined according to art, and carefully imbibe the oil, drop by drop, while continuously stirring the calx Saturni. Then put it ten days and nights in the heat, in the furnace of secrets, and let the fire that this furnace contains, increase every other day by one degree. The first two days you give it the first degree of fire, the second two days you give it the second degree, and after four days and nights you put it into the third degree of fire and let it remain there for three days and nights. After these three days you open the window of the fourth degree, for which likewise three days and nights should be sufficient. Then take it out, and the top of the Saturnus becomes very beautiful and of a reddish yellow colour. This should be melted with Venetian Boreas. When this has been done, you will find that the power of our oil has changed it to good gold. Thus you will again have subsistence, so that you may better expect the Great Work. We now come back to our purpose where we left it earlier. Above you have heard, and have been told to distill the Spiritum vini with the Oleum Antimonii over the helm into the recipient as well as the work of changing the Saturnum into gold. But now we wish to make haste and report about the second tinctural work. Here it will be necessary to separate the Spiritum vini from the oil again, and you shall know that it is done thus: Take the mixture of oil and wine spirit put it into a retort, put on a helm, connect a receiver and place it all together into the Balneum Mariae. Then distill all the Spiritum vini from the oil, at a very gentle heat, until you are certain that no more Spiritus vini is to be found within this very precious oil. And this will be easy to check; for when you see several drops of Spiritu vini ascend over the helm and fall into the recipient, this is the sign that the Spiritus vini has become separated from the oil. Then remove the fire from the Balneo, though it was very small, so that it may cool all the sooner. Now remove the recipient containing the Spiritu vini, and keep it in a safe place, for it is full of Spiritus which it has extracted from the oil and retained. It also contains admirable virtues, as you will hear hereafter. But in the Balneo you will find the blessed bloodred Oleum Antimonii in the retort, which should be taken out very carefully. The helm must be very slowly removed, taking care to soften and wash off the Lute, so that no dirt falls down into the beautiful red oil and makes it turbid. This oil you must store with all possible precaution so that it receives no damage. For you now have a Heavenly Oil that shines on a dark night and emits light as from a glowing coal. And the reason for this is that its innermost power and soul has become thrown out unto the outermost, and the hidden soul is now revealed and shines through the pure body as a light through a lantern: Just as on Judgement Day our present invisible and internal souls will manifest through our clarified bodies, that in this life are impure and dark, but the soul will then be revealed and seen unto the outermost of the body, and will shine as the bright sun. Thus you now have two separate things: Both the Spirit of Wine full of force and wonder in the arts of the human body: And then the blessed red, noble, heavenly Oleum Antimonii, to translate all diseases of the imperfect metals to the Perfection of gold. And the power of the Spiritual Wine reaches very far and to great heights. For when it is rightly used according to the Art of Medicine: I tell you, you have a heavenly medicine to prevent and to cure all kinds of diseases and ailments of the human body. And its uses are thus, as follows:

— Oil of Antimony —

Ref. Bacon, De oleo Antimonii Tractatus

" The most secret way of the wise to distill the very praised oil of Antimony "

Vitriol 1½ pts
Sal Ammoniac 1 pt
Arinat (alun) ½ pt
Niter 1½ pt
Sal Gemmae 1 pt
Alumen Crudem (entali) ½ pt

Broken alum/Rulandus

→ Mix well → Distill
slowly at first

May get violent
if urged to fast

[Strong Water] "Aqua Regia"
" the water "

[Stibnite] → Powder finely → Dissolve the Antimony
in the water

Collect the solution of dissolved
Sb_2S_3 as soon as possible
(ie. minimize long acid contact)

Final Distillation / oil distills over → [Oil of ☿]
hotter

Gentle Distillation of Spirit

Add distillate
to residue &
repeat   Collect the Liquid Extract
(discard feces)

Extract with Spirit of Wine
4 days in BM

Red Powder

Wash with H_2O & dry

Precipitate
the Antimony
& wash it well   w/ ♂ ♀

Place into vial
and add distilled vinegar

Digest in BM 40 days

Solid   ← Evaporate the
Residue   Vinegar out   ← Red Vinegar Extract

(discard feces)

ROBERT ALLEN BARTLETT

$FeSO_4$

$$\left[\begin{array}{ll} FeSO_4 \cdot 7H_2O & 1.3g \\ NH_4Cl & 1g \\ KAlSO_4 & \frac{1}{2}g \\ KNO_3 & 1.3g \\ NaCl & 1g \\ K_2SO_4 & \frac{1}{2}g \end{array}\right\}$$ ground separately & mixed → YELLOWISH POWDER   12/11/08

↓

DISTILLED to RED HEAT   12/14/08

↓

clear Distillate $pH\ 1$ HCL ?

[STIBNITE POWDER] → MIX BUBBLES & DISSOLVES

↓

ADDED Deliquesced until Neutral

↓

GREY ppt

↓

H_2O WASH ppt

↓

DRY Moist ppt + VINEGAR Let Digest @ 40° 12/14/08

ADDITION of SbF CAUSES WHITE ppt

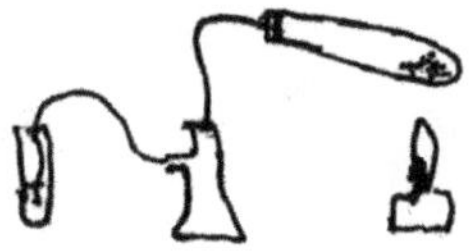

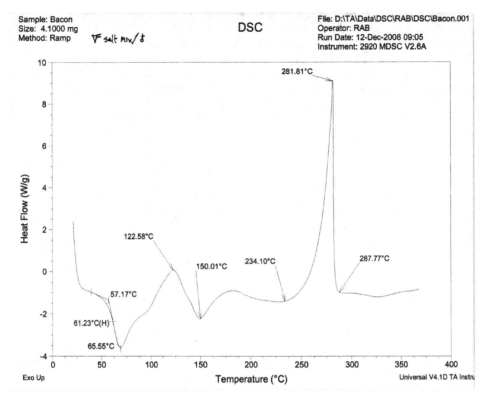

Above: DSC of Bacon's Aqua Fortis salt mixture;
Below, TGA and DSC of the Salt blend recommended by Bacon

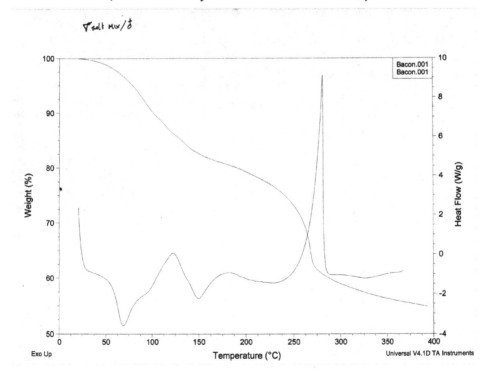

Living Mercury Extracted from Antimony

Take the Regulus of Antimony, made in such manner, as I above taught, eight Parts. Salt of Humane Urine clarified and sublimed, one Part. Sal-Armoniack one Part, and one Part of Salt of Tartar. Mix all the Salts together in a Glass, and having poured on strong Wine Vinegar, lute it with the Luting of Sapience, and digest the Salts with the Vinegar for an entire Month in convenient Heat; afterward put all into a Cucurbit, and in Ashes distill off the Vinegar, that the Salts may remain dry. These dry Salts mix with three Parts of Venetian Earth, and by Retort distil the Mixture with strong Fire, and you will have a wonderful Spirit. This Spirit pour upon the aforesaid Regulus of Antimony reduced to a Powder, and set the whole in putrefaction for two Months. Then gently distil the Vinegar from it, and with what remains mix a fourfold weight of the filings of Steel, and with violent Fire distil by Retort: then the Spirit of Salt, which passeth out, carries over with itself the Mercury of Antimony in the Species of Fume. Wherefore in this Operation you must apply a great Recipient with a large quantity of Water in it, so doing, the Spirit of Salt will be mixed with the Water, but the Mercury collected in the Bottom of the Glass into true living Mercury.

—*Triumphal Chariot*

Salt of Antimony

Make a Regulus of Antimony, by Tartar and Salnitre, as I have above taught, grind this subtily, put it in a great round Glass, and place it in a moderate heat of Sand. This way the Antimony will be sublimed: whatsoever shall be sublimed, that dayly put down with a Feather, that at length it may remain in the Bottom, and there persist until nothing more of it can be sublimed, but the whole remains fixed in the Bottom. Then is your Regulus fixed, and precipitated per se. But consider, here is required a sufficient time, and repetition of the Labour often, before you can obtain that. This Red Precipitate take out, grind it to a subtle Powder, which spread upon a flat and clean Stone, set in a cold moist Place and there let it remain for six Months; at length the Precipitate begins to resolve it self into a red and pure Liquor, and the Feces or Earth is separated from it. The Salt of Antimony, I say, only resolves itself into Liquor, which filter, and put into a Cucurbit, that it may be condensed by extraction of the phlegm; and again set it in moist Place, then will yield you fair Crystals. Separate these from their Phlegm, and they will be pellucid, mixt with a red Colour; but when again purified become white. Then is made the true Salt of Antimony, as I have often prepared it.

—*Triumphal Chariot*

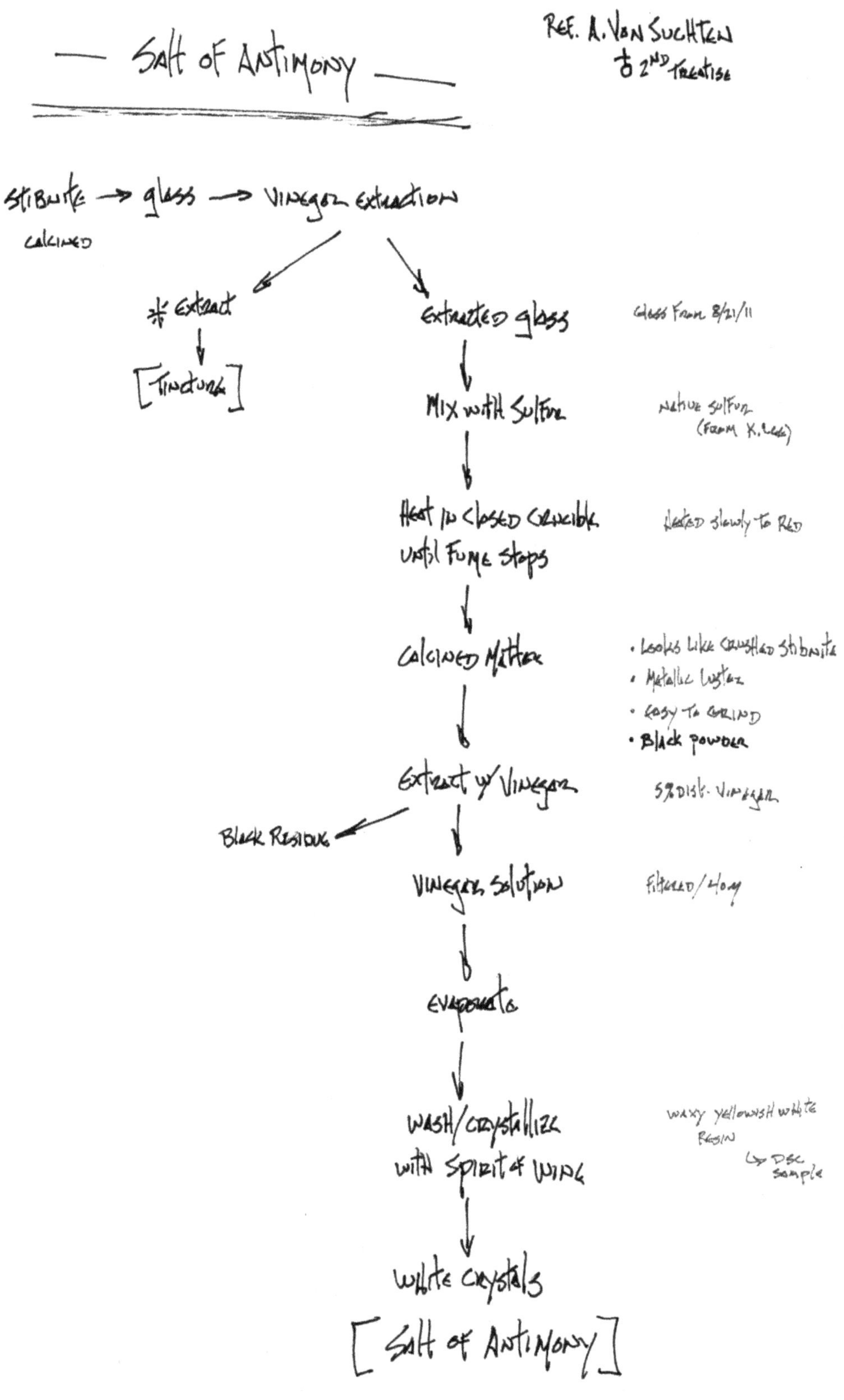

— Salt of Antimony —

REF. A. Von Suchten
♁ 2ND Treatise

Stibnite → glass → Vinegar extraction
calcined

✳ Extract

[Tincture]

Extracted glass   Glass From 8/21/11

MIX with Sulfur   Native sulfur
                       (from X.Lee)

Heat in closed crucible   Heated slowly to Red
until Fume stops

Calcined Matter   • Looks like crushed Stibnite
                   • Metallic Luster
                   • Easy to Grind
                   • Black powder

Extract w/ Vinegar   5% Dist. Vinegar

Black Residue ←

Vinegar Solution   Filtered/Hot

Evaporate

Wash/Crystallize   Waxy yellowish white
with spirit of wine   Resin
                       ↳ DSC
                         Sample

White crystals

[Salt of Antimony]

Previously extracted antimony glass is mixed with an equal measure of native sulfur

TGA of the antimony glass and native sulfur mixture

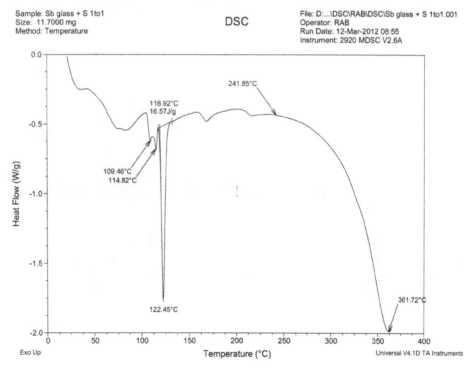

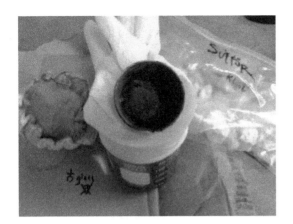

The so-called "Fire Stone," or "Lapis Ignis," represents the summit of work on antimony itself. Utilizing the preparations of antimony as detailed above, the Fire Stone is confected in a manner similar to the plant stone, where purified Body, Soul, and Spirit are reunited and congealed. Basil Valentine describes its preparation as follows.

The Tincture of Antimony prepared fixed and solid, or the Stone of Fire (as I name it) is a certain pure, penetrative spiritual and fiery Essence, which is reduced into a coagulated Matter, like the Salamander, which in Fire is not consumed, but purified and conserved. [...]

Yet the Stone of Fire tingeth not universally, as the Stone of Philosophers, which is made of the Essence of Gold itself. [...]

PREPARATION Take in the Name of the Lord, of the Minera of Antimony, which grew after the Rising of the Sun, and Salt Nitre, of each equal Parts; grind them subtily and mix them; burn them together with a moderate Fire very artificially and warily; for in this the principal Part of the Work consists. Then you will have a matter inclining to Blackness. Of this matter make Glass, grind that Glass to a subtile Powder, and extract from it an high red Tincture with sharp distilled Vinegar, which is made of its proper Minera. Abstract the Vinegar in B.M. and a Powder will remain, which again extract with Spirit of Wine highly rectified, then some feces will be put down, and you will have a fair, red, sweet Extraction, which is of great use in Medicine. This is the pure Sulphur of Antimony, which must be separated as exactly as is possible. [...]

If of this Extraction you have one pound two ounces take of the Salt of Antimony, as I taught you to prepare it, four ounces and on them pour the Extraction, and circulate them, for a whole Month at least, in a Vessel well closed, and the Salt will unite itself with the Extracted Sulphur.

If Feces be put down, separate them, and again abstract the Spirit of Wine by B.M. The Powder which remains urge with vehement Fire, and not without admiration will come forth a varicoloured sweet Oil, grateful, pellucid and red. Rectify this Oil again in B.M. So that a fourth part of it may be distilled, and then it is prepared.[...]

This Operation being completed, take living Mercury of Antimony, which I taught you how you should make, and pour upon it red Oil of Vitriol made upon Iron, and highly rectified. By Distillation in Sand remove the Phlegm from the Mercury; then you will have a precious Precipitate, in Colour such, as never was any more grateful to the Sight; and in Chronical Diseases and open Wounds, it may profitably be used for recovering the Pristine Sanity. For it vehemently dries up all Symptomatical Humors, whence Martial-Diseases proceed; in which the Spirit of the Oil, which remains with the Mercury, and conjoins and unites itself thereto, powerfully helps.[...]

Take this precipitate, and of the Superior Sweet Oil of Antimony, equal parts, pour these together into a Phial, which well closed set in convenient heat, and the Precipitate will in time resolve and fix itself in the Oil. Also the Phlegm by the Fire will be consumed, and what remains become a Red, dry, fixed and fluid Powder which will not in the least give forth from itself any Fume.[...]

Now my Follower, and Disciple of Arcanums, I will speak after a Prophetic manner. When you have brought your Philosophic Studies (in the Method by me prescribed) to this end, you have the Medicine of Men and Metals.

—*Triumphal Chariot*

Another method of preparing the Fire Stone, advocated by contemporary artists, begins with the preparation of Kermes as detailed above.

The Kermes is rinsed with rainwater until neutral. Be careful in this rinsing that the water does not become acidic, as that is a sign that some of the vinegar of antimony is beginning to come out and be lost with the rinse water.

Decant as much of the water from the Kermes as you can and then extract the still moist Kermes with a strong vinegar solution, at least 30 to 60% acetic acid. Let this digest at about 60 °C, until the solution becomes golden yellow to orange in color.

Decant the solution and repeat the extraction with fresh vinegar. Combine all of the extracts and filter until clear. Now gently concentrate the solution by distillation or simple evaporation in a dish and allow crystals to form.

The collected crystals are then dry distilled as in the acetate path using a suitably sized apparatus. The distillation train shown below is suitable for this part of the process.

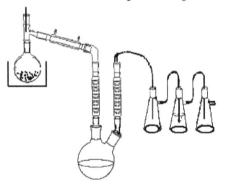

The distilling flask on the left can be heated using a sandbath. The central flask of the bubbler train is partially filled with alcohol; the other two flasks are left empty and act as guards against sudden pressure changes.

As the distillation proceeds, a clear watery "phlegm" will come over. Save this aside and continue heating. Soon the white vapor and red oil, as seen in other acetate distillations, will come over.

The red oil is the Sulfur of Antimony. The alcohol in the bubbler will become saturated with the Mercury of Antimony.

This Mercury of Antimony is not fixed as it is in the preparation of Vinegar of Anti-mony, so the alcohol solution must be kept cold or the Spirit will escape. Since it does not stay around for very long, it is a good idea to use it as a menstruum soon after preparation. It will extract the Sulfur from most prepared minerals and metals.

Collect the red oil and save it aside in a tightly sealed vial until we are ready to use it later. It has great medicinal virtues on its own, but our aim here is to unite it with a prepared body and form the Fire Stone.

The body we need for this is hidden within the solid residue remaining in the distillation flask. This black residue is called the "Black Lion."

Remove the black residue from the flask and grind it very fine, then place it into a clean, unglazed crucible. The crucible is then heated in a furnace to about 1000 °C. The Black Lion will become lighter and possibly seep through the crucible, so it is usually set on an unglazed tile or pottery shard with a layer of Kaolin (from a pottery supplier).

Once cool, the crucible is placed into a strong glass container and covered with water. If the crucible leaked out onto the tile and kaolin, these are added to the container of water as well.

Heat the water to a boil so that the contents of the crucible will be leached out and dissolved into the water. Filter the liquid and gently evaporate until crystals form.

Collect these crystals and keep them dry and out of air contact, as they will readily deliquesce. This is the Salt of Antimony. The crystals are called the "Magnets of the Philosophers"; they have the property of fixing the Philosophical Mercury.

Recharge the distillation apparatus with a fresh load of "Kermes Acetate" and instead of placing alcohol into the bubbler train, place the dried crystals you collected.

Now repeat the acetate distillation to collect more red oil. In addition, the crystals in the bubbler train will become saturated with the Mercury of antimony and it will be fixed by the Salt.

Place the crystals into a vial; this is now the Salt united with the Mercury of antimony.

ROBERT ALLEN BARTLETT

Use the collected red oil to saturate the Salt and Mercury, then seal the vial and digest at 40 °C initially. After about a week, increase the temperature to 60 °C and continue the digestion. Similar to the plant stone, the matter will congeal into a translucent red solid, the Fire Stone.

Via Humida with Antimony

The alchemist Artephius described a process for confecting the Philosopher's Stone using Antimony around 1150 CE. It became known as the Wet Way or Via Humida.

The method involved two processes he called the First and Second Perfections. In the First Perfection, pure antimony metal is formed from stibnite when iron substitutes for the antimony in a liquid mixture. Iron sulfide forms a dull matte that is fused to the Regulus. During the process, Antimony Trichloride is also formed and distilled from the reaction mixture.

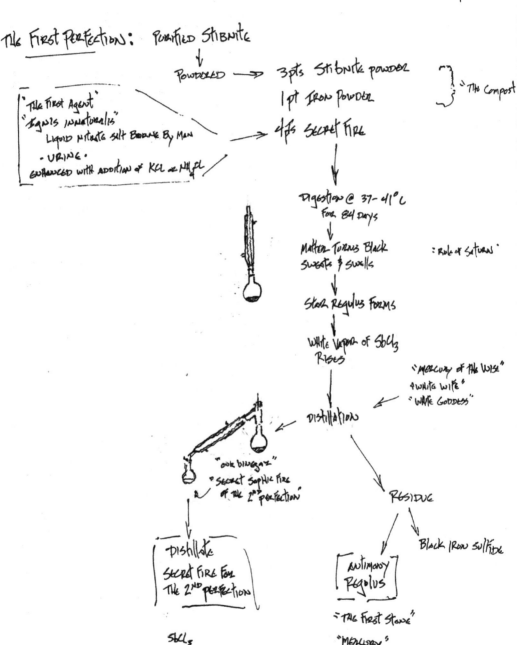

— VIA HUMIDA WITH ANTIMONY —

REF. S. NETHERTON / ALKHEMY KEY
SEE ALSO LAPIDUS / PURSUIT OF A
ARTEPHIUS 1120 – 1150 AD
THE WET WAY TO THE STONE

THE FIRST PERFECTION: PURIFIED STIBNITE
↓
POWDERED → 3 pts STIBNITE POWDER
1 pt IRON POWDER   } "THE COMPOST"

"THE FIRST AGENT"
"IGNIS INNATURALIS"
    LIQUID NITRATE SALT BORNE BY MAN
    - URINE -
ENHANCED WITH ADDITION OF KCL or NH4Cl
→ 4 pts SECRET FIRE
↓
Digestion @ 37 – 41°C
For 84 Days   : RULE OF SATURN
↓
MATTER TURNS BLACK
SWEATS & SWELLS
↓
STAR REGULUS FORMS
↓
WHITE VAPOR of $SbCl_3$
RISES
↓   "MERCURY OF THE WISE"
↓   "WHITE WIFE"
DISTILLATION ←   "WHITE GODDESS"

"OUR DISOLVER"
"SECRET SOPHIC FIRE
OF THE 2ND PERFECTION"

RESIDUE

Black Iron Sulfide

DISTILLATE
SECRET FIRE FOR
THE 2ND PERFECTION

[ANTIMONY
  REGULUS]

$SbCl_3$

: THE FIRST STONE"
"MERCURY"

The reaction takes place through the agency of Ignis Innaturalis or Secret Fire, which is prepared from urine enhanced by the addition of potassium chloride, which was called Muriate of Potash.

The powdered stibnite and iron are mixed to form the "Compost," which is moistened with the secret fire and placed into a distillation train. The proportions are 3 parts pulverized Stibnite; 1 part Iron powder; and 4 parts Secret Fire (urine saturated with Potassium Chloride).

11/1/05

900 mg Sb₂S₃ / Stibnite
300 mg Fe
1200 mg Secret Fire / U/KCl

} MIXED IN 40ml VOA VIAL & SEALED → Black SUSPENSION

[Looks almost like a
  Mercury amalgam as
  the Liquid wets the Powder]

12/1/05 Material appears Solidified. Red at Surface / Black at Bottom, But it is Still Liquid. Digestion at 40°C

1/1/06 Material is Becoming a Uniform Black color

3/20/06 Matter is Black and Nearly Dry — Added 1 ml of Sat. Sol'n of KNO₃ : K₂CO₃ / 1:1

6/20/06 Matter is Black like Pitch, increased Temp.

7/05/07 Removed Matter from Vial. Dark Blk & Brown with Metallic Streaks

└ Sb Regulus

2ᴺᴰ PERFECTION: COMBINED ½ cc Gold Powder
11/27/07   ½ cc ♂ Regulus
                     4 cc Deliquesced SbCl₃

} Placed into 10 ml Volumetric Flask Sealed & Digest @ 40°C

5/29/2011 A white sublimate has formed around the exterior of the stopper joint Scrapped this off with a knife and returned it to the flask. (a small sample was saved for analysis)

White sublimate
Red Brown Solids & Liquid

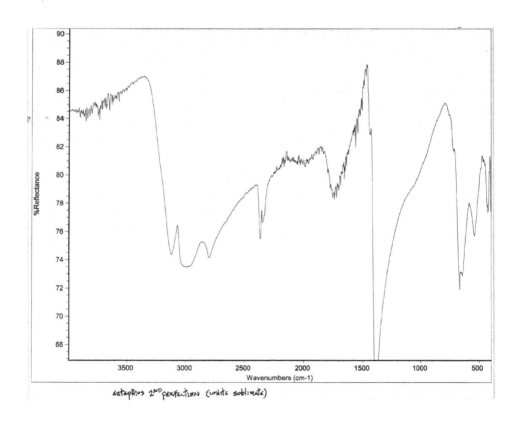

Antephius 2ND perfection (white sublimate)

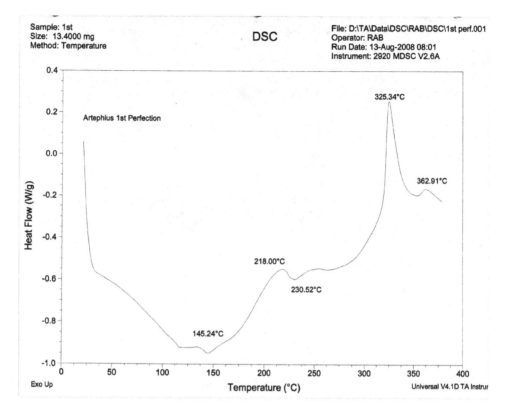

Sample: 1st
Size: 13.4000 mg
Method: Temperature

DSC

File: D:\TA\Data\DSC\RAB\DSC\1st perf.001
Operator: RAB
Run Date: 13-Aug-2008 08:01
Instrument: 2920 MDSC V2.6A

Artephius 1st Perfection

325.34°C

362.91°C

218.00°C

230.52°C

145.24°C

Exo Up

Temperature (°C)

Universal V4.1D TA Instrument

The neck of the flask must be kept cold so the vapor of the "Mercury" will condense.

Gently heat the flask in a sand bath, at a temperature of 40 °C held constant for about three months.

There is a slow reaction as the Compost absorbs the liquid in the first few days. It swells, and sweats with a dark and rusty appearance. This is the Rule of Saturn of the First Perfection.

At the end of this digestion, a shiny star appears on the surface. This is the Regulus, which is pure metallic antimony. Antimony Trichloride vapors start to rise only after the Regulus forms.

The vapor of Antimony Trichloride forms as a white "metallic, volatile humidity," called the "Mercury of the Wise," the "white wife" or White Goddess of the First Perfection. This vapor, when distilled, becomes a clear shining liquid, the "water that does not wet the hands."

The condensed Antimony Trichloride is kept sealed in the receiving flask. It will fume slightly in air and is very corrosive, irritating and hygroscopic. This Mercury of Antimony Trichloride becomes "our vinegre" or Secret Sophic Fire in the Second Perfection.

Remove the matter from the distilling flask and separate the regulus from the black matte of iron sulfide. This is the "First Stone." Pulverize the Regulus in a mortar and pestle and save it aside. In the Second Perfection, this Regulus is called Our Mercury.

The Second Perfection is performed in a "Philosophical Egg," which is a flask having a long neck sealed with a ground glass stopper or silicone rubber stopper. The "egg" is filled to one quarter of its volume with the "Azoth," which is analogous to the Compost of the First Perfection. It is made from a mixture of Gold Leaf, Regulus, and the Secret or Sophic Fire of Antimony Trichloride produced in the First Perfection.

The ratio is Gold, 3 parts; Regulus, 1 part; and 4 parts of the Secret or Sophic Fire.

THE SECOND PERFECTIONS:

Gold Leaf   3 Drachms (10.8mL) 2½ tsp
Regulus   1 Drachm (3.6mL) ¾ tsp
Secret Fire from 1st perfections 4 Drachms (14.4mL) } "The AZoTH"
(SbCl₃ Distillate)   ≈ 3 tsp (180 drops)

$19.32_{g/cc} \times 10.8cc \rightarrow 208.6_g$ Au

$6.697_{g/cc} \times 3.6cc \rightarrow 24.1_g$ Sb

$3.14_{g/cc} \times 14.4cc \rightarrow 45.2$ SbCl₃

Digestion 37-41°C
40 to 50 Days
* Vapors must circulate/reflux

Rule of ♄
NIGREDO

Colors change to Black

Rule of ♃
Peacocks Tail

Increase Heat to 41°C
Colors appear

Rule of ☽
ALBEDO

RED POWDER "The Stone"

22-24 More Days
• Whitening begins
• White cream forms

Heat increased to 150°C

Powder Begins to form

Rule of ♀
King & Queen Unite
Green Lion Forms

Slowly increase Heat
to 66°C - 77°C
40-42 Days

"The Red Rose"

Sparkling Red Oil
of Fiery Vermillion

42 Days
Green Lion is overcome
Colors change to RED

Rule of ♂
RUBEDO

Rule of ☉

Slowly increase Heat
to 110-121°C
40-42 Days

"The Red Earth is called Sulfur"

The Red Sulfur fixes the White Mercury
and they dissolve into a liquid state

Sample: Artephius 2nd perf subl
Size: 7.7000 mg
Method: Temperature

DSC

File: D:...\DSC\Artephius 2nd perf subl.001
Operator: RAB
Run Date: 31-May-2011 11:12
Instrument: 2920 MDSC V2.6A

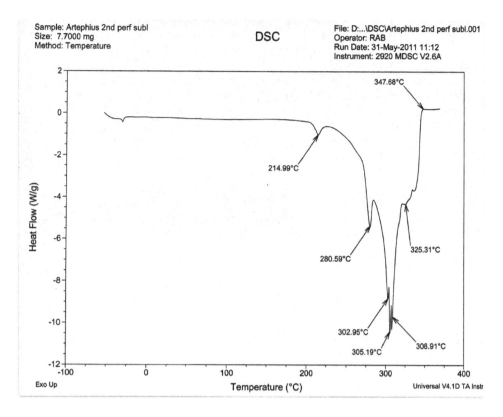

A period called the Rule of Saturn takes about two months for the matter to form a black mass. Keep the heat at about 40 °C during this period. The matter will sweat and circulate in the flask, passing through the "Solve et Coagula" phase.

With time, the moist slime changes to a dry coagulated substance. The so-called Lyon or Toad's exhalations are the vapors seen in the neck of the flask, often compared to two fighting dragons, one with wings and the other without. Seven or eight successive volatilizations are necessary. Some alchemists call the volatilizations Eagles. These Eagles feed on the Lyon and drip back down on the Earth as dead eagles.

By the end of this period, the matter swells and becomes dark. A phase of calcination begins, which to leads to the black or Nigredo phase. The fumes cease. The Earth bursts and reduces into a black powder called the Raven. The Nigredo brings the end of the Rule of Saturn.

The Rule of Jupiter now begins. It takes about two more months before the "Peacock's Tail" appears. Slowly increase the temperature to 45 °C. Then a water washes the Nigredo and beautiful colors appear, Alchemists called this the Peacock's Tail. It signals the end of Jupiter's Rule.

The Rule of Luna now begins. It takes about 28 days in Luna's Rule to achieve the Second Stone, which is when the matter turns white. This period was called the "albedo," or whitening, or the white dove. It floats on the water like a cream.

The Rule of Venus is 42 days more with heat increased to about 70 °C. The King (gold) unites with the Queen (albedo). The Queen is also called Philosophical Mercury, *rosa alba* (the white rose). In uniting, the king and queen remove impurities from each other. The King and Queen produce the Green Lion.

The Rule of Mars is 42 days. During this time azure, gray, and citrine overcome the

Green Lion, which finally changes to a red color. This red matter is now called "Sulphur." The red Sulphur fixes the white Mercury and they dissolve into a liquid state.

The Rule of Sol is another 42 days, with the temperature increased to between 100 °C and 121 °C. In a short time, a crimson or Tyrian purple color forms as a sparkling oil. Alchemists call it the Red Rose; the perfect fixation and perfection; the Red Poppy of the Rock; and the precious tincture. This is at last the Philosopher's Stone or "Third Stone." When powder forms from the solution, the alchemist slowly increases the temperature to 150 °C.

The red powder is a form of gold chloride. Traditionally, the blood red powder is the completed Philosopher's Stone.

For transmutation, melt metallic gold in a crucible, then add the red powder of the Philosopher's Stone in equal part to the crucible and pour the mixture into an ingot where it cools.

Now break away part of the ingot and pour ten parts of heated Mercury onto it. Melt the new mixture, which becomes tinged into pure gold.

Via Sicca with Antimony

The alchemical text *Coelum Philosophorum* (The Heaven of the Philosophers), by the German alchemist Phillipus Ulstadius around 1536, presents detailed instructions for working with many mineral and metallic substances. Be careful not to confuse this text with a work by Paracelsus with the same name. Ulstadius sheds a great deal of light on the subject of antimony and particularly the use of antimony regulus.

By far the greatest interest surrounding the regulus is its fixed spirit or Mercury, which can be transferred to other metals in order to reanimate them and awaken their generative power. This path leads to confecting the Philosopher's Stone and is referred to as Via Sicca or the Dry Way with antimony. With some operative variations, this is the path of Flamel, Philalethes, and Newton. It is said to be one of the fastest and most reliable ways to make the Stone of the Wise, but filled with many dangers.

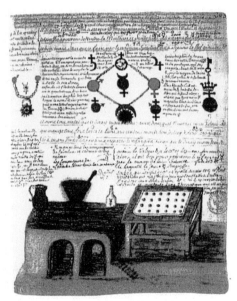

A page from Flamel's notebook

DRY PATH of ANTIMONY

1. ASSATION

2. PURGE : Melt stibnite To separate it from The Gangue (SiO₂· Al₂O₃)

3. Separation : Separation of The Regulus from Stibnite with Iron
   and Suitable Salts ($\oplus$/$\overline{\oplus}$) ← Recrystallize from Dew

   ⎫ separates, orders,
   | Purifies, and assembles
   | The elements of the
   ⎭ MINERAL CHAOS ($\overline{\ominus}$)

4. Purification : To Bring out the star / fusions with Niter
   Also to extract the vitriol or GREEN LION

5. THE Eagles : alloy with Silver and Copper → Amalgamate with Metallic Mercury ⇒
   Distillation of Hg · Repeat 3 To 7 Times

6. Digestion To Stone : secret fire (salts)

To begin, stibnite must be purified by the liquation process as described on the next page. The purified stibnite is powdered and dried, then mixed with an equal amount of fluxing powder consisting of 2 parts salt of tartar and 1 part niter. Grind these together carefully and dry.

Next, a crucible is heated red hot and the dry powder mixture is slowly added spoonful by spoonful with a cover placed on top with each new addition. A scoria will form at the top and regulus will fall to the bottom of the crucible. Pour the melt into a hot cone-shaped iron mold and tap the sides to help the regulus fall to the bottom. Once cool, the regulus can be separated from the scoria easily by a hammer blow. Save the scoria aside; it contains the "seed of gold."

To purify the regulus, it is melted in a clean crucible and niter is sprinkled on top to form a thin molten layer. Keep this in flux for about 15 minutes, then pour it again into the iron cone. Repeat this purification two more times at least.

Antimony Dry Way

1. Purification of Stibnite

Removes the Sb_2S_3 from its matrix of SiO_2 & Al_2O_3 and also eliminates other sulfurs ("parasitic sulfurs")

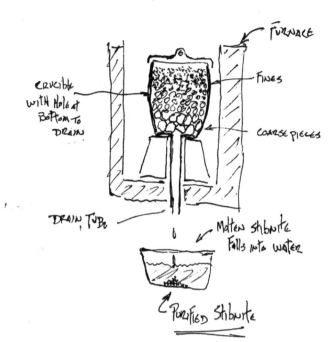

CRUCIBLE WITH HOLE AT BOTTOM TO DRAIN

FURNACE

FINES

COARSE PIECES

DRAIN TUBE

Molten Stibnite Falls into Water

Purified Stibnite

2. Reduction of Stibnite to Regulus

$$2pts\ K_2CO_3$$
$$1pt\ KNO_3$$ $$\rightarrow 1pt$$

Stibnite $\rightarrow 1pt$

$\rightarrow$ GRIND well & DRY it $\rightarrow$ ADD 1Tsp at at time to a RED HOT CRUCIBLE (COVER AFTER EACH ADDITION)

Pour into a <u>Hot</u> Ingot Mold (USE AN IRON BLADE TO SCRAPE OFF SCORIA)

Repeat the Fusion until the Metal is clean of Sulfur

Purification of the Regulus
Ref. Coelum Philosophorum

1. Melt Regulus
2. Slowly Sprinkle Hot KNO_3 onto surface
3. Keep in Flux ≈ 15 Min. with a thin layer of Molten KNO_3 on Top.
4. When the melt is quiet, Pour into Iron Cone Tap with Hammer to settle
5. Separate Scoria and Regulus then Repeat the Process

The next step is to form the Martial Regulus. The recommended proportions are 1 part regulus to $^1/_{10}$th part iron or steel nails. Iron is said to have a volatile magnetic quality and steel, a fixed magnetic quality. Steel is preferred here, but not stainless steel. Heat the nails red hot in a crucible, then slowly add the regulus as a powder. Keep in flux for 15 minutes, then pour into the iron cone which has been preheated. When cool, break the regulus away from the remaining undissolved nails. Purify the regulus as described above until you see the starry crystal surface.

Now melt your "Stellate Martial Regulus" in a clean crucible and slowly add pure silver metal filings until they stop melting, signaling it is saturated. This is now a Lunar Martial Regulus.

This is sufficient if you plan to make the White Stone which can transmute metals to silver. If you wish to make the Red Stone which transmutes metals to gold, you will need to add a small amount of copper.

Melt the Lunar Martial Regulus and slowly add pure copper metal powder slowly until the melt takes on color, it won't take very much. Cast the metal out and you will have a Lunar Venusian Martial Regulus with a beautiful violet sheen. Save this regulus aside for the amalgamation phase of the work.

3. Martial Regulus:

Regulus 1 pt
IRON Nails ⅒ Pt. } ADD Regulus to Red Hot Nails in Crucible

IRON - Volatile Magnetism
* Steel - Fixed Magnetism
4-5% dissolves into Regulus

Martial Lunar Regulus:

1. Melt Martial Regulus
2. ADD Metal (☽) Filings slowly To saturation (ie. Dissolution ceases)

1 oz Ag
½ oz ☿ } Von Suchten / Amalgamate w/4-5 oz Hg

Lunar Venusian Regulus:

Melt Lunar Martial Regulus
ADD 20% Copper Powder

Equal parts of martial regulus and copper form an alloy having a beautiful violet color known as "Regulus of Venus"

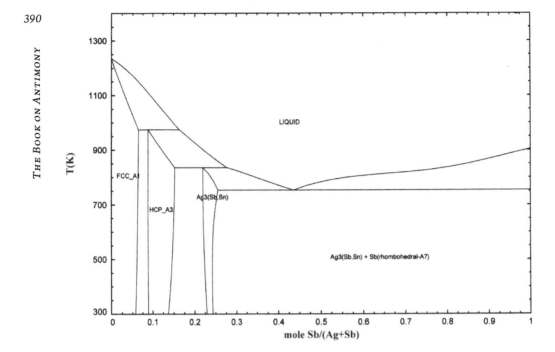

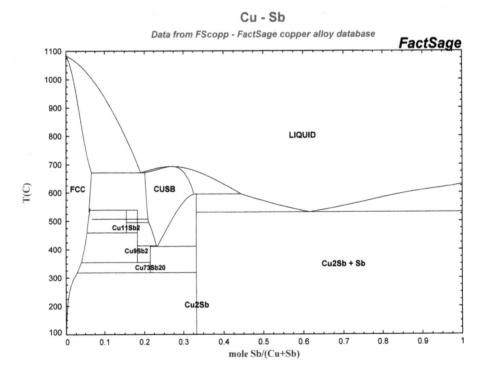

Above: Phase diagram of Antimony alloyed with Silver
Below: Phase diagram of Antimony with Copper

Above is a photo of "Regulus of Venus" and below are various pours of "Martial Regulus"
and "Lunar Martial Regulus"

The Stone of the Philosophers is nothing more than a subtilized, exalted and seminal gold.

Mercury is the agent which penetrates and effects such a subtilization and exaltation. But it must be prepared first for use in this Art.
—*Coelum Philosophorum*

Before we can use the prepared Lunar Venusian Regulus to "animate" metallic mercury, we need to purify mercury with some of the Martial Regulus.

Ideally we should use a very pure Native Cinnabar for this process, but if that is not available, we can use high purity metallic mercury (triple distilled) from the chemical supply store. It is a good idea to purify it in the old ways prior to use. It's not so much aimed at getting the mercury any more pure as at exalting it alchemically, opening the body to receive new life.

For this, take your mercury and wash it well with rainwater, then squeeze it through a piece of chamois or other thin pliable leather.

Now cover the mercury with dried and powdered sea salt. Mix these two completely using a mortar and pestle. Depending on the impurities in the mercury, the salt will darken even to blackness. Wash this dirty salt out using rainwater and repeat the salt washing once or twice. The mercury will retain some of the subtle essence of the salt which is important for the rest of the processes.

Put the mercury into a mortar and add an equal amount of sea salt. Saturate this mixture with strong distilled vinegar (about 10% acetic acid) and begin vigorously mixing the mass for about 10 minutes. Now wash this salt out with rainwater until the mercury appears shiny and bright. Press it through a chamois; there should be no residue left in the chamois. The mercury should leave no trail when rolled across a smooth surface and should be without any appearance of scum at the surface.

Another method to clean metallic mercury, borrowed from Indian Alchemy, is to grind the metal with garlic into a thick paste. You will need a pinch of salt to help the grinding or else it will become a very sticky mess. Once the paste is made, it is poured into a large vessel of water, whereupon the mercury will rain down to the bottom and the impurities stay suspended with the garlic in the water. Decant, wash, and pass the collected mercury through the chamois to dry it.

Mix the mercury with an equal amount of native sulfur in a mortar, grinding it together well. The matter will turn black during this process, forming mercury sulfide. Examine the matter closely with a magnifier. There should be no tiny globules of mercury remaining. Grind with additional sulfur if there are. The resulting black mass is a crude form of cinnabar, which is the sulfide ore of mercury. We can proceed with the black variety of cinnabar or we can improve this matter by sublimation to obtain the beautiful orange variety of cinnabar which is best. This is a difficult and dangerous process which requires careful control of the heating. This can be performed using the "Bottle Firing" method detailed above and a small firing pit. This way it can be set up safely outside. The pit is ignited and then you can move away to a safe location upwind to watch until it cools.

An alternate method for turning the black mercury sulfide into the red form is done chemically through the use of potassium hydroxide:

ROBERT ALLEN BARTLETT

— CinnaBar Via Humida —

70g Metallic Mercury
30g Native Sulfur ⟩ Grind To Black (Ethiopian Mineral)
[HgS] B Form
Cubic

↓

Place into Flask
Cover with 3g Caustic Potash (KOH)
which has Deliquesced or Just
Dissolved with Rainwater

↓

Seal Flask and
Digest (65°C Max)

↓

Matter Becomes
Red (CinnaBar)   Protect From Light

↓

Wash the CinnaBar ppt
with Rainwater To Remove Salt

↓

Collect & Dry Gently

↓

┌─────────────┐
│ CinnaBar   │ α Form   "Vermillion"
└─────────────┘ Hexagonal
Store in Dark

Now mix 1 part of the cinnabar with ½ part of powdered martial regulus and grind them together very well in a mortar.

Place the powder into a strong glass retort with the distilling arm immersed in a container of water.

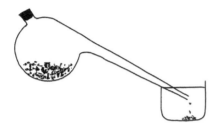

Begin the distillation slowly at first, and then gradually raise the heat until metallic mercury distills over. The temperature will be about 320° to 380°C as the mercury distills. When the distillation is complete, remove the receiver first, before removing the heat, or the cooling retort may draw the water into itself and explode.

The black residue remaining in the retort is mostly antimony sulfide which can be used to make more of the Martial Regulus.

The mercury which distilled over is ground together with Native Sulfur until a homogeneous black powder of cinnabar is formed. Again, we can sublimate this black form of cinnabar into the red orange variety, but either form will work.

The process of mixing the cinnabar with Martial Regulus and distilling is repeated at least three times. The metallic mercury from the final distillation is now purified and prepared for the amalgamation phase.

Take 1 part of the Lunar Martial Regulus for the White Work, or 1 part of the Lunar Venusian Martial Regulus for the Red Work, as prepared earlier. Powder the regulus and add 4 parts of the purified mercury in small increments, grinding the matter very well in an iron mortar with each addition. Continue grinding the mass for 10 to 20 hours total. At the end of this grinding, add rainwater and continue to grind until the water is black. Pour out this dirty water and add fresh rainwater. Continue this water wash until all of

the blackness is out and the resulting amalgam appears bright and clean.

Now place the amalgam into a strong retort as above or into a distilling flask set up as shown below.

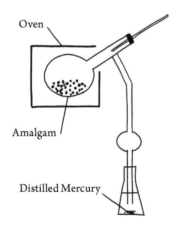

Oven

Amalgam

Distilled Mercury

The baked potato method of amalgam distillation

ROBERT ALLEN BARTLETT

The oven should be able to reach about 400° C. The bulb in the distilling arm prevents water from being drawn into the hot flask if there is a sudden pressure change. The receiver is partially filled with water to condense the mercury vapor distilling over.

Distill the amalgam and collect the mercury from the receiver. Wash the mercury several times with water, and then dry it with a paper towel.

Remove the black silver and regulus residue from the distillation flask and weigh it, then grind it to powder. Melt half its weight of fresh regulus in a crucible, then slowly add the powder until it melts. Cast out the melt and powder it.

Use the distilled mercury to form the amalgam again with this fresh regulus as you did above. Now repeat the distillation.

The amalgamation and distillation process is repeated 7 to 10 times and is often referred to as "letting the eagles fly." The regulus of antimony won't amalgamate very easily with mercury metal, so the silver is added to absorb the fixed spirit of antimony and transfer it to the mercury.

A flowchart summary of the process is shown on the following page.

In seeking optional methods for distillation of the mercury amalgams, I found an interesting trick used by miners in South Africa. It involves placing the amalgam in the center of a large potato and wrapping the two halves together with several layers of aluminum foil. The potato is "baked" in a shallow pit, whereupon, the mercury vaporizes and distributes throughout the potato, leaving the gold or silver at the center. Loss of mercury can be detected by damage to the foil liner. The now baked potato is crushed in a container of water and a rain of fine mercury particles fall and collect at the bottom.

The silver then, often called the "Doves of Diana," acts as a medium to transfer the life force of the antimony into the mercury. After the distillation, the residue of silver which remains in the retort, called now the "Dead Doves of Diana," is cleaned and used again each time with the addition of fresh regulus. With each cycle of amalgamation and distillation, the mercury metal becomes more enlivened and ultimately is called "Animated Mercury," or "Sophic Mercury," containing the generative power of the metallic realm.

This is the "Philosophical Mercury" of the Dry Way. Thus common mercury becomes reanimated by the fire of antimony and the principles of life hidden in the iron and copper. It is the fertile field wherein the seed of metals is sown.

For the White Work, purified silver is "seeded" into this animated mercury; for the Red Work, we use purified gold.

The purification of the precious metals begins with the preparation of sea salt. The salt is fused in a crucible at about 800° C, then dissolved in rainwater. Filter the solution into a distillation train and distill out ⅔ of the water. Save this distilled water aside, and pour the remaining salt concentrate into a dish.

Crystals will form in about a day, which are then collected. Dissolve the crystals in

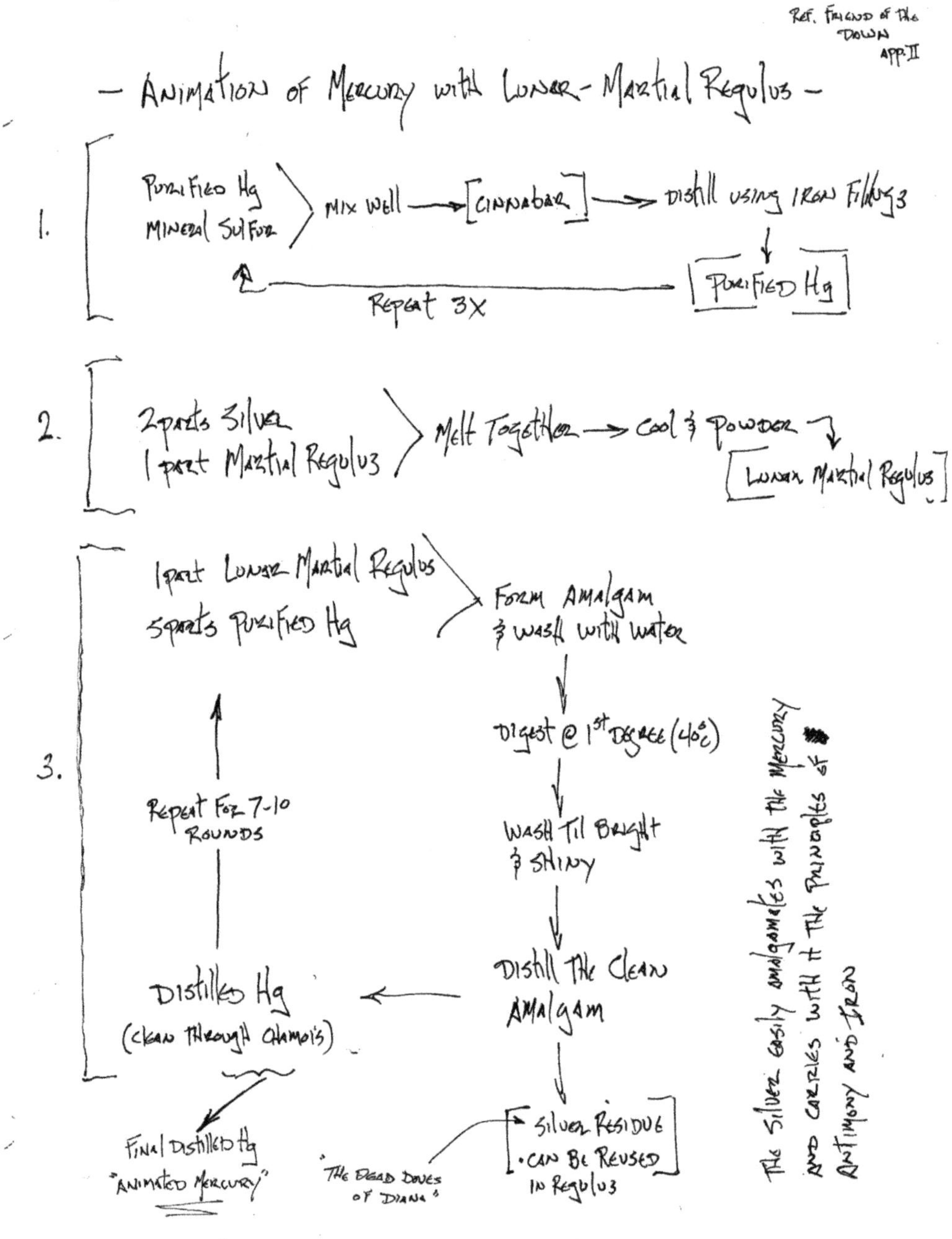

REF. FRIEND OF THE
DOWN
APP II

— ANIMATION OF MERCURY WITH LUNAR-MARTIAL REGULUS —

1. PURIFIED Hg, MINERAL SULFUR > MIX WELL → [CINNABAR] → DISTILL USING IRON FILINGS

Repeat 3X → [PURIFIED Hg]

2. 2 PARTS SILVER, 1 PART MARTIAL REGULUS > MELT TOGETHER → COOL & POWDER → [LUNAR MARTIAL REGULUS]

3. 1 PART LUNAR MARTIAL REGULUS, 5 PARTS PURIFIED Hg > FORM AMALGAM & WASH WITH WATER

DIGEST @ 1st DEGREE ($40°C$)

WASH TIL BRIGHT & SHINY

DISTILL THE CLEAN AMALGAM

REPEAT FOR 7-10 ROUNDS

DISTILLED Hg (CLEAN THROUGH CHAMOIS)

FINAL DISTILLED Hg "ANIMATED MERCURY"

"THE DEAD DOVES OF DIANA"

[SILVER RESIDUE • CAN BE REUSED IN REGULUS]

THE SILVER EASILY AMALGAMATES WITH THE MERCURY AND CARRIES WITH IT THE PRINCIPLES OF ANTIMONY AND IRON

— "Baked Potatoe Distillation of Hg Amalgams —

OLD MINERS TRICK

TRIAL RUN: 12/5/10 FORMED a SOLIDIFIED
amalgam with Hg and Ag Crystals
washed w/water until clear
Bright Shiny MASS

1. Slice a potatoe in half

2. Scoop out a space in the center to hold the amalgam

3. Wrap Tightly with several layers of Aluminum Foil

4. Bake in Coals

12/11/10 FIRED in Half gaga pits
• REMOVED after 3 Hrs

RAIN INHIBITED THE FIRE
Potatoe crispy on outside
More dried than Baked
Little change in the Amalgam

NO MERCURY
To RECOVER

5. REMOVE [Metal] FROM Center

6. CRUSH Baked Potatoe in Hot Water

Mercury Falls out

[Collect Hg]

One of Glauber's Philosophical Furnaces used to prepare the mineral acids.

the distilled water you collected. Filter the solution into a dish and allow it to crystallize. Collect and gently dry the crystals. This is now purified salt to be used in preparing the gold and silver metals.

For the White Work, silver metal is dissolved in Aqua Fortis or nitric acid. Filter the solution through glass wool, and dilute it with about ten times as much water. Now pour the solution into a clean dish made of copper. Some of the copper will dissolve and fine crystals of silver metal will form on the bottom of the dish. Wash this fine silver powder several times with rainwater, and then dry it.

Grind together one part of the dried silver powder with six parts of mercury which has been purified with vinegar and salt. Press the resulting amalgam through a leather chamois to squeeze out the excess mercury.

Take the ball of amalgam remaining in the chamois and grind it together with the previously purified salt. Add the salt in small amounts and continue grinding until you cannot see the metallic amalgam in the powder. Place this powder into a distillation train and distill out the mercury. The residue remaining in the distillation flask is rinsed several times to dissolve and remove the salt. A very fine "silver calx" will remain.

Repeat the process of amalgamation with mercury, grinding with purified salt, distillation of the mercury, and washing the silver calx, two more times. The resulting fine silver calx will be suitable for seeding into the animated mercury and preparing the White Stone.

The ancient artists thought of this process as a type of calcination of the precious metals, wherein they are reduced to a fine ash like consistency, and hence the name "calx" of the metal.

The calcination of gold, for the Red Work, can be easily performed by dissolving gold in aqua regia and then diluting with a little water. This solution is then poured into a strong solution of vitriol (ferrous sulfate). The gold will immediately precipitate in the form of very fine metallic particles.

Philosophical Furnace #1

Robert Allen Bartlett

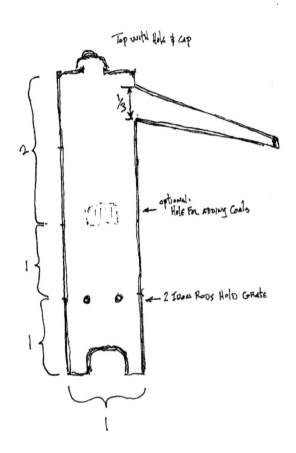

Top with Hole & Cap

1/3

← optional.
Hole For Adding Coals

← 2 Iron Rods Hold Grate

1. Have Live Coals Ready

2. Load Coals into Body Nearly To The Bottom of The Pipe

3. Leave Cap off and Let Heat apply Receiver

4. Cast in Spoonfuls of Matter To Distill & Quickly Close The Top So Vapors Rush into Receiver

"In This Furnace are Distilled only such Materials, which Being Distilled, Yield an Incombustible Humidity, as Common Salt, Vitriol, Alum and other Minerals and Metals"

"There are By The Help Hereof, Made most Subtle, Volatile, Sulfurous spirits of salts, and minerals, as of common salt, vitriol, alum, niter, antimony and all other Minerals and Metals, which otherwise, without This Furnace, could not Have Been Made, with which spirits, wonderful Things are performed in Medicine and Alchemy"

* Many of the Materials need To Be Prepared specially Before They are Cast IN To The Coals

    * Flowers of Many Metals and Minerals can Be easily Made with This Furnace.

RECEIVER

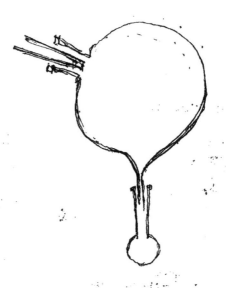

For Spirit of Salt : Quench Hot coals in saturated Salt (NaCl) solution
Let Dry & soak up Salt
cast into Furnace Heated with charcoal & collect Distillate
Rectify

HERBS :

~~Plante~~ " How an Acid Spirit, or Vinegar may be Distilled out of all
Vegetables, as Herbs, Woods, Roots, Seeds, etc "   P. 61

Simply set the Material in upon the coals and collect the Distillate
which is the Acid Spirit. Rectify For use.
Also called Vinegar of Woods

" Heavy woods; For by how much Heavier the woods are, by so much More
Acid spirit do they yield."

— Vitriol —

REF Glauber/Centuries
P 219

"Forasmuch then as we know that Vitriol is an Universal Acid, and Chief of all Salts, and the Spirit it Yields by Distillation, Much more Fiery than that which is Forced from other Salts, Therefore we may make use of the Oil of Vitriol, For a Basis with the help of other salts To prepare several sorts of Saline Spirits, with small labor and charges"

2pts Niter
(Dissolved in water)

1pt Oil of Vitriol

> Distill → [Aqua Fortis
(For ☽, ♄, ☿)]

1Lb Salt
1Lb Niter
3Lbs Water

> Dissolve, then add
1 Lb Oil of Vitriol → Distill → [Aqua Regis
(For ☉ ♀ ♂ ♃)]

2Lb Salt
3Lbs Water

> Dissolve → Add 1Lb
Oil of Vitriol → Distill [5Lbs Spirit of Salt
Residue = Sal Mirabile]

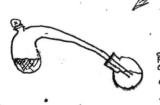

RECEIVER
CONTAINING WATER
OR USE A BUBBLER TRAIN
* HCL DISSOLVES IN THE WATER

"THE STONE DRAGONS"

· H_2SO_4
· HNO_3
· HCL

Now that we have prepared the metal calx and the Animated Mercury, we are ready to proceed with the next phase of the work.

This part of the work consists of planting our precious metal "seed" into the Sophic Mercury.

Ref MIN 80 p9 / Coelum Philos.

6. SEEDING THE ANIMATED MERCURY

✱ ANIMATED Hg MADE WITH LUNAR MARTIAL Regulus IS SEEDED WITH SILVER FOR THE WHITE WORK

✱ ANIMATED Hg MADE WITH LUNAR VENUSIAN MARTIAL Regulus IS SEEDED WITH GOLD (RED WORK)

THE NOBLE METALS MUST 1st BE PREPARED FOR USE:

● Preparation of the Gold:

PURIFIED POWDERED GOLD 1pt
TRIPLE DISTILLED MERCURY 4 pts ⟩ AMALGAMATE WELL

↓

PRESS THRU CHAMOIS TO REMOVE EXCESS Hg

↓

WASH THE AMALGAM WITH SALT, VINEGAR & RINSE WITH H_2O UNTIL BRIGHT

↓

DRY IN SUN OR BY GENTLE HEAT THEN PULVERIZE

↓

1pt DRIED AMALGAM
3pts PURIFIED SEA SALT
GRIND INTO BLACK POWDER

PLACE MIXTURE INTO WATER TO COLLECT Hg

DISTILLED Hg (RE-USE)

GOLD CALX RESIDUE

WASH SALT OUT WITH H_2O & DRY

DRIED GOLD CALX

Repeat 3 Times

FINAL GOLD RESIDUE IS

[PURIFIED GOLD CALX]

Take one part of silver calx (for the White Work) or one part of gold calx (for the Red Work) and grind it together with two parts of the Sophic Mercury for about ten hours. The resulting amalgam is then washed with rainwater until no more blackness comes out in the water and the amalgam appears clean and bright.

Place the amalgam into a dish and cover it with a paper to keep dust out. The amalgam will become dry and firm up enough so that it can be shaped. Cut pieces of the amalgam off and form them into small balls about the size of a pea. Set the balls into a dish, and let dry gently in the sun.

Place the dried amalgam balls into a heavy walled digestion flask with a ground glass stopper. The flask should be no more than a third full. Cover the flask with a piece of paper to keep dust out, then place it into a sandbath at a gentle heat of about 50° C for a day.

When you perceive that all of the moisture has gone out, seal the flask tightly with the ground glass stopper. Continue the digestion at a gentle heat.

After about a week, the balls of amalgam will come together as a mass which begins to swell and puff up. Gradually raise the temperature and continue digesting the flask.

The matter will become very dark but soon will begin to look lighter and finally take on a reddish hue. Increase the heat still higher and the red will become more pronounced after about three months. After six months of continuous digestion, the matter will be of a uniform red color.

This is the "Philosopher's Gold" and represents "the true radical and central calcination of gold." These are "the ashes of the philosophers, wherein the Royal Diadem is hidden" and is "the nearest matter of the Stone, out of which the Great Work may be made."

This "Sophic Gold" provides the foundation for confecting the Red Stone of the Philosophers, but first we must augment or multiply its virtue and quantity.

Place 3 parts of the Sophic Gold into a clean digestion flask as above and heat it until you can barely stand to touch it for very long. Using a heated glass funnel, you must add 1 part of preheated Sophic mercury in small portions. Add about the quantity of a pea each time and allow about half an hour to pass before the next addition. Each time the moisture should be allowed to vapor away.

When the full 1 part of Sophic Mercury has been added and all of the moisture has disappeared, seal the flask with the ground glass stopper. Continue the digestion in a sandbath for four weeks, gradually increasing the heat during this time. At no point should the temperature rise high enough to sublime or distill the mercury within the flask. After four weeks of digestion, the added mercury will become fixed by the Sophic Gold.

Increase the heat until the flask is almost glowing red hot and the matter will fuse without fuming. Allow the flask to cool slowly, then break it free of the digestion flask.

You can repeat this process of multiplication as many times as you like and thus have a constant supply of Sophic Gold.

Now take 1 part of the Sophic Gold reduced to powder and place it into a clean digestion flask. Add two parts of Sophic Mercury all at once, then gently warm the flask to exhale all of the moisture. Seal the flask and continue the digestion until the powder and mercury form a fluid amalgam. Pour the amalgam into a clean glass mortar and begin gently grinding it with rainwater until no more blackness enters the water. When the wash water comes off clear, pour the amalgam into a dish and let it dry in the sun.

Place the dried amalgam into a clean digestion flask and gently heat to remove all moisture before sealing. The flask is digested in a sandbath at about 40° C and left undisturbed.

The matter will ferment, swell and bubble, then turn black like pitch. This is called "The Regimen of Saturn." Keep up this gentle digestion for 40 or 50 days and the mercury will begin to circulate. Within several months, the matter will become lighter, and finally a pure white powder will form. This is the "White Sulfur of the Philosophers."

The final phase of this process is the preparation of the White and Red Stones from this White Sulfur. For the White Stone we use pure silver metal and for the Red Stone we use Pure Gold. In each case the method is the same, so we will only describe here the preparation of the Red Stone.

Place the White Sulfur into a digestion flask and add small portions of Sophic Mercury until the matter is a soft dark mass.

Warm the flask to exhale all moisture, then seal it tightly.

Digest with a gentle heat in a sandbath for 30 days and the darkness will begin to lighten. Continue the digestion for another 30 days and the matter will take on a greenish hue, then a blue green, similar to a peacock's tail, which is what this phase of the work is called. As the digestion continues, the matter will become increasingly yellow, then reddish. At last, the entire mass will become a beautiful red powder which is called the "Red Sulfur of the Philosophers."

Take 1 part of this Red Sulfur and encase it in a shell of beeswax. Now melt 2 or 3 parts of pure gold in a crucible and cast the Red Sulfur wax ball into it. Cover the crucible and let remain molten for half an hour. Once cool, break open the crucible and you will find a glassy material which you must reduce into powder.

Place 1 part of this powder into a digestion flask and add 2 parts of the Sophic Mercury. Exhale the moisture out, then seal the flask. Digest the flask with a gentle heat as before. The matter will become dark at first but will turn red much quicker than the first time.

Repeat the digestion with fresh Sophic Mercury several times. The matter will turn red more quickly each time. At the end of this process, you will have "The Red Stone of the Philosophers," "The Medicine of Metals," which can transmute impure metals into gold.

The process of transmutation of metals into gold is called Projection. Making a judgment of how much metal your stone will transmute requires a little experimentation.

Take about 4 parts of pure gold and melt it in a clean crucible. Cast in 1 part of your Red Stone wrapped in beeswax and keep the matter in flux for half an hour. When cool, break out the resulting red glassy mass from the crucible and powder it.

Now heat 100 parts common mercury in a crucible and cast in 1 part of the Red Stone wrapped in beeswax. Keep the matter in flux for half an hour, then cast it out into an ingot mold. If the metal is still brittle, you must remelt it with more mercury. If all of the metal did not change into gold, you must add more of the Stone. After a few trials, you will be able to judge the proportions in future transmutations.

In order to multiply the Stone in quantity and virtue, melt 1 part of it with 2 parts pure gold. Powder the resulting glassy mass and place it into a digestion flask. Add Sophic mercury until it becomes a soft mass, then seal the flask. Digest at a gentle heat and it will become fixed into the Red Stone in a short time.

With slight modifications, this is the same process for confecting the Philosopher's Stone advocated by Flamel and Philalethes. Some modern artists even refer to this as the Flamel Work because his was one of the earliest descriptions of it.

Facing page: Above: flowchart of the Flamel Path developed by the PON; below: phase diagram for gold and mercury amalgams

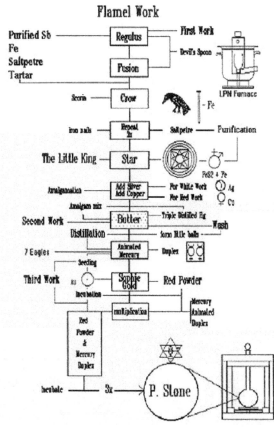

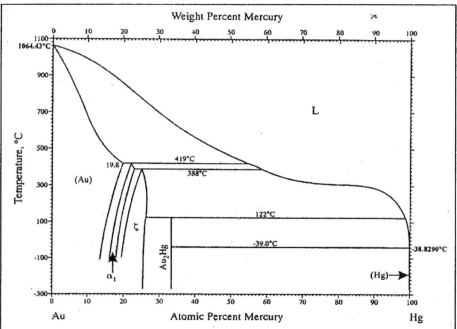

Figure 2.70. Phase diagram for gold in mercury. Stability of crystal forms and liquids a s a function of concentration (x axis) and temperature (y axis). Source: Phase Diagrams for Binary Alloys. H. Okamoto, ASM, Materials Park, Ohio, 1995.

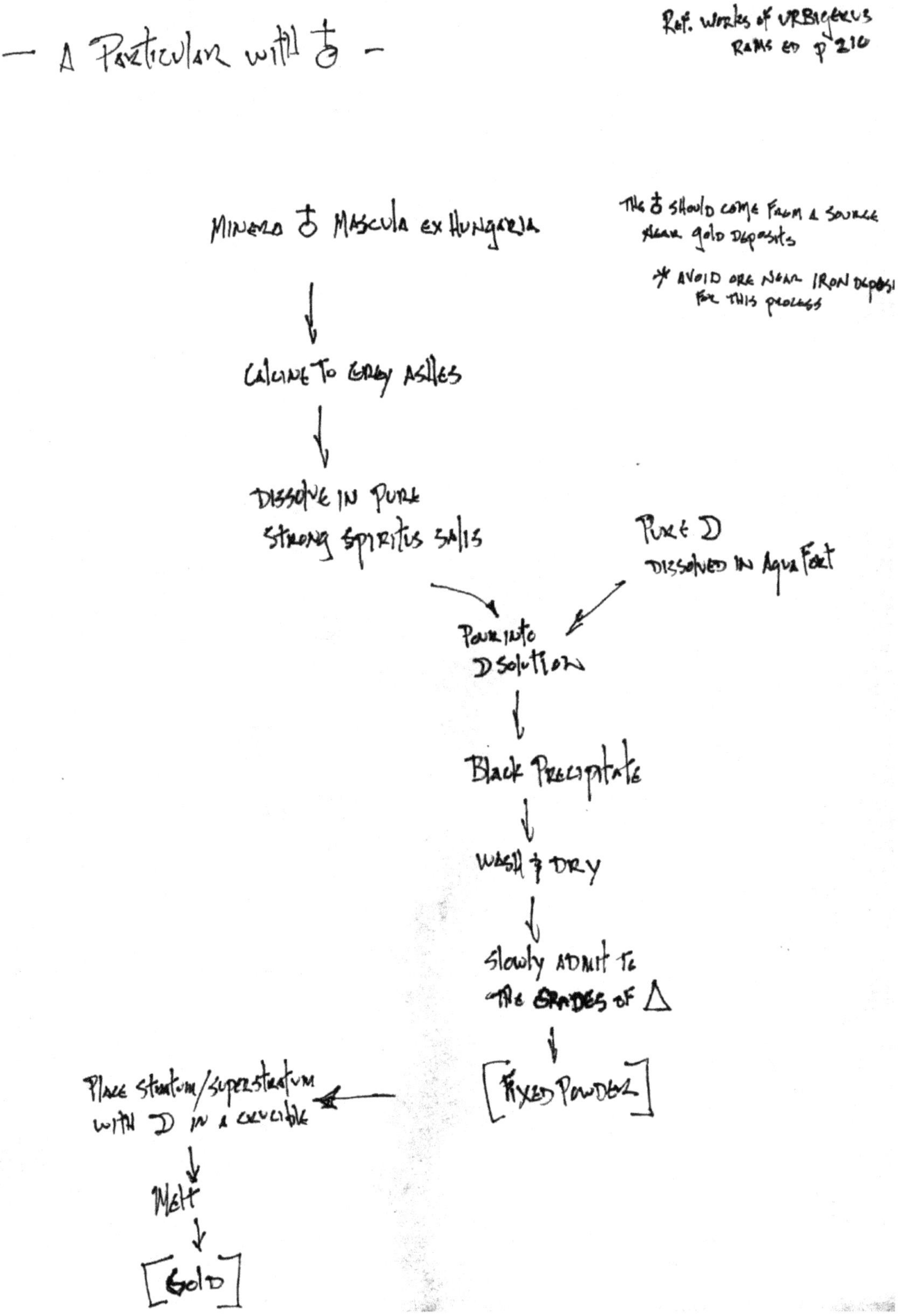

— A Particular with ☿ —

Ref. Works of URBIGERUS
RAMS ED p 210

MINERA ☿ MASCULA ex HUNGARIA

This ☿ should come from a source near gold deposits

✳ AVOID ORE NEAR IRON DEPOSIT FOR THIS PROCESS

↓

CALCINE TO GREY ASHES

↓

DISSOLVE IN PURE STRONG SPIRITUS SALIS

PURE D DISSOLVED IN Aqua Fort

Pour into D SOLUTION

↓

Black Precipitate

↓

WASH & DRY

↓

Slowly ADMIT TO THE GRADES OF △

↓

[FIXED POWDER]

Place stratum/superstratum WITH D IN a crucible

↓

Melt

↓

[GOLD]

— A RUBY RED GLASS FROM ☿ WHICH FIXES ☿ —

RGP Jugels Exp. Chym.
Exp. 13

ROBERT ALLEN BARTLETT

♀   1 Lb

↓

FUSION

↓

ADD ♂   10-12 oz

↓

Let cool &
Do Not Stir

↓

Break crucible
& Separate

↙   ↘

Top   Bottom
Scoria   Brown Glassy Regulus
Dark   Metallic w/ Rays
Brown   Like Sb

                 10g

Powder & Let   Regulus is Soft Like
Deliquesce   Pb (Sampled For DSC)
Clear
Liquid   ↓
& Black
Solids   Powder

↓   ↓

Liquid Per   Place into Flask   No immediate
Deliquium   →   RXN 11/2/10
Clear
Liquid   ↓

pH 11   EXTRACTION

↓   ↓

RIED   Ether off Liquid
PLR   Clear
FOR DSC
                 Evaporate To   ↓
                 Thick Liquid

                 Place into a
                 Small Flask   →   Bury in Sand Bath
                                     within a crucible

Keep in a Thinly Fluxed
State

Test Fusion: 10/30/10
to 1-2 oz ♀
FUSED IN CRUCIBLE
Added Powdered ♂ By
Small Spoonfuls
* ERUPTS/sparks from
crucible Like a SHOWER
          Use a Lid

[RUBY RED VITRIFIED
  MASS]

↑

Cool & Break glass

↑

Maintain Red Heat

↑

gradually increase Δ
To Red Heat

↑

Beat To Fine Powder &
* 1 pt Fixes 100 pts ☿ so it
can be Melted without Loss.
Cools To a Brittle Regulus

* A pea size portion can
Tinge 4 oz ☿ To a
white Metal not D

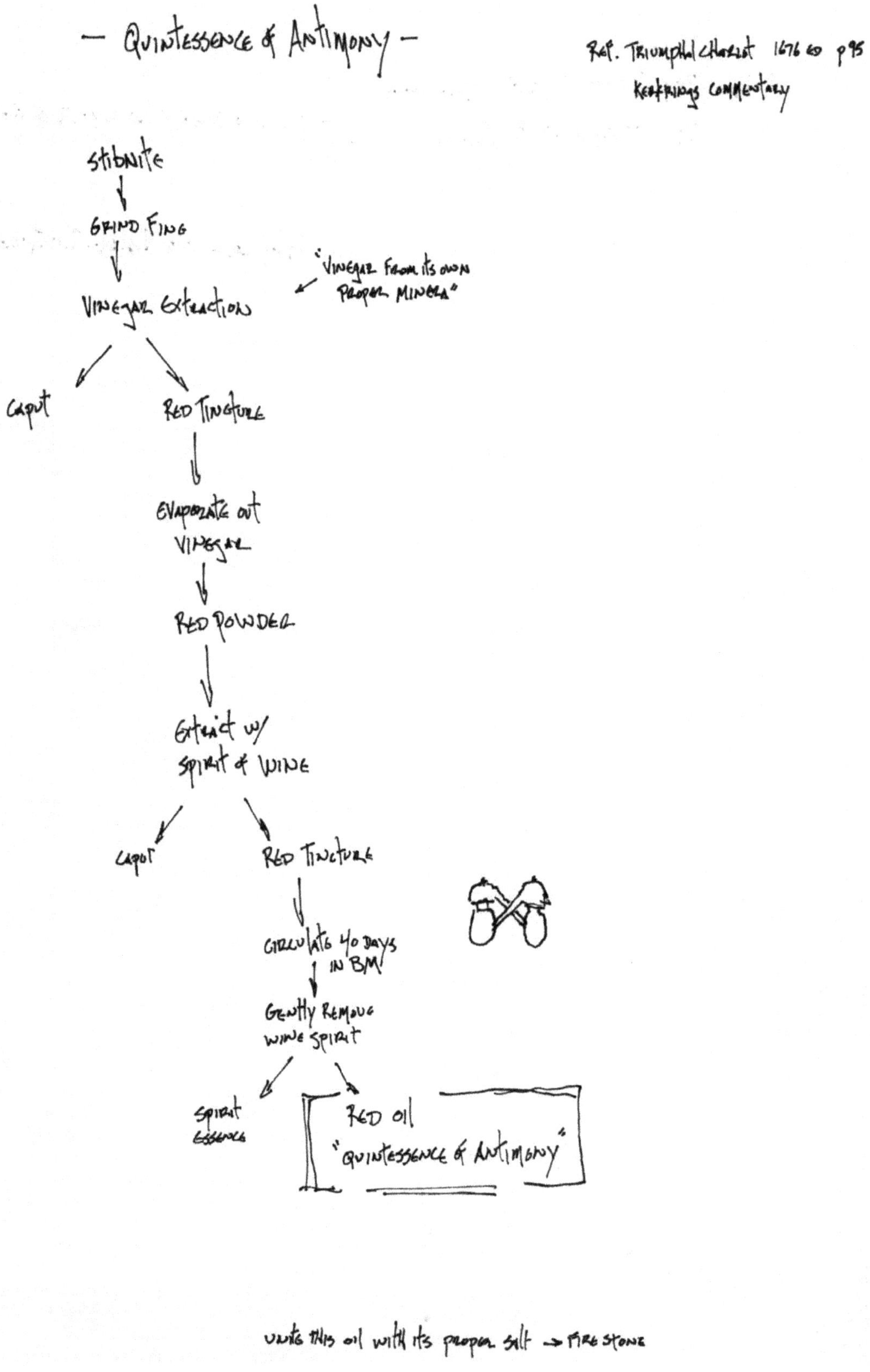

— QUINTESSENCE OF ANTIMONY —

Ref. Triumphal Chariot 1676 ed p95
Kerkrings Commentary

Stibnite
↓
GRIND FINE
↓
VINEGAR EXTRACTION   "VINEGAR FROM ITS OWN
                            PROPER MINERA"

Caput   RED TINCTURE
                   ↓
               EVAPORATE OUT
               VINEGAR
                   ↓
               RED POWDER
                   ↓
               Extract w/
               SPIRIT OF WINE

       Caput   RED TINCTURE
                          ↓
                      CIRCULATE 40 DAYS
                            IN BM
                      GENTLY REMOVE
                      WINE SPIRIT

             SPIRIT
             ESSENCE   RED OIL
                            "QUINTESSENCE OF ANTIMONY"

UNITE THIS OIL WITH ITS PROPER SALT → FIRE STONE

The following experiment is performed in tandem with the next. The first experiment produces a Fixed White Powder of Antimony, said to have healing and even rejuvenative powers. In this, powdered stibnite is mixed with niter to essentially form weak gunpowder. The powder is "Detonated" by touching it with a glowing coal. Make sure this is done in the open or in a fume hood and in an open dish, as it will get very active and smoke a lot. Once it burns off, gently calcine what is left, being careful not to melt it.

The residue is washed out with water and allowed to dry. The wash water (labeled as "soluble salts" in the flowchart) is the subject of the following experiment to produce "Fixed Antimonial Niter" so they are saved aside. The niter's association with antimony has altered its medicinal and metallurgical qualities.

Save the wash water from all three detonations and recrystallize together. Store in a glass container for future work.

Stibnite is ground separately and then mixed with powdered niter. A cast iron ladle works well for the detonation.

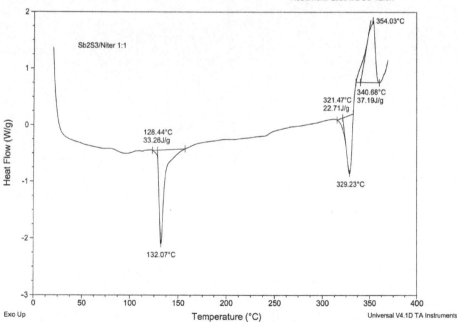

Sample: Sb2S3 niter
Size: 9.8000 mg
Method: Temperature

DSC

File: D:\TA\Data\DSC\RAB\DSC\Sb2S3 niter.001
Operator: RAB
Run Date: 02-Jun-2010 08:19
Instrument: 2920 MDSC V2.6A

DSC scan of the Stibnite/Niter mixture

— FIXED WHITE POWDER OF ANTIMONY —

Ref. Triumphal Chariot

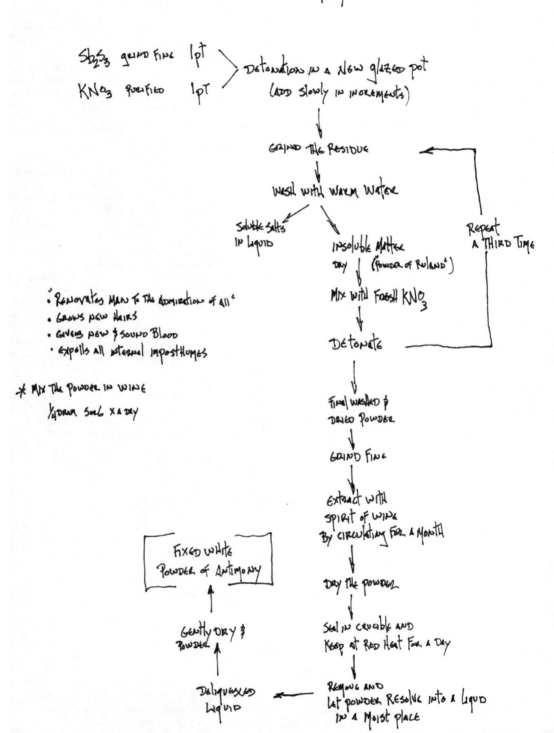

Sb_2S_3 grind fine 1pt
KNO_3 purified 1pt

Detonation in a new glazed pot
(add slowly in increments)

GRIND THE RESIDUE

WASH WITH WARM WATER

Soluble salts in liquid

Insoluble Matter
Dry (Powder of Ruland')

Mix with fresh KNO_3

Detonate

Repeat a third time

Final washed & dried powder

GRIND FINE

Extract with
spirit of wine
by circulating for a month

Dry the powder

Seal in crucible and
keep at red heat for a day

Remove and
let powder resolve into a liquid
in a moist place

Deliquesced liquid

Gently dry &
powder

FIXED WHITE
POWDER OF ANTIMONY

• "Renovates man to the admiration of all"
• Grows new hairs
• Gives new & sound blood
• Expells all internal imposthumes

✱ Mix the powder in wine
½ dram so L x a day

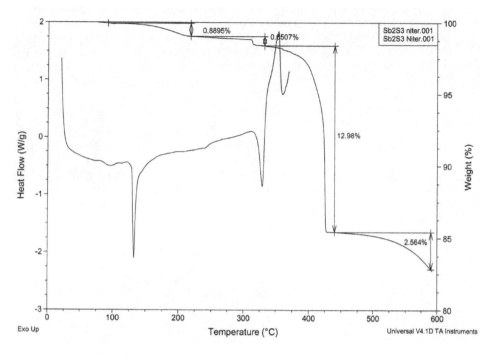

Overlay of the DSC and TGA results for the Stibnite/Niter mixture

Once ignited, the mixture burns rapidly to completion

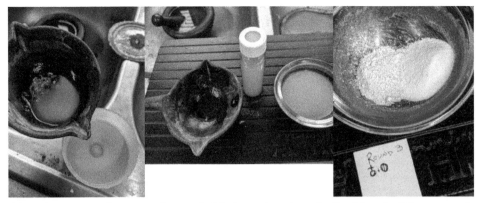

The salts are rinsed out in each round of deflagration. Save the liquid and solids separately

After the third ignition and washing, the Fixed Powder is ready to digest in wine spirit. The wash waters are seen crystallized on the left and the subject of the next experiment

The dried Fixed White Powder is digested in Spirit of Wine for a month.

= Fixed Antimonial Niter =

Ref: Starkey's Notebooks
P322
Newman/Principe

ROBERT ALLEN BARTLETT

Stibnite 1pt
Niter 1pt   Powder separately then mix well

↓

Place into an iron dish and
ignite with a coal
Stir with an iron spatula

↓

Continue sprinkling with niter
until deflagration stops

↓

Calcine in Reverberatory
Do not melt

| white ash
↓

Leach out salts with
hot water

↓

Crystallize

↓

[White Salt of Antimony]   H₂o Sol.
not Deliq.

• Burns like slow gunpowder
• Smokes alot

Uses:

• It resolves old obstructions

• Provokes urine

Ingested with desireable success in all internal Heats

Dose: 1 scruple to a drachm

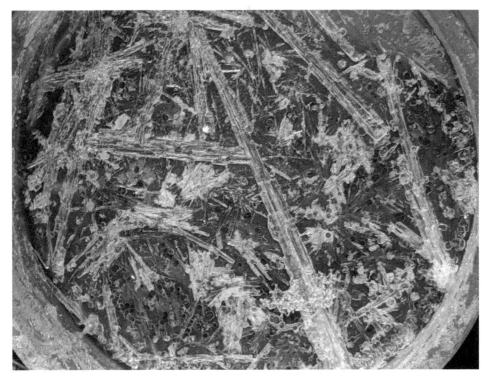

Fixed Antimonial Niter

Ref Golden Manuscripts
Hermetic Art

Heinz Fischer Lichtenthal

Volpierre (Niklaus Burtschell)
(1892 ~ 1952)

3 parts to the work   * Best started when ☿ is △ ♃, ♀, or ☉ or △ with well aspected ♂

#1. Metal carefully dissolved by Art yields a Red Juice ⌐Menstruum
                                                        └Blood of the Red Lion

    └→ *a useful medium capable of extracting the essential
        vitality found in all creation and then being
        able to retain it. *

#2. Gradual & Repeated distillation of the Red Juice and its Residue to form ⌐Menstruum Universal
                                                                              │Radical Solvent
                                                                              │Virgins Milk
                                                                              └Flying Dragon

    * "wherin all natural essentials can be dissolved
       while their inherent characteristics are still retained"

    * It contains the flying Mercury in the form of tiny silver colored scales which evaporate in air
                                        Remora - "Little fishes"

    distillation ⟜→ "A yellow vinegar" (HCl) followed by phlegm, then H_2SO_4 ←Hi Temp Distillation
                 └→ Residue = 2 Volatile salts at Bottom / elliptial - orient to N-S poles
                    1 is white (Hermetical salt)
                    1 is yellowish (Hermetical Sulfur)

#3 Cohobation of the Salts and their Fixation.   "Cementation"

#1.

Mix: 1 part powdered Sb_2S_3
6 pts Iron Filings

> Place a 3/4 CM Layer into a 5 Liter Flask

↓

Repeat 2 more time →

Add 3 ml HCL
2 ml H_2SO_4 *
Seal & Digest @ 37°C 24 Hrs

* The H_2SO_4 Should Be Produced By The Lead Chamber Process using $CuSO_4$

↓

4TH Acid Addition Consists of
6 ml HCL
$4\frac{1}{2}$ ml H_2SO_4

** Repeat every 4TH Day No Matter
What the contents Look Like.

* Break up any Lumps

* Color changes Black → White → Yellow Green

* a Dark Floating Ring Appears & enters the Mass

* Matter Expands To 15 or 16 CM

* Matter Becomes Blue w/ a Radiance

* Blood Red Lines Appear

At this point, circulate 3 or 4 Months until the Rising Red Juice Reaches The Top of The Mass.

Should Have a Green Luster
If it is Brown, its No good

↓

Residual Mass

| Pour off the Red Juice For Use |

"Dragons Blood"

↓

Add More Acid in
10 to 30 Fold Increase
Like 60 HCL + 45 H_2SO_4

→ Digestion Produces More | Red Juice |

"As Much As 80 Liters Has Been Obtained out of a 5L Bottle"

$Sb_2S_3 + Fe \longrightarrow 2Sb \quad 3FeS$

$3FeSO_4$

3
1
4

DRW ⊖ ✳

☿
♂
□/KCL

♂

☿
♁⊖

♂ martial regulus
♂ Butter (as sacret △)

⊖

☿ ♂ 3
⊙ 1
sacret △ 4

Valporro
1/100th Scale
50 mL   VOA Vial]

.75 cm
7.5 mm
0.08 mm light

2000 mL   2000 mL
↓   ↓
38 mL HCL   20 mL H₂O₂

1. Wash Fe w/ HCL (cleans surface & activates)
2. Grind ☿ ♂
3. Grind ⊙ ⊖ 1:3
4. Mix
5. Moisten w/ HCl wash
6. Seal & digest

1 : 3 : 4
♂ ☿ △

6/21/08

@ 1/2 g = 1 pt

Stibnite   3pts   1.5
Iron   1pt   0.5

1pt NH₄NO₃ ⎫ 4pts   2
3pts NH₄Cl ⎭

4g ⟶ 40mL VOA VIAL

* MIXED 6/22/08
  GRAY POWDER
  ↓
  6/23/08
  MOISTENED W/ WATER
  & DIGESTED @ 40°C
  ↓
  5/11/09 1yr later
  DARK GRAY & CRYSTALLINE
  STRONG NH₃ ODOR
  SAMPLED FOR DSC ANALYSIS

1. RINSE IRON WITH HCL TO CLEAN ⟶ Filter
                                    ↓   ↓
                                  IRON   ACID SOL'N
                                            ↓
                                          Dilute
                                            ↓
   ACTIVATES THE Fe   Let settle
   LIKE A CATALYST   ↓
                                          USE CLEAN
                                          SOL'N TO IMBIBE
                                          MATTER

Sample: Sb2S3/Fe
Size: 9.0000 mg
Method: Temperature

DSC

File: D:\TA\Data\DSC\RAB\DSC\Sb2S3-Fe.001
Operator: RAB
Run Date: 12-May-2009 10:59
Instrument: 2920 MDSC V2.6A

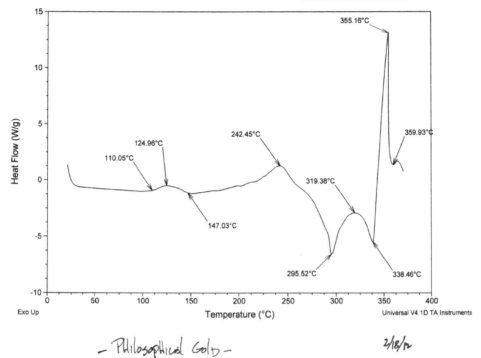

Exo Up

Universal V4.1D TA Instruments

— Philosophical Gold —

2/18/12

* Regulus From K.Lee ☿ w/♂ ♃ ☉
Fused 3x

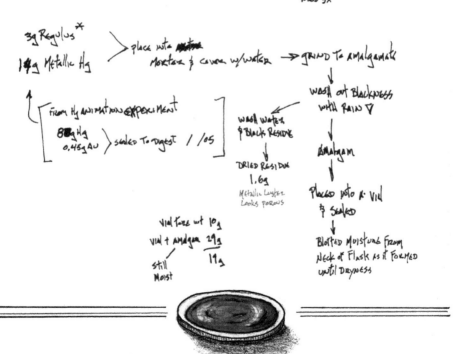

3g Regulus *
14g Metallic Hg
} place into Mortar & cover w/water → grind to amalgamate

↓

Wash out blackness
with rain ▽

↓

Amalgam

↓

Placed into a vial
& sealed

↓

Blotted moisture from
neck of flask as it formed
until dryness

From Hg animation experiment
80g Hg
0.45g Au } sealed to digest 1/05

wash water
& black residue

↓

Dried residue
1.6g
Metallic Luster
Looks porous

Vial tare wt 10g
vial + amalgam 29g
_____
19g
still
moist

LaPort Work

Mentioned earlier was the highly recommended text by the modern alchemical researcher, J. Erik LaPort, *Cracking the Philosophers Stone*, wherein he develops a unifying interpretation of confecting the Philosophical Stone of the ancients. Tracing processes from Maria Prophetissa in ancient Alexandria to Isaac Newton in 17th-century Europe, a pattern develops where we see the Sun and Moon married by Mercury under so many guises and the Glorious Child resulting from that union. There is only one way to make the Stone but many paths that can be taken to achieve it. The following experiments were inspired by that text and so I dubbed them "The LaPort Work" in his honor.

One thing that piqued my interest in this method is the combination of gold and antimony producing something new and powerful among medicines. I had seen this in the past many times, but produced in a different way. The combination of Fixed Oil from Antimony and the Oil of Gold prepared in a separate process has proved to be one of the most powerful healing agents I have ever used.

Case in point, our old friend Karl Lee collapsed one day and was rushed to the hospital. It was bad, Acute Myelytic Leukemia, and without treatment the doctors said he had about a month. Immediate chemotherapy was recommended, but Karl was reluctant and instead sought me out to see if I could send him something that would help.

I took a spagyric combination of aloe, saffron, and myrrh then heavily dosed it with the prepared oils from gold and antimony and sent it to Karl as quickly as possible. In the meantime, the doctors convinced Karl to try a short round of chemotherapy during which his legs ballooned up with fluids and he went into cardiac arrest, damaging his mitral valve. Some days later, Karl received the bottle I had sent and immediately started taking it. Three days later, Karl walked out of the hospital and his doctors were "Flabbergasted," scratching their heads saying it's impossible. His blood analysis showed no signs of the leukemia and his cardiogram showed a perfectly normal heart. I kept in touch with Karl over the next few years as we would talk alchemy via phone calls quite often and all during that time he was seeing his doctor on a regular basis for monitoring. The leukemia never came back and his heart was beating strong.

This is just one of many stories people have related to me concerning this combination of gold and antimony; somehow the two bring out the best in each other.

The method for uniting gold and antimony in the LaPort work opens many possibilities because once the general premise is understood there are many options to achieve it as seen in the works of various alchemists through time.

The following scans from my notes introduce the theoretical background of the work:

✠ CHRYSOPOEIA ✠

Page 1

Ref. P.S. Cracked
LaPort 2015

TRANSMUTATION IS UNDERSTOOD TO MEAN A CHANGE IN THE PROPERTIES OF MATTER.
PERFECTION IN THE ALCHEMICAL SENSE IMPLIES INCORRUPTIBILITY, INDESTRUCTABILITY, AND IMMORTALITY WHILE
ALSO BEING IMBUED WITH PROPERTIES OF GROWTH AND REGENERATION.

THE PRIMARY INGREDIENT IN THE ARCHETYPAL PHILOSOPHER'S STONE RECIPE
IS ALWAYS ALCHEMICALLY PREPARED GOLD.

"IN SPECIES IT IS GOLD, MORE PURE THAN THE PUREST; IT IS FIXED AND
INCOMBUSTIBLE LIKE A STONE, BUT ITS APPEARANCE IS THAT OF VERY
FINE POWDER... IT DOES NOT EXIST IN NATURE, BUT HAS TO BE
PREPARED BY ART IN OBEDIENCE TO NATURE'S LAWS"

George Starkey

INGREDIENTS AND CHEMICAL REACTIONS COMMON TO MOST RECIPES:

Gold	Antimony	Flux/Menstruum
High purity/Fine particle size	Stibnite/Regulus/Flucks	Key to the whole Art
Au - Metallic gold Calx	Sb_2O_3 = Flucks/$Sb_2O_2SO_4$ = Glass	$SbCl_3$ = Butter of ♁
Fixed & Non-Flammable	Volatile & Unchanged	Volatile & Changeable
First Principle	Second Principle	Third Principle
Red Man	White Woman	~~Corona~~ Spirit of ♄
Red Gumm	White Gumm	Lunaria
Sulfur	Mercury	Salt
Salt	Mercury	Sulfur
Body	Soul or Spirit	Soul or Mediator
Sol	Luna	Mercury
Sun	Moon	Venus or Sirius
Perfect Body	First water	Second Mercurial water
Father of Life	Fountain of Life	Center of Life

According to the Testimony of All Philosophers There Are Three parts belonging to the Elixir, viz., Soul, Body and Spirit.

1. The Soul is nothing else but the Ferment or the Form of the Elixir (antimony)

2. The Body is the paste or Matter (gold)

3. The Third part of the Stone is the Spirit (Salt/Flux/Menstruum)

If this Mediator (Flux) were taken Away The Soul (Sb) could never Be centrally and permanently united with The Body (Au). This spirit is called by the Philosophers: Heaven, Dissolving Mercury, Menstruum, Azoth, Quintessence, etc..

This Fluxing Agent/Mediator, is the key to The entire Art and its Most Closely Guarded Secret.

The spirit attracts the soul and Returns it to the Dead Body

The First Principle, The groundwork and Foundation of the Whole Art is Gold — common pure Gold, without Any Ambiguity or Double Meaning
       This is "our Sulfur"
                                          S. Bacstrom

Sophic Sulfur = Gold Calx.

Problem with Gold is that Having Reached Perfection — it Has no growth or Regenerative principles Left to impart.

The Alchemical Work Required The infusion of a new Growth/Reproductive principle into the Body of Gold.

To enable such an infusion, Gold's Remaining Soul & Spirit Had To Be Killed or Destroyed. only Then will The Gold Be Able To Receive The Transplant of Soul-spirit From its Donor (Sb)

— CHRYSOPOEIA —   Page 2   Ref: Cracking The P.S.
                                              LaPort

GOLD NEEDED TO BE REDUCED TO XÉRE/IKSIR FIRST IN ORDER TO ACHIEVE THERAPEUTIC
OR TRANSFORMATIVE Potential

ELIXIR = XÉRE = XERION = MEDICINAL POWDER   PHARMAKON

PURE GOLD CALX WAS CONSIDERED PHILOSOPHICAL, MEANING REDUCED TO ITS ORIGINAL
NATURE AND FIT FOR ALCHEMICAL USE.

GOLD SOLUTIONS IN AQUA REGIA CAN TAKE ON A GREENISH TINT AND CALLED THE GREEN LION
PRIOR TO THEIR REDUCTION (OFTEN WITH VITRIOL - ANOTHER GREEN LION) AS METALLIC CALX

ANTIMONY WAS A GREEN LION IN THE FORM OF IMMATURE OR UNRIPE GOLD.

THE REBIS IS PREPARED BY CASTING THE GOLD ELIXIR INTO MOLTEN ANTIMONY,
SOMETIMES REFERRED TO AS SOPHIC MERCURY, IN ORDER TO ACHIEVE A
GOLD-ANTIMONY GLASS OR ALLOY.

Sophic Sulfur   Sophic Mercury
MALE   FEMALE
GOLD   ANTIMONY

REBIS

THE SECOND MARRIAGE IS THE PROCESS WHEREBY THE REBIS IS SEALED IN A
VESSEL AND CONCOCTED OVER LOW HEAT. THE FINAL PRODUCT IS THE RED STONE.

ROBERT ALLEN BARTLETT

Sophic Mercury — The second principle is Mercury, not common quicksilver, but that substance to which the philosophers have given the name of "our Mercury", "our Diana", "our Moon", "our Luna", "unripe Gold", and many other names.

Backstrom

The prime material, "our lead", is Stibnite (Sb_2S_3)

"The black secret lead of the wise" R. Bacon

Once antimony and gold are alloyed, the antimony can then be removed by vaporization. This process leaves behind purified gold, in alchemical terms, this process "kills" the dual soul of gold and leaves the body behind soulless.

Antimony = "Golds Assasin" = Chalybs = Sword
= Magnesia = Magnet

Because of antimony's affinity to gold, its ability to join so easily with gold and to purify it in a manner similar to Mercury, alchemists believed these 2 substances to be related

"The whole secret of our preparation is that you take that mineral which is next of kin (related) to gold and to Mercury" G. Starkey

The spirit and soul - or the Growth and Regenerative principles - inherent in antimony served as a perfect dual soul transplant donor into the soulless gold calx.

— CHRYSOPOEIA —   Page 3   REF: CRACKING THE P.S.
                                            LE PORT

Antimony — SUMERIAN = ŠEMBI   AES STIMMI = ANTIMONIAL BRONZE
            GREEK = STIMMI, STIBI   = MOLYBDOCHALKON
            MSDMT = MESTEM = KHOL   KAJJALI = RASA SHASTRA EQUIVALENT

" THIS IS CERTAIN, THAT NOTHING IS BETTER SUITED TO ALTER THE NATURE OF METALS THAN ANTIMONY "
                                                    H. BOERHAAVE

The First Perfection REFERS TO THE INITIAL PROCESS OF ANTIMONY PURIFICATION.

   IN THE ALEXANDRIAN TRADITION, THIS MEANT CREATING FLOWERS OF ANTIMONY

      $Sb_2S_3 \rightarrow Sb_2O_3$ BLACK → WHITE   "FIXED FLOWERS"

[Metallic Antimony WAS KNOWN AS Regulus OR "Little King" AFTER THE BRIGHTEST STAR
   IN LEO - ALPHA LEONIS. ♌ ANTIMONY IS THE HEART OF GOLD
   ... ITS SOUL IS IN ITS HEART " ZOSIMUS   (USE OF METALLIC Sb WAS POPULAR IN LATER EUROPEAN ALCHEMY)]

Antimony WAS BELIEVED TO CONTAIN THE SEED OR SPERM OF GOLD AND,
BECAUSE OF THIS, WAS CONSIDERED INTIMATELY RELATED TO GOLD AND TO THE SUN..

   IT WAS THE CROWN PRINCE, UNRIPE OR IMMATURE GOLD. SOMETIMES DEPICTED AS GREEN LION

      SON OF SATURN = OUR LEAD = STIBNITE

Pliny THE ELDER DISTINGUISHED BETWEEN MALE AND FEMALE FORMS OF ANTIMONY;
      STIBNITE = MALE   Sb FLOWERS = FEMALE   Regulus = FEMALE

Antimony ISOLATED FROM ITS SULFUR AND IN A PURIFIED FORM WAS KNOWN AS
" THE STONE OF THE FIRST DEGREE " OR " STONE OF THE FIRST ORDER "

      $Sb_2S_3 \xrightarrow{\Delta} Sb_2O_3$

Sophic Salt / Eudica / Spirit Water $Sb\,Cl_3$

ROBERT ALLEN BARTLETT

The THIRD principle is what they Call their "SECRET FIRE", "our Mercurial water", "Dissolving water", "Fire Against Nature", Spirit of Life, The Moon, The Priest, etc.

Bacstrom

Secret Fire - Ignis Aqua   Its identity a closely guarded secret

Purified Antimony was The Mercury of The Philosophers

The Liquid Solvent was the SEED, SPERM or the very ESSENCE of Antimony.

Sophic Mercury is Butter of Antimony ($SbCl_3$) Also called the Salt.

Sophic Salt is the MEDIATOR Between Sophic Sulfur (gold) and Sophic Mercury (Sb), By Distilling This special Salt, A SOLVENT is CREATED That DISSOLVES Fine gold-Antimony glass Calx First into a Liquid, After Which It then Solidifies The Composition into the Philosopher's Stone.

Also called AZOTH - The agent of Transformation By which the Philosopher's stone would self-synthesize.

When the REBIS is Joined with AZOTH, The FIFTH element Facilitates the CREATION of a NEW Composite KNOWN To Alchemists as the QUINTESSENCE - Better KNOWN as The Philosopher's Stone.

According To Alexandrian Methodology only Sal Ammoniac, By which all of their work was Accomplished, is Required To Confect The Stone. Generally they used only Two Salts in The Actual Confection of the Stone - Sal Ammoniac and Butter of Antimony.

The Secret To Confecting The Philosophers Stone Has Always Relied upon the identification and The Manipulation of these Salts.

THE BOOK ON ANTIMONY

— Chrysopoeia —   Page 4   Ref. Cracking the P.S
                                                        LaPort

— Latten, Body, Earth, the Rebis —
[Gold-Antimony Glass ($Au \cdot Sb_2O_3SO_4$)]

"The First Principle being well purified, and the second principle properly prepared, they are then joined together, and the compound is called Rebis and is reduced to powder and mixed with the Third. Thus are all the three Principle united in proper proportion."

                                                        Backstrom

The Rebis is the Stone of the Second Degree or Stone of the Second Order. The secret to the Rebis is one of Proportion.

Creation of the Rebis is a two step process:

1. Union created by fusing refined & reduced Gold Calx with purified Antimony in just the right proportion to make the Gold brittle. This process is called Vitrification - literally to make Glass.

2. Once cooled, the Gold-Antimony Alloy is then ground to a very fine powder and combined with the Third Principle, Butter of Antimony or Liquid Antimony Menstruum in the proper proportions.

Rebis means Dual Thing or union of opposites likened to a Hermaphrodite It is the Sacred Marriage of Sun (gold) and Moon (antimony). Often depicted as a two headed Eagle with outstretched wings.

"Sol or Luna must be calcined philosophically with the first water (molten glass of ☉) that the perfect Body may be opened and become porous to enable the second water (Butter of Antimony) to have the readier ingress"

                                                        KHalid

The Chemical Wedding is the process of finishing the stone, which upon completion is known as the Stone of the THIRD ORDER or STONE OF THE THIRD DEGREE.

The 3 orders refer to Antimony passing through 3 stages:

1. Purification
2. Union
3. Fixation

- Red Man   o white woman
- Lions Blood • Eagles Glisten
- Sol   o Luna

The entire mass comprised of a matrix of Gold, Antimony, and Butter of Antimony should have the consistency of a dough or soft clay with no excess moisture. The mass is then placed into a digestion vessel and sealed airtight. The Digestion vessel is then subjected to low heat and the mass need only be monitored for color indicators that signal the alchemist to adjust the temperature accordingly. Final union is achieved when the chemical reaction results in the Philosophers Stone.

(Proportions can be determined from the molecular weights of the reactants)

Regardless of which approach one takes, the foundational principle of joining Gold to Antimony via the medium of a salt/menstruum is present in all Genuine Philosopher's Stone recipes.

The identity of the basic Philosopher's Stone from a chemistry perspective is a species of Gold-Antimony Salt.   [Gold-Antimony oxysulfide]

There is only one path to confect the Philosopher's Stone, yet achieved in a variety of ways

An initial experiment for proof of concept was performed on a small scale using three different ratios of reactants:

Latten + Eudica

9/10/15   .5g Gold Calx/Prs
           3g Glass ə/weathered By   } Fusion of Glass → Cast glass

                                          Ground Fine ə
                                          Placed into Vial

                                          Added SbCl₃ Soln
                                          To Full Saturation
                                          + small excess

                                        Sealed and Let Digest @ 80°F

10/1/15   Turning white

               Almost all white

11/15/15   Increased Heat To 45°C

12/10/15   Increased Heat To 120°C

2/12/15   Heat off/Let cool

                ——— Power outage 5 days ———

           Stopped ə stored Vials at Rm Temp.
           For all 3 Test Runs of 9/10/15

9/10/15 — 0.5g Glass ☉/Weatherby
0.5g Gold Calx/PPt
⟩ GROUND & PLACED INTO TEST TUBE

↓

IMBIBED w SbCl₃ & SEAL

↓

TURNED DARK

↓

DIGESTION @ 80°F

↓

TURNING WHITE

↓

11/15/15 — INCREASED HEAT TO 45°C

↓

12/10/15 — INCREASED HEAT TO 120°C

↓

2/12/16 — HEAT OFF/Let cool

9/10/15 — Glass ☉/Weatherby
AU Calx/FeSO₄ PPt
⟩ GROUND & PLACED INTO TEST TUBE

↓

IMBIBED WITH
EXCESS SbCl₃

↓

BLACK THICK
SOLUTION

↓

SEALED TO DIGEST
80°F

↓

11/15/15 — INCREASED HEAT TO 45°C

↓

12/10/15 — INCREASED HEAT TO 120°C

↓

2/12/15 — HEAT OFF/Let cool

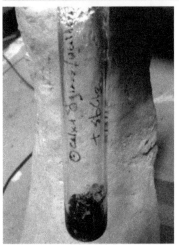

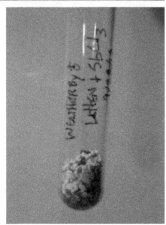

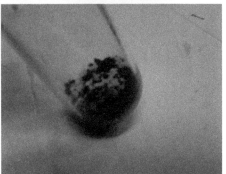

The power went off during the digestion just when the initial blackness was turning white, the Albedo stage. All looked well, the color sequence was going in the right direction and the matter going through active changes. Another round of experiments were begun, focusing on preparation of the "Latten."

Latten

The term "Latten" is used here to describe alloys of Antimony and Gold, usually in the form of the Glass of Antimony fused with refined Gold powder but potentially also the Regulus of Antimony fused with Gold. The phase diagram below can be used to develop relatively low melting point alloys of the metals.

In this next experiment, the Latten was fused using the power of the Sun focused through a large Fresnel lens. Once focused, the concentrated light fused the powder on contact and I was able to fuse it, grind it and fuse it again within an hours time start to finish.

The Au-Sb (Gold-Antimony) System

196.9665   121.75

By H. Okamoto and T. B. Massalski
Carnegie-Mellon University

Equilibrium Diagram

The equilibrium phases of the Au-Sb system are (1) the liquid; (2) the fcc terminal solid solution, (Au), having less than 1.2 at.% solid solubility of Sb in Au; (3) the rhombohedral terminal solid solution, (Sb), with no reported solubility of Au in Sb; and (4) the Fe_2S-type intermetallic (line) compound $AuSb_2$ (Fig. 1). The peritectic temperature is at 460 °C. The intersection of the peritectic temperature, horizontal with the liquidus boundary, is 66.6 at.% Sb, which almost coincides with the composition of $AuSb_2$. The eutectic point is at 360 °C and 35.5 ± 2.5 at.% Sb.

The phase diagram, calculated on the basis of thermodynamic experimental data obtained at 750 and 1100 °C for the liquid phase, the specific heat and heat of fusion for the $AuSb_2$ compound, and the peritectic equilibrium at 460 °C, agrees with the experimentally determined phase boundaries by [06Vog] within about 2 at.% error (see "Thermodynamics", Fig. 5).

Liquidus. The melting point of Au and Sb are accepted as 1064.43 and 630.755 °C, respectively [81BAP]. The liquidus curves of [Hansen], which were based on the thermal and microscopic examinations by Vogel [06Vog] and [29Gri], are accepted here with only minor modifications of

the peritectic and eutectic temperatures and compositions, as discussed below.

Peritectic Temperature and Composition. The intersection of the L/L + (Sb) liquidus and the L/L + $AuSb_2$

Table 1 Au-Sb Liquidus and Invariant Temperatures [06Vog]

Composition, at.% Sb	Temperature, °C	
	Liquidus	Invariant
0	1064	...
15.24	728	360(a)
22.21	581	361(a)
28.80	472	360(a)
35.03	...	357(a)
40.95	396	360(a)
51.89	443	360(a)
56.96	455	360(a)
61.80	458	359(a)
66.41	460	460(b)
70.82	494	460(b)
79.06	543	458(b)
86.62	580	460(b)
93.57	608	450(b)
96.84	618	450(b)
100	631	...

(a) Eutectic.   (b) Peritectic.

Fig. 1 Assessed Au-Sb Phase Diagram

Weight Percent Antimony

L

× 06Vog
○ 29Gri
▲ 450We
□ 59Mul

(Au) $AuSb_2$ (Sb)

Atomic Percent Antimony

Au   Sb

H. Okamoto and T.B. Massalski, 1984

Inspired by old works of art, a large Fresnel lens, mounted to swivel around, easily fused the Latten by concentrated Sunlight.

First fusion of Antimony Glass with Gold powder using the Sun

First fusion of Latten, ground and fused again by the Sun

The final test piece of Latten

The prepared Latten was ground fine and placed into a test tube and then imbibed with a concentrated solution of the Butter of Antimony. This time the matter did not turn black immediately but stayed a light brown color for over a month as it sat in a 40° C incubator. The blackness did finally come but an additional month saw no changes, so the vessel was placed into a hotter digestion of 120° C.

It took about six weeks for the color to become entirely white, and an additional month saw no changes. At this point, I decided to push the issue and heat it with a propane torch just to see if it would indeed turn red in the final stage. I heated it until the glass was beginning to soften but saw no indication of yellowing or reddening.

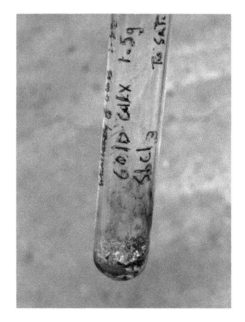

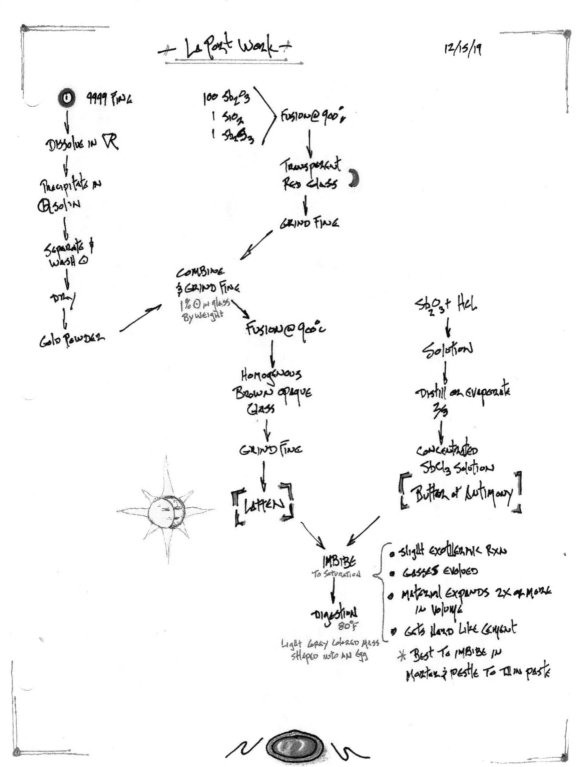

— La Port Work —   12/15/19

① 9999 Fine

100 Sb_2O_3
1 SiO_2 ⟩ Fusion @ 900°c
1 Sb_2S_3

Dissolve in VR

↓

Precipitate in
① Sol'n

↓

Separate &
Wash ①

↓

Dry

↓

Gold Powder

Transparent
Red Glass

↓

Grind Fine

Combine
& Grind Fine
1% ① in glass
By Weight

↓

Fusion @ 900°c

↓

Homogenous
Brown opaque
Glass

↓

Grind Fine

↓

[Laffen]

Sb_2O_3 + HCl

↓

Solution

↓

Distill or Evaporate
⅔

↓

Concentrated
$SbCl_3$ Solution
[Butter of Antimony]

Imbibe
To Saturation

↓

Digestion
80°F

Light Grey Colored Mass
Shaped into an Egg

• Slight Exothermic Rxn
• Gasses Evolved
• Material Expands 2x or more
  in volume
• Gets Hard like Cement

✳ Best to Imbibe in
   Mortar & Pestle to Thin paste

Preparation of the Glass. I took this piece as a good omen

Fusion of the Latten

The final Latten showing a homogenous material

The ground Latten ready for imbibing with Butter of Antimony

The Latten was saturated with concentrated Butter of Antimony,
but this time didn't darken. It was set on a 90° F surface to digest.

After 2 months, a red sublimate appeared and at the bottom, a mottled black and white mass.

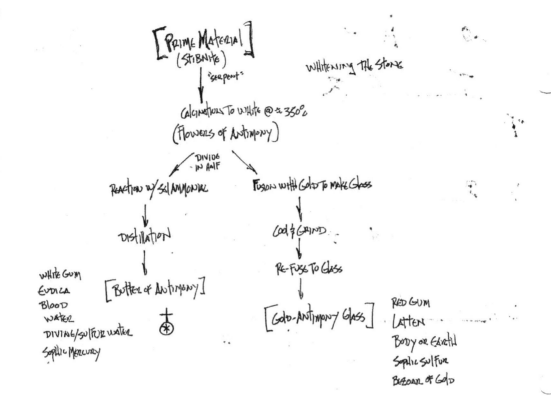

[PRIME MATERIAL
(STIBNITE)]
"SERPENT"

WHITENING THE STONE

↓

CALCINATION TO WHITE @ ± 350°
(FLOWERS OF ANTIMONY)

DIVIDE
IN HALF

REACTION W/ SAL AMMONIAC   FUSION WITH GOLD TO MAKE GLASS

↓   ↓

DISTILLATION   COOL & GRIND

↓   ↓

                                 RE-FUSE TO GLASS

WHITE GUM
EVDICA
BLOOD   [BUTTER OF ANTIMONY]   [GOLD-ANTIMONY GLASS]
WATER
DIVINE/SULFUR WATER   ☿   RED GUM
SOPHIC MERCURY   LATTEN
                                                               BODY OR EARTH
                                                               SOPHIC SULFUR
                                                               BEZOAR OF GOLD

SAL AMMONIAC REACTS WITH GOLD-ANTIMONY GLASS OR ALLOY TO CREATE THE PHILOSOPHERS STONE.
Metallurgical Techniques include Detonation, Ignition & Layers/Stratum Superstratum ──▷
Projection of Sal Ammoniac onto Molten Gold-Antimony Glass to initiate an instant reaction.

SALT-Saturated URINE is a Low-Cost Readily Available Alternative to Sal Ammoniac

According to Paracelsus, the Astrum residing in the Body of a substance was the soul-spirit
principle responsible for its nature and hidden power, which could be isolated via
alchemical preparations and applied. He also held that each substance contains an astrum
as its vital principle in correspondence with a celestial body.

THE ASTRUM OF THE SUN IS SAL AMMONIAC

See Isaac Holland
Hand of Philosophies

Ref Cracking The P.S.
La Porte CH8

441

ROBERT ALLEN BARTLETT

The crux of confecting the philosopher's stone is to create Glass of Antimony as a precursor to Latten (Gold-Antimony Glass).

Latten or REBIS are cover-names for what Maria called RED MAN or RED GUM and Morienus termed Latten, Earth, Body, or Almagra and Newton referred to as GREEN LION; basically a Gold-Antimony Glass or Alloy of varying proportions.   IMAGE: GREEN LION DEVOURING THE SUN It is based on the most ancient metallurgical technique for creating the philosophers stone. Latten satisfies the Gold-Antimony content while serving to divide Gold's particle size even further. Latten is a matter of choice rather than necessity, but it does speed up the process of confecting the stone.

Latten is described as having a red or green coloration. The difference is mainly due to residual sulfur content of the calcined Antimony.

examples: Red Glass of ☉: 1pt Sb_2S_3
8pts Sb_2O_3 ⟩ MIX & FUSE at 1000-1050°C 15-30 MIN

Green Glass of ☉: 1pt Sb_2S_3
3pts Sb_2O_3 ⟩ MIX & FUSE at 1000-1050°C 15-30 MIN

Glass of ☉ may have been produced synthetically by Basil Valentine. His recipe calls for adding a small amount of hot "spirit of iron vitriol" (Hot sulfuric acid) to Living Mercury of Antimony (Antimony oxychloride)

$$H_2SO_4 + 2SbOCl = Sb_2O_2SO_4 + 2HCl$$

$$2H_2SO_4 + Sb_4O_5Cl_2 = 2Sb_2O_2SO_4 + 2HCl + H_2O$$

~Operational Notes~ P31

Ref Cracking P.S.
Laport P401

Temperature & Color Regimen

The Color Regimen is based on Temperature Control rather than Time Duration. Heat control is crucial to Success.

1. **Blackening** - occurs only when gold is united with antimony as Gold-Antimony Glass or Alloy (Latten) The Black Stage, known in European Alchemy as **Sophic Decomposition** is catalysed at 40-42°c

   The $SbCl_3$ should be Molten then added to the Alloy. product becomes pitch Black

2. A **Greenish Transition** around edges transitions to Grey. This green-yellow-Grey transition, known traditionally as **Vegetative Germination** is catalysed at 47-50°c. The changes are subtle and unspectacular

3. **Whitening** occurs as a Liquifying stage that Begins like a Frost or snow that spreads throughout the matter as it transitions from Grey to White, the white stage, known as **Volatilization By Evaporation** is catalysed at 70-80°c or higher

4. **Yellowing to Reddening** - as the matter dries the yellow to Red Transition occurs known as **Volatilization By Sublimation** it is catalysed at 100-110°c

5. **Fixation** Begins at 120-130°c and finishes around 150°c. Upon Cooling, the matter appears as a Heavy Reddish-Purple-Brown Colored Powder

— Operative Notes —

Alchemical Aurum Potabile

'All substances are poisons; there is not which is not a poison. The correct dose differentiates a poison from a remedy' Paracelsus

From the text 'Tractatus de Lapide', (an anonymously authored tract) part of the collection of writings in "Auri Fontina Chymica", London 1680, come these clear instructions on How To Convert The Philosopher's Stone into Potabile Gold of a safe and effective dose.

1. Take the quantity of 4 grains of gold weight (200–212 mg) and dissolve them in a pint (≈ 568 mL) of white or Rhenish wine. Put it into a great clean glass, and it will color the wine almost instantly the highest red. Let it stand so, close covered from dust, four days.

2. Then add to this a pint more by degrees, until it is not so red, stirring with a wooden stick, not metal or glass, and so continue pouring on wine, until it be just the color of gold, which is a shining yellow. Beware there be no redness in it; For so long as there is redness in it, it is not sufficiently dilated, but will fire the body and exhaust the spirits

3. Neither is it sufficiently brought to yellow, until the wine have round about the sides a ring like hair, of a whitish film. Filter to remove the white film (insoluble $\varnothing$ products) and the liquid will be like yellow gold. This is the token of truth, that you cannot wrong yourself by this liquor; and without this token, it will be either too weak or so strong that it will fire the body. Know this to be a rare secret.

4. Of this golden water let the patient — whatever sickness he may have, take a tablespoon every morning, and it will drive the sickness, whatever it may be away with pleasant perspiration. For it does not purge, nor does it cause vomiting, nor does it call forth perspiration so strong and so much that it causes tiredness. On the contrary, it is rather invigorating.
If the sickness has lasted several years, or if it is chronic, it will go away in approximately 12 days, but otherwise in 24 hours or 2–3 days at most. This is the way it must be used for all internal diseases.

Part Nine: The Future

Basil Valentine says one man's life is not long enough to search out all of the mysteries
hidden in Antimony; I think he is right, but I'm still going to try. Maybe I should
label this as volume one of the *Book on Antimony* for there is more to this story.
There are experiments at play as I write, and many others are planned
for the future so my dance with the dragon is not over.
And that has been my dance
with the Black Dragon
to date.

FINI

CPSIA information can be obtained
at www.ICGtesting.com
Printed in the USA
BVHW021615130622
639652BV00010B/130

9 781947 544420